NEW WRITING 10

Penelope Lively has published twelve novels and three collections of short stories. Her work has received several literary awards, including the Booker Prize in 1987 for *Moon Tiger.* Her memoir of childhood in Egypt, *Oleander, Jacaranda: A Childhood Perceived,* appeared in 1984.

George Szirtes was born in Budapest in 1948 and came to England as a refugee following the 1956 Uprising. He was trained as a painter and started to exhibit and publish at roughly the same time. He has published nine books of poetry, most recently *Selected Poems* (OUP, 1996), *Portrait of My Father in an English Landscape* (OUP, 1998) and *The Budapest File* (Bloodaxe, 2000) and has translated some ten books of poetry, fiction and drama from Hungarian. He won the European Poetry Translation Prize (1995) for his translations of the poet Zsuzsa Rakovszky (*New Life*, OUP, 1994), was shortlisted for the Weidenfeld Prize in 1999 for his translation of Gyula Krúdy's Sindbad stories (*The Adventures of Sindbad*, CEUP 1999) and, for his own work, has won the Faber Prize (1980) and the Cholmondeley Award (1986) and has been shortlisted for the Whitbread Poetry Prize (1991) and the Forward Prize (1999).

NEW WRITING

10

edited by **PENELOPE LIVELY**

and **GEORGE SZIRTES**

PICADOR

In association with **The British Council**

First published 2001 by Picador
an imprint of Macmillan Publishers Ltd
25 Eccleston Place, London SW1W 9NF
Basingstoke and Oxford
Associated companies throughout the world
www.macmillan.com

ISBN 0 330 48268 8

Collection copyright © The British Council 2001
Edited by Penelope Lively and George Szirtes
For copyright of contributors see page 317

9 8 7 6 5 4 3 2 1

A CIP catalogue record for this book is available from
the British Library.

Phototypeset by Intype London Ltd
Printed and bound in Great Britain by
Mackays of Chatham plc, Chatham, Kent

The tenth volume of *New Writing* is dedicated to the memory of Clarissa Luard, Senior Literature Officer of the Arts Council of England, who died on 4 November 1999. She was always a champion of the new writer and it was because of her vision that the Arts Council is now associated with the publication of the series.

Preface

I would like to welcome Picador, as this is the first volume of *New Writing* for which this distinguished imprint has had responsibility, and to thank the Arts Council of England for its enterprise in co-funding this volume with the British Council. Public money is being put to good use!

We look forward to the continuing vitality of this series, in which for the first time translation takes its proper place beside other forms of literature. The collection will be widely used around the world, often in countries where book deprivation may make it the only easily available gateway to new writing. We hope, too, that British readers will continue to see within it evidence of the health of Britain's literary life.

I would like especially to thank Penelope Lively and George Szirtes, two of the hardest working editors I have ever encountered, combining good judgement with tireless attention to their commission.

Alistair Niven
Director of Literature
The British Council
31 January 2001

New Writing 11, edited by Andrew O'Hagan and Colm Tóibín, will appear in March 2002. Though some work is commissioned, submissions of unpublished material for consideration (stories, poetry, extracts from forthcoming works of fiction, essays and translations) are welcome. Three copies of submissions should be made double-spaced, with page numbers. Due to the number of submissions we are unable to return the material. They should be sent to:

New Writing
Literature Department
The British Council
11 Portland Place
London
W1B 1EJ

The deadline for *New Writing 11* is 30 April 2001.

Contents

Introduction

The brown envelopes thudded onto the doormat, week after week. To edit *New Writing* is to be on the receiving end of a seemingly unstoppable supply of literary endeavour – good and bad, innovative and conventional, arresting and dismaying. The established writers from whom we had solicited contributions would come up with something of a high standard, that we knew, but the great mass of hopeful entries would provide the surprises – and it did. This tenth edition of *New Writing* is as wide ranging and eclectic as any of its predecessors, covering a considerable spectrum of British writing today: poetry and prose, work by tyro writers alongside that from the well-known, contributions from the young and from the considerably less young.

It would be impossible to find a common denominator, which is as it should be in such an anthology. We looked simply for writing that seized us in some way, that made us sit up and pay attention because it moved us, or startled us, or impressed us by reason of content, expression or presentation. We both read everything that came through, whether this was verse or prose, and were usually in agreement about obvious exclusions, as well as about submissions that we wanted to include if we possibly could. Inevitably, a fair number of these had to fall by the wayside if *New Writing 10* was not to end up the size of a mini telephone directory.

We were jubilant when something fresh and interesting arrived from a hitherto unknown name. We homed in on submissions from writers already published but whose work, we felt, could do with more and wider exposure. A geographical distribution seemed to impose itself, without us having consciously set about making sure that there was one – writers from north, south, east and west, and writers from overseas who write in English and whose work is intended for publication in Britain – work, in short, likely to form part of the developing consciousness of British readers and writers.

For the first time, translation is included in the anthology. All three translators are notable writers in their own right, and in contributing translations they draw attention both to the nature of the task, which is by no means a lowly mechanical activity but a high art, and to the revitalizing effect of literatures of other languages and cultures on a culture that itself tends to the insular. And when we looked at the final assemblage, at the ultimate harvest from those hefty piles of typescript, at the survivors of all that reading and discussion, we saw that while there was no thread of unity, there were certain distinctive themes. It seemed appealing, under the circumstances, to range these in some kind of pattern, for while anthologies – like volumes of poetry – are notoriously devoured in haphazard order, there is, all the same, a happy driving force to a book that seeks some narrative sequence: if nothing else, certain coincidences of motif or approach might come to the reader's attention. These are of course incidental pleasures and the book's contents are bound by slender threads rather than clanking chains.

In terms of genre or treatment, realism seemed to be the dominant mode: there was less by the way of fantasy or speculative literature on offer than we had anticipated. That said, the range both of matter and of manner was remarkable – everything from the crisp mass-market story to material of sophistication and complexity. The twenty-first century British writer speaks with tongues, it could seem. Here and there the whiff of derivation was apparent – offerings that were less a nod of respect in the direction of a high-profile contemporary or a fashionable theme than outright obeisance. But the writing of merit was gratifyingly *sui generis* – distinctive voices with original things to say.

Penelope Lively

George Szirtes

Julia Darling

Love Me Tender

The supermarket rears up with brash colour even in the middle of January, when the branches of trees are hard wet bones and the gutters are full of torn brown envelopes. It rises up, full of choice and promise between roundabouts and frostbitten terraces. Lolly is walking to work, thinking about food again. Buttery, creamy food. Also she considers her thighs and the way her skin rubs together at the top when she walks, and her uncomfortable underwear that presses down on her voluminous belly. Then she reruns her interview with Doctor Wooler on Friday, in his sparse, aloof office with the white orchid in a vase on the desk. The way he stared at his hands palm down in front of him, as if he was holding the desk in place, and everything else in the room. Neddy, the car park attendant, looks up from sweeping the tarmac as she passes and says her name. 'Lolly.'

It sounds like a dollop of custard.

There's a thin, older woman waiting for the store to open, wrapped in a leathery coat with a high collar. She's wearing rather bright make-up, applied quickly. Her lipstick is leaking into the lines around her mouth. She stands smoking impatiently by the trolleys. It's Sunday and there are dank bells ringing in the distance. Lolly smiles helpfully at the woman as she slides her card through a silver box that magically opens the shining glass doors. The woman doesn't respond. She drops the cigarette end and grinds it into the ground with the tip of her shoe. Lolly's seen her before. She's always there on Sunday mornings. She looks like she's looking for something she left behind.

Inside it's warm and humming with food. The polished oranges and apples are piled up high, dazzling and fresh. Lolly puts on her pink and white overall and her starchy hat and sits at her checkout keying in numbers. Other women either side of

1

her take their places too. The Tannoy plays an Elvis song, and Lolly sees that they are all singing along quietly, to themselves. Love me tender, love me true. It's like they're all whispering the same prayer.

The aisles are nearly empty. Lolly likes this time of day, before the crowds come, with their messy children. When everything is ready and clean. Out of the corner of her eye she can see the thin woman, moving slowly along the aisles, picking up packets and looking at the ingredients. She wonders what it's like to be inside that wafer of a body, with your hip bones sticking out and your ribs rattling. She feels like a cushion. She had said that to Doctor Wooler, 'I feel like a fat cushion,' and he had nodded in a serious and understanding way.

At this time of day the shoppers are leisurely, as if they want to be there. Lolly thinks they must be escaping from something; their sulky husbands, wives and children. You can tell what people's houses are like from what's in their trolleys. There's the organic types: the posh dirties, with dirty potatoes and red lentils, who don't clean their baths and who don't watch television; and the large grabbing families with formica and carved pine kitchen tables, buying sliced loaves and cheap tins of spaghetti, and supermarket cider. And then there's the childless couples with their chicken breasts and bottles of French wine, who would have plain sofas and candles in holders, and things that match. When she applies the same test to herself, she sees the frilly edges of her mother's curtains, the dolls that she still displays in her bedroom, the big fluffy slippers. Like a great big baby, she thinks, with a trolley full of cream cakes and potato waffles. A big, tender baby that can't leave home, which is why she ended up with Doctor Wooler, with her savings in a post office book clamped in her handbag. She can't believe that she is going to spend the money. She imagines that after it has gone it will be like a blockage has been removed from a drain, and that everything will happen very quickly: leaving home, finding love, making babies. Her mother will become a gritty speck on the edge of her life as she rides down a river of opportunity.

The thin woman, whose name is Winters, has lost her first name. It just disappeared one day when she was signing something, and she has never been able to get it back. She is ostensibly buying food for her enormous son Harry. Harry works for the council; something to do with pavements. She always comes to the supermarket at this time on a Sunday, leaving Harry drinking milky coffee with the *Sunday Telegraph* on the sofa. Sometimes she has a fantasy about never returning to her oversize son, and fluttering away like a piece of tissue paper on the wind. She hopes to meet someone in the aisles one day. She read somewhere that supermarkets are really singles clubs. She might suddenly fall in love by the jellies, or in the shadow of a tower of mangoes, or be spotted by a lonesome widower fingering a guinea-fowl. Harry and the police would find her shopping in the back of her car, with the frozen food all sodden and limp. She isn't keen on food. If she lived on her own she would eat small pieces of exotic fruit, or little lumps of cheese. She prefers smoking cigarettes. They taste evil and definite, and you know what you're going to die of. She finds most food in the supermarket suspicious. It's like doll's house food; there's nothing there when you open the packets, or peel off the outer rind. Her son is also rather artificial; a huge package of a man. He sits in chairs, he talks, he eats, but he has no real substance. She is thin, but articulate, and her edges are not blurred. But still she shops every Sunday morning, although she isn't sure why. Perhaps because shopping is like dreaming. Somnambulistic. You can reinvent yourself in a supermarket. You can imagine that you are somebody else.

Winters is looking at the French biscuits, while Lolly turns the pages of a slimming magazine. In Ponteland Doctor Wooler is standing in a grey bathroom examining his face in the mirror, noticing the gradual aging of his facial skin. Harry is reading a story about anorexia and worrying, not for the first time, about his mother.

Winters sees the back of a man by the gourmet soups. His hair is neatly cut, as if he's just been to the barbers. He is wearing a thick, comfortable coat. She likes the way he turns the can around in his large hands, as if he has never seen a tin of soup before. She goes right up close to him. He smells of pipe smoke. She reaches over and picks up a can of consommé, and makes a sighing sound as she drops it into her trolley. The man turns round and looks at her. His face is a disappointment. It's not carved and sombre as she had hoped, but rather tight and small, with pursed lips, beady little eyes and a sharp chin. She replaces the consommé and moves on briskly to the bakery where she longs for someone with shoulders like loaves and comfortable doughy cheeks, but there is no one there but a young man with loping hands who roots through the organic breads, and who she imagines has a family in a camper van outside.

*

By the time Winters reaches the checkout her trolley is half filled with frozen packet meals for Harry. Fisherman's pie and Chicken Kiev. Lolly smiles at her again, and Winters recognizes her as the fat girl she saw before in the car park, and she smiles back. When Winters smiles it's as if her face unravels, like knitting falling off a needle. She looks right at Lolly, noticing her pasty complexion, her blonde permed hair, her bluish spectacles and she thinks, poor girl. Lolly, looking at Winters, thinks of a stiff little peg doll with a glued on face.

'It's very quiet today,' remarks Winters.

'It's like this on Sunday morning,' says Lolly. 'Everyone else is in bed.' And, she would like to say, probably with someone else's arm wrapped lazily around their neck.

Lolly starts swiping. She can't connect the food that Winters is buying with the woman. The food implies a large lazy person, with a colour TV and a stuffy sofa, but the woman is all mahogany and straight-backed chairs.

One of the packets isn't priced, so Lolly rings her bell and waits for the supervisor to come clipping over. The two women stand there, Winters tapping the floor with her foot, and Lolly with her eyebrows raised, with food piled between them. Lolly says, to pass the time, 'I'm having an operation next week.'

'Oh dear,' says Winters. 'Is it serious?'

'Yes,' says Lolly, and to her surprise her eyes start filling with tears. Winters doesn't know what to do. She leans over and touches Lolly's shoulder, and there is a sudden shift in the atmosphere. Perhaps the music changes key, or maybe an iceberg suddenly collapses into the arctic sea on the other side of the world and for a moment everything melts.

The supervisor comes back and says, 'Two pounds.' Lolly slumps back into her seat.

'I'm a guinea-pig,' sobs Lolly. 'I'm the first one in this country to have it. Doctor Wooler says it's a very simple procedure.'

Winters sees guinea-pigs in cages. Harry had a guinea-pig when he was little. They used to clean out the cage together and make it cosy. He wasn't so large then. He was sweet and talkative. Harry's father would be in the greenhouse spraying the greenfly with a detergent bottle. There would be something large cooking in the oven that smelt of sleep.

'What kind of operation?' asks Winters. Lolly wipes her eyes beneath her spectacles and giggles tearfully.

'A slimming operation,' she mumbles. 'I'm always hungry,' she says, 'I love food.'

'You want to be thin,' states Winters.

'Yes, thin.'

'You're not fat. My son's fat. You're plump.'

Plump, she thinks, is a word that women hate. *Thin* is a word that they respect.

'But maybe your son doesn't care. I care. The Doctor, he's putting a balloon in my stomach. It will stop me wanting food.'

'Isn't that a bit drastic,' says Winters, who is feeling confused and sorry for Lolly, and amazed at the emotions that course through her. Why should she care about an overweight checkout girl in a supermarket?

'I've got to do something,' says Lolly. 'I can't sit here all my life. They do it all the time in America.'

'But will it make you happy?' asks Winters.

'Yes it will,' says Lolly. 'It will make me happy. I know it will.'

'So why are you crying?' asks Winters, putting the last packet of potato waffles into a carrier bag.

'Because I love food. You know I really love it. I like the feeling of it inside me. I like chewing it, and planning what to eat, and cooking it. I love everything about food.'

'You should meet my son,' says Winters wistfully. 'He loves food.'

'Is that why you're so thin?'

'Perhaps. He puts me off eating. I'm hoping he'll leave home soon.'

'What will you do when he goes?'

'I'll stop shopping. I'll go on a cruise.'

This idea has never occurred to Winters before. It fills her body with a kind of blue nourishment.

'How will you pay for it?' asks Lolly, with red eyes.

The blueness turns grey. Winters can't think of an answer.

'I'd sell my own mother,' says Lolly. 'To be thin.'

Winters wavers between thinking that Lolly is deranged, and considering selling Harry for a new and better body. The type of body that would find itself in Tahiti. A body with soft skin and curves. A body that loved itself. A body that never went to supermarkets, and knew how to lie down. A body that leant over the side of a ship with the wind blowing into her face. But then a sensation creeps up her spine, and she sees Harry's big hungry face looking at her over the *Sunday Telegraph*, and his expression is frightened and lost.

'I wouldn't sell Harry,' she says.

Lolly blinks.

'But would he sell you?' she says. Then she is frightened by her own words; they were far too intellectual. It is not the kind of thing that Lolly would say.

'I don't think so,' says Winters. 'Of course not. Why would he want to do that?'

They are both aware of the supermarket filling up, of people moving up the aisles, the everyday leaking into the sides of their fantasies.

'Of course he wouldn't,' Lolly says. 'That's forty-eight pounds.' She sadly takes Winters' card.

'I'm his mother,' says Winters. 'He wouldn't dare.'

Lolly hands Winters the receipt.

'If I could just love someone,' says Lolly, 'the way I love food!' But then she acts as if she doesn't know her any more, and

Winters hesitates, then starts to walk away, leaning on her trolley as if it's a zimmer frame.

She turns round to look at Lolly, who is disappearing behind a pile of someone else's white sliced loaves.

'I hope . . .' she begins, but Lolly can't hear her.

*

Winters feels very thin as she emerges into the bleak car park. Her heart is small and cold within the cave of her ribs, and she feels the harsh grind of her hip bones. She can't stop thinking of the young woman lying on the operating table, with the firm-faced doctor dangling a creamy white balloon above her gaping stomach.

About how her helpful smile will have sagged away.

And then she lights up a cigarette and puts Lolly in a cupboard somewhere in her hard body, and drives back home, with her Kievs still hard and cold in their packets.

Barbara Trapido

Frankie and Stankie

Dinah knows that she's weedy: she's always been little and thin, and she has no meat on her bones. She has asthmatic's black smudges under her eyes, and she breathes through her mouth, which is always open. This makes her look daffy as well as weedy. In addition, her parents tell her she is edgy. There are various anecdotes about her early life that testify to this. Dinah is edgy because her mother was edgy during the pregnancy, and she was born premature because her mother had got overexcited on the day. First of all she had had a big surprise because Dinah's father was declared unfit to serve in the Dutch army in the war against Hitler because his eyesight was much too bad. This ought not to have come as a surprise since he'd always been as blind as a mole without his glasses. He'd always needed someone to lead him to the water's edge when he went swimming, once he'd left his glasses behind on his bundle of clothes on the sand.

In addition, Dinah's mother'd had a shock later that day. While Dinah's dad was out teaching an evening class, a man, after trying to break down the front door, had gone tramping round and round the garden. He banged on the bedroom windows, and called out, 'Open up there, Dolly! C'mon, Dolly, give us a kiss now. Let me in, damn you.' Dinah's mum thought he was the multiple rapist currently on the loose in Cape Town and since she had no telephone in the flat she made a dash for the phone box, clutching Dinah's fourteen-month-old sister to her bosom, while the rapist was busy trampling the arum lilies to death round the back. She dialled the police, who came at once, only to discover a drunken Australian soldier asleep in one of the flower beds. His troopship was docked in Cape Town for a few days and he had been trying to make his way back to a woman who had been very free with her affections the previous night.

Dinah was born later that night in the lift during a wartime power cut because her mother couldn't hold on even though the nurse had told her that she had to. 'You've got to hold on,' the nurse said, 'I've never done a birth before.' The poor girl was a wartime stand-in. Next morning, the regular day-nurses remembered Dinah's mother from the previous year. They all groaned at the sight of the new baby, who weighed just over four pounds. They'd seen her older sister into the world fourteen months earlier, and they'd called her 'Angel-Face'. Now, with a flash of originality, they called Dinah 'Tiny-Mite'. 'Tiny-Mite is going to give poor Angel-Face a very hard time,' they said.

Angel-Face by this time is a healthy, smiley, auburn-haired cherub with four pearly incisors, two up, two down, who gurgles and bounces so charmingly from her cot on the balcony of the apartment that total strangers come by and bombard her with presents. They throw cloth monkeys up onto the balcony for her and little jerseys they've knitted out of their scratchy wartime wool rations. What the nurses don't know is that Tiny-Mite is already giving Angel-Face a hard time, because, after the waters broke, Dinah's dad has leaped into a taxi with his wife, meaning to drop her off at the hospital and hurry back, so he's left poor Angel-Face sound asleep and all alone. And then he's stuck in the lift. Plus he's forgotten that it's Bonfire Night, so when he gets back two hours later, Angel-Face, who's been woken by the neighbourhood rocket display, is standing at her cot bars in paroxysms of terror with her poor little face caked in snot and her gingernut curls spikey with sweat. Remember remember the Fifth of November/ The Gunpowder, Treason and Plot. A mad lady in the hospital foyer tells Dinah's dad that Scorpios always have the rockiest journey through life. Dinah isn't meant to be a Scorpio. Maybe that's why she's so ill-equipped to deal with it.

Angel-Face is called Lisa. Tiny-Mite is supposed to have been called Amaryllis, after a song her dad sings while her mother accompanies him on a borrowed piano. 'Amarilli, mia bella.' It's in a collection of seventeenth-century Italian love songs from the Accademia di Santa Cecilia in Rome. Instead Dinah's dad changes his mind on the way to the registry office next day. He finds himself whistling a pop song that goes 'Dinah, is there anyone finer, in the state of Carolina?' He likes to make decisions without consultation because it's quicker, and anyway he Always Knows Best.

Dinah's mum has the girls so close together because she doesn't Always Know Best. She's been told that you don't get pregnant while you're breastfeeding and to her credit she's been breastfeeding Angel-Face for fourteen months on demand, since she hasn't read Truby King, who has created a fashion for formulas and four-hourly regimentation. She does so even though Angel-Face, who has a hearty appetite, frequently bites the nipple. In between feeds Angel-Face even takes bites out of the bath soap, leaving little tell-tale toothmarks behind. Her favourite soap comes a dark, marbled green and it's called Cuticura.

Dinah is kept in a cardboard box at first and wiped down with olive oil because she is too small to have proper baths. This is at a time when olive oil is still strictly medicinal: it's well before Elizabeth David has spread the good news from Aix-en-Provence to the British Isles, courtesy of Penguin Books, and then all over the empire including Cape Town, where Lisa and Dinah live. Angel-Face goes stiff with terror when she first hears Tiny-Mite's unearthly mewling cry, and she won't go near the cot for days. For two years afterwards, she's even afraid to approach lifelike dolls. Unlike Angel-Face, Tiny-Mite is not a good eater. She drops off the nipple and will not suck. 'We had to smack you to make you eat,' her dad tells her. He's always been a ready smacker. Her dad is called Ta, which is a corruption of Da, though Dinah's mum has diminutized this to Tätchen-herz because she's come from Germany. His real name is Fred.

Dinah continues to be a non-eater throughout her childhood. When one of her dad's colleagues visits with a packet of biscuits, he says they're 'for Lisa to eat and Dinah to play with'. The biscuits are called Iced Zoological but the girls call them Animal Biscuits. Each biscuit is a scalloped rectangle with pastel icing on the top and with an animal piped onto it in a contrasting colour. There are yellow giraffes on rose-pink icing and white tigers on sky-blue icing. Dinah loves to play with the biscuits. She's always good at playing. Angel-Face isn't introspective enough to make up games. She likes visitors and outings and treats. Best of all she likes Toffo-lux. She hangs around saying 'I'm bored. I've got nothing to do. What can I do now? What's there to eat? What's for pudding?' So it's Tiny-Mite who thinks up the games. Sometimes she leads Angel-Face into the garden shed, where families of daddy-long-legses live on the walls. If she touches their lovely fragile legs very gently with her index finger they scurry up and down the walls so deftly that it leaves her feeling quite heady. She loves to climb walls and trees herself but she knows she'll never be able to abseil like that down sheer vertical walls. For some reason Angel-Face hates the creepy-crawlies, especially when they move. When Dinah makes them scurry up the walls she yells and screams in panic. This makes Dinah keep on doing it because, being so much smaller than her sister, it's one way to redress the balance of power.

Mealtimes are hell for Dinah, when she clamps her mouth shut against the approaching spoon. 'This one's for Teddy,' her dad will say, 'this one's for Panda. This one's the last one. This one's the very last one.' She knows it will never be the last one until the bowl is empty. Sometimes he eats a spoon himself to encourage her, and because like Angel-Face he has a hearty appetite. Finally he says 'This one's for Co.' Co is Dinah's rag-doll, whose name is really Ro. Ro is short for Rosema, which is not short for Rosemary. When grown-ups ask her, she says firmly 'No. Her name is just Rosema.'

She only gets to know one Rosemary. She's a girl in the neighbourhood who has high status in the child community because she's blonde to excess. Rosemary is white-mouse blonde with a small whiffly nose and little see-through ears. Lots of the children are blonde-ish but not so blonde that the light shines right through them as it does with Rosemary. This whiteness is associated with purity. Rosemary has very little brain, but her dad is immensely rich, even though he can't read and write. He is said to sign papers with an X. This is an achievement that Dinah's mum remarks upon, a little pointedly, from time to time, since the girls' dad is not at all rich even though he can read and write in eight languages, having been rigorously taught between the wars in one of those gymnasiums they have in Holland for clever boys and girls. His best thing, along with teaching himself to play musical instruments, is maths. For a while he works as an actuary in a bank but he finds it boring so he now works for a pittance as an untenured junior lecturer in the maths department at the university in Cape Town. The girls' mum calls his mathematical activities 'puzzling'. She uses the word as a verb. 'Tätchen-herz is puzzling,' she says. It is just one example from her range of Germanic verbal peculiarities.

The flat is small and poky and if he is marking exam scripts at the only table, then the girls' dad has to clear them away at mealtimes. Dinah's horror times. Sometimes, presumably to blot out the girls' chatter going on in the same room, he will start to puzzle out loud.

Angel-Face and Dinah are amused by his mathematical gibberish and chant bits of it at each other. 'Pi to the curve,' they say. They say it as they take turns to climb onto a big wooden box called 'the klapkasten' and jump off. 'Pi to the curve.' Dinah envisages triangles of gooseberry pie with crimped edges. They do the same sometimes when he sings his Italian songs to their mother's accompaniment. There's one about a beautiful mouth, 'O bocca bella. O bocca, bocca bella'. For years they think it's about malted corn porridge because one of Lisa's many culinary favourites is a chocolatey porridge called Maltabela. The song keeps repeating the phrase so they giggle and sing along in silly voices, 'Oh Maltabela, oh Malta, Maltabela'. They suffer a similar misunderstanding with a mournful Italian worker song that makes reference to comrades who have died in the struggle. One is called Carlo Franchi. Since the struggle has wearied them, there is a reference to the Italian word for exhausted. Stanchi. It rhymes with Franchi. Dinah envisages it as a song about two clowns called Frankie and Stankie and she explains this to Lisa. She pictures them in orange bloomers and very small orange bowler hats. When Frankie is the right way up, then Stankie is upside down and vice versa. Lisa says that Beethoven is her favourite composer and Dinah says Mozart. If Dinah listens to some early Beethoven on the radio and mistakes it for Mozart until the radio announcer says it's Beethoven, then she'll say, 'That's why I didn't like it all *that* much.' Lisa does the same, only the other way round.

The absence of money is a trial to Dinah's mother whose family used to have lots of it, but now the money's all gone up in smoke – some of it literally, because the family houses in Berlin and Furstenwalde and Frankfurt-am-Main have been bombed to dust along with the businesses in which they had their investments – and the rest of it vanished when Dinah's mum's parents got cheated out of it as new immigrants in Cape Town. It's hard for Dinah's mum to be always thinking about saving tuppence on tins of beans and to get her head around the idea that the world she grew up in isn't there any more. Not even the streets are in the same place. And she's sometimes sad about her Aunt Ella, who is currently living like a pauper in one room of her own villa in East Berlin – or what had been her own villa until she was 'invited' to make it over to the state and watch it turn into a doss-house. Aunt Ella never married, having in her youth broken off her engagement to a Danish count. She decided to stay single and became Dinah's mum's favourite. She had made herself responsible for her niece's coming-out and took her on trips to Copenhagen on a boat called the *Schleswig Holstein*, where Dinah's mum used to win at deck quoits. She still has a china sailor doll with a hat that says 'Schleswig Holstein' in gold Gothic script on the hatband. And she still has one of the winning rope deck quoits. She keeps these in her knicker drawer and she sometimes lets the girls play with them. Dinah who loves poking about finds that her mum also hoards dark chocolate and Nescafé and Lux Flakes in her drawers from time to time, whenever there's a whiff of further trouble in the world. This is from living through the First World War in Germany. Swiss chocolate, Nescafé and soap powder are this life's greatest necessities. If you're German.

Dinah's mum has lots of stories about her childhood, unlike her dad who only has three. At the drop of a hat she will tell stories about skiing holidays in the Harz mountains and about her two boy cousins, the skiing champs, whose mum was Tante Berthe and whose dad was the judge. She'll tell about the seafaring trips she took with her father and her three brothers on their motor launch called the *Sophie*. Sophie is Dinah's maternal grandmother's name, but she never went along on the boat because she didn't have sea legs. She had no head for heights either, because when she was chosen, as the auburn-haired beauty of Wiesbaden, to represent the new century on new year's day in 1900, she fainted while waving regally from a specially constructed obelisk and her huge feathered hat wafted slowly downwards into the square from a great height, like a winged angel. In all the photographs, she's shown to have a fine hourglass figure and a thick mass of wavy hair. She doesn't look at all like Dinah's mum who is tall and thin with high cheekbones and widely spaced blue eyes and fine baby-blonde hair. Dinah's mum looks like her father who comes from the Danish Friesian Islands, but got sent to school in Berlin where the boys called him 'Bahne Banana', because his name is Jacob Bahne Jacobsen. All that Dinah's mum tells about holidays on the island, is that when you posted a letter you didn't need to buy a stamp. You just posted your fourpence into the box along with the letter and the postie knew it was yours.

She tells stories about the family dog, who was called 'Deena', but spelt just like Dinah without the 'h'. She tells about how Dina had been taught not to kill the chickens but couldn't resist taking them in her mouth and giving each one a little squeeze, so the chickens in the garden at Lindenstrasse vier-und-achtzich all walked with a limp. She tells about how her dad had bought Lindenstrasse from the estate of a reclusive old army colonel who'd lived surrounded by dogs and cats; and how the overgrown garden of the house was a mass of animal gravestones as far as you could see. 'Dogs to ze right; cats to ze left,' Dinah's mum tells the girls. There were the stories about the *Tiergarten* and the opera house, where the boat carrying off the Wagnerian lovers got derailed on stage on account of the singers' excessive, combined weight.

Now occasionally letters get through from the Eastern Zone in which Aunt Ella, old and sick, pleads for parcels of smoked bacon. Dinah's mum sends these wrapped in linen sewn up with a darning needle, though she doubts whether they ever arrive. Dinah watches her write the address in marking ink with a tiny dipping pen that she longs to have for her dolls, to use at their pretend school. Dinah has lots of dolls, the favourites of which, other than Rosema and the baby dolls, are Deborah, Naomi and

Jennifer. Rosema is closest to her heart, even though she has the look of a candidate for facial surgery and Dinah has replaced her original hair, which went matt and couldn't be brushed, with some unsightly black knitting wool. She has sewn this on with back-stitch along the line of Rosema's centre parting so that if she turns Rosema upside down she looks like a Mohican doing a head-stand.

At first Dinah despises Rosema because she is a rag-doll and proper dolls are made of china or celluloid or bakelite, and they can open and shut their eyes. Click, clack. So at first Rosema always dies when Dinah and Lisa play hospitals. They pick her up by one of her lanky limbs and hurl her into the corner. At this stage, the baby dolls command their strongest affections. These are called Wet 'Ums dolls and you can feed them from miniature babies' bottles filled with water. Put the dolls to sleep in their cots, and three minutes later their nappies will be soaked through. 'Oh, you naughty baby,' Dinah and Lisa say. They whack the babies on the bums before changing their nappies and putting them back in their cots.

Dinah, unlike Lisa, becomes obsessed with her dolls. They begin to exist in real time. They have school every day and Dinah makes them all miniature school books and school uniforms. Each chair in the living room is a different classroom, depending on the dolls' ages and their home time is staggered. She has to remember to fetch them all from school at different times. The neighbourhood boys who spy on her games, manage to pick up that Rosema is an abuse victim. They promptly follow suit, because all Rosema's body language is screaming at them to abuse her. They barge in and kick her round the garden like a football. They toss her high into the tallest trees so that she hangs for a moment in the branches by her hair before falling onto the red earth in a heap, like a poor broken spider.

Then, one day, a boy called David Cruise gets into a frenzy. Dinah watches as he shakes Rosema violently between his teeth, tossing his head from side to side. Then he throws her into the air and catches her in his mouth. He growls at her like a tiger and rips off the end of her nose. Dinah's eyes are opened. In a fit of guilt she takes Rosema to her heart and swears to love her best for ever. Having rejected her child, she now adores her with an extreme devotion. She has a total conversion experience. Having sewn up Rosema's nose with a needle and some of the flesh-coloured thread that her mother uses to cobble together holes in silk stockings, she announces, 'Rosema is my favourite.' She and Rosema become inseparable. Rosema is always Top Girl in school.

Anthony Thwaite

At the Millennium

It was a dead time. Ice on the river,
Snow on the banks, snow on the far field,
Sky white to the top, trees bare.

And nothing moved. Stiffly, the landscape held
Steady as rock, steadier than ice. The wind
Had dropped into a wide unmoving stare.

Till something moved: a thing with wings came down
Looking for something there, whatever it was.
There on the snow a brilliant patch, a stain

Concentrated, and still. And there it lies,
One spot of colour, gathered, focused, where
Whatever happened happened. What it was

Disturbs the landscape, hides itself away.
It is as if some angel in the air
Came to its aim on the appointed day

And touched the other's tongue with a cinder of
           dead fire.

Stephen Knight

So Early in the Year

Presumably the whole point is that there should be no
continuum: of anything. That failures of memory are
but a proof of a living organism's subordination to the
laws of nature. No life is meant to be preserved.

Joseph Brodsky: *In a Room and a Half*

'I really ought to stop
climbing trees,' you said,
nipping the filter off
another low-tar cigarette
then settling your arm
lightly on my shoulder,
giving me a squeeze
as if you didn't know
that you were dead.

— THUMP THUMP
thumpthumpthump . . .
The builder opposite
plays Capital all day.
His hammer in the air,
a nail between his teeth,
he dances,
dances like a little boy
till everything's OK.

The Green, fluorescent
after rain, is buzzing,
with ZIPPOS' grimy
Day-Glo trailers

scattered like toys.
While men lug rope,
funambulists in tights
pitch in, or practise
death-defying feats.

You looked quite wrong —
your eyes too far apart,
your hair too long
and coppery — and yet
the way in dreams
we know, I knew
(deep down) that it
was you, knee-deep
in reams of leaves.

The golden chain tree's
flowers blew away
so early in the year,
now wizened seedpods
hang above the path,
but they're juggling fire
out there, balancing –
on long broom-handles
– children, who throw

their arms out wide.

Carol Baxendale

The Flag

Kerry looks in the mirror and thinks, Ma, don't make me wear this dress, and watches her mother's reflection button the dress all the way down her back. She wants to call her Ma because that's what she would say if she was joking with her; she wants to make it funny so that when she says it, it won't hurt. She wants to say, Ma, why are you dressing me? But she's not going to say that either, because it would feel strange to speak to her properly – after nearly seven months. And the strange contented smile – reflected in the long mirror – stops her saying anything. It's been a long time since she saw a smile like this one; she noticed it a few minutes ago, when her mother bunched the dress up over Kerry's head. At first she liked being dressed. It made her feel warm and cosy, like in the old days, when she was very small and was dressed in clothes warm from the radiator. She smiled back, but her mother's eyes seemed to be focused on something hidden in the folds of the dress.

Kerry fixes her eyes on the floor, just in front of the mirror; she doesn't want to see herself being dressed. If the dress were different it wouldn't have been so bad, then she would have felt more like a model or an actress being assisted in her wardrobe change; she could imagine that. But this is strange. Can't she see I'm not a little girl any more? she thinks, and imagines herself suddenly sucking her thumb and making baby noises; she can see her mother's shocked face as her daughter turns into a dribbling baby; then she'd see what she'd done; she would cry and admit her mistake and talk much more to her. But then, what if Kerry behaved like it was too late, too late to be sorry, and not understand a word that was said, and carried on talking like a baby; talking like she really *was* telling her something in her own baby language, but couldn't get through to her. Too late. Too late.

'I know it's not new, darling, but it's a nice dress. Looked nice on Jenny,' she says in the flat, hollow voice that Kerry has come to dread, and is glad her mother rarely speaks to her. She wants to say, why don't you stop using that pathetic voice? She keeps her eyes fixed on the floor because she doesn't want to see the face that goes with the voice every time; her head will be tilted a little to one side – now that she's looking into the mirror – and she'll look kind of sad. Her eyes will get that distant look in them, as if she's in some kind of daydream. And she'll have that smile again: not the happier one that's come recently, but the old familiar one, the half-a-year-old one that's made Kerry start to think, Just snap out of it, Mother, you don't get people feeling sorry for you that way. It was Auntie Annie who'd said money could be a bit tight – seven months ago. It wasn't her mother who told her, it was Annie. And now all she can feel is bad about growing out of her clothes. But she's not going to say anything about that either.

So now she's wearing her cousin's dress. The dress had suited Jenny. But as she looks at herself in the mirror she feels a strange tightness in her chest; she's still breathing all right, but she can see in the mirror that it's all wrong, like her reflection is all in a panic, and might even cry soon. Somehow the mirror makes everything more real – the woman bending to concentrate on the hook at the top of the dress, blonde hair falling forward, making her look, suddenly, like a teenager; the hot flush of pink in Kerry's face, making her blue eyes too bright and feverish looking. The dress had suited Jenny.

Ma, she thinks, I can't wear this to a beach party, no way. The voice she wants to use is a pleading one. Anyone can see it's too tight. And another thing: she might have worn a flowery dress when she was ten, even eleven, but not now she's twelve; she had imagined saying something like this ever since her mother showed her the dress two days ago. She had dreaded this moment. If they see me in this, she thinks, they'll remember it for ever. It won't matter what I wear after this – they'll remember it for ever. Ma, I'm at the big school now. She could say it with a silly accent and her hands on her hips, pretending to tell her off, like – how could she have missed it.

Her mother steps back when she's finished straightening the dress and runs her eyes over bare legs, dress, shoulders, face; she sucks air between her teeth and frowns. Kerry remembers that she herself used to do that – even used to practise it in the mirror. She'll see now, thinks Kerry, watching her comb her fingers through blonde hair, a segment of long fringe falling over her face when she lets it go; sometimes she wishes she hadn't had her own hair cut short.

'Right,' her mother says, suddenly – brushing her hands on her jeans. She turns and looks vaguely round her bedroom. She's looking for something to lend me, thinks Kerry. She's seen it: Look, Ma, I'm nearly your height. But the tightness in her chest crawls into her throat when she sees her pick up the hairbrush from the drawers, and begin plucking from it a tangle of blonde hair.

'Good, good,' she says, vaguely, when she's finished with the brush. Kerry looks at herself in the long mirror, and watches her leave the room. Half a year ago she wouldn't have just left like that, she would have said a lot more, teased her a bit, laughed, noticed the dress was all wrong. And even if she hadn't noticed, Dad would have, and he would have said something because he couldn't help being honest, and it would have been all right – him saying it.

'Stupid dress,' she says out loud, 'I'd be better in some of the stuff I've grown out off.' She feels bad as soon as she's said it, claps her hand over her mouth, and watches her eyes grow big. 'How could you say that?' she whispers to her reflection. 'Mum's been to Hell and back in the last seven months.' She'd heard her say so on the phone; she'd heard it a lot recently. Even Auntie Annie had said it to Kerry – in a hushed voice as if they were in church or some museum. She'd also heard them talk in low voices in all the other rooms, but never in the same one as her. It's all she knows now – these hushed voices. No one shouts in this house any more.

She sits on the edge of the bed for a long time, staring at her reflection. Yes, it suited Jenny. For one thing she had long hair when she wore it – which had seemed right with this dress; shoulder-length hair like a shiny chestnut, fringe cut like a sharp blade.

The flowers on the dress look like they're meant to be rose-buds, but remind her more of glace cherries. And there are brown shapes that look vaguely like sultanas. All this on a background of cream. Like a cake. But the worst of it is, the dress is meant for a smaller girl. What's her mother thinking of?

'This foul frock,' she sneers, remembering a word her grand-mother used. 'Makes me look like a stupid doll.' She thinks of the time when she dressed her Sindy doll in a dress belonging to a smaller doll. It had big black cross-stitching across the front, gathering the cloth. It looked fine on the smaller doll because it nearly reached her cute big feet. But it made Sindy's legs look longer than ever. It wasn't Sindy at all, especially with her hair cut short like that – just like Kerry's.

The sleeves are long, but too short for Kerry's arms, and the hem fringes her knobbly knees, making the shallow dents on them look like eyes. It's totally the wrong length, and the sleeves are already cutting into her armpits.

'Tight!' she tells her reflection. 'It's too tight,' and she hides her face in her hands. Even crying hurts in this dress; it cuts across her stomach in tight pleats, making it hard to breathe. This is worse than Dad's funeral. It was bad enough then, having to wear a gross black dress. But Auntie Annie had said never mind, just keep your coat on. It'll be all right. And it had been; nobody cares much at funerals. Everyone had looked the same: all dark. And the dress, then, had been just a bit too big, but that didn't seem so bad. She'd forgotten about the funeral until she found the black dress again. Her mother must have been looking for something for her to wear, found it at the bottom of the cupboard in Kerry's room, and left it right there at the front – folded up on top of the other clothes she'd grown out of. It was a shock to see the dress, because she'd forgotten about it. She'd forgotten about kneading it like bread, into the floor – angry at Dad for leaving her with someone who didn't look like her mother, but stared through the kitchen walls and turned her face away from her when she walked into the room. Turned her face away, as if she couldn't bear to look at her. Why am I thinking about it now? she thinks. It must be seeing the black dress again; she remembers – after squeezing the dress into a tight ball – hiding it under a pile of shoes and toys. She's even started to notice things that have been there all along, like the photos of Dad on the mantelpiece in the front room; it's occurred to her that he's alone in them. Now she thinks of him as alone and separate from her and her mother; thinks of him being in the front room – every time she passes that door.

Remembering how small the black dress looked when she found it, she can't stop herself wondering how much she's grown. She knows it's a lot. She doesn't like thinking about it, because she doesn't like to think of her bones growing in the night. That's when it happens; Auntie Annie told her once. And not long ago she'd said: 'You must have grown a foot last night,' and laughed at her own joke.

So two nights ago – when an ache in her shins had woken her – she remembered what Annie said, and she knew – right then, right that very minute – that her bones were growing. She stayed awake for a long time, listening to her sister's tiny breath across the room, listening in case it ever stopped. Once she thought it did stop, so then she had to keep herself awake in case it happened again. She lay on her back – had to – to stop herself from hearing her own heart beating through the pillow. Then she started thinking of ways to change the dress, or maybe she could just wear her rucksack and hide a change of clothes in it, but the present she's got for Tracy is small and her mother might wonder why she needed the bag. Just for show, for effect . . . with that dress? I could dye it, she thought; go into town with Auntie Annie and choose a colour. Annie would help her; she was always dyeing stuff. Purple. Yes, purple. Tone the flowers down. A picture of herself flashed in her mind like a magazine shot. Black tights, purple dress, and the starry platforms Annie got her last Christmas. The dress in her mind had no particular shape, but it would have long sleeves – too long – that almost reached the knuckles, but that was good. And red streaks, magenta – just a couple – in her hair. Maybe one or two bleached strands, too, but it might not show in her hair because it's blonde and the sun had bleached it anyway. Then the dress grew into a shape; it was like Jenny's dress, but a little less tight. It became much shorter, but still the sleeves were extremely long, and now covered her knuckles, and dangled – with frayed woolly edges – to her finger-nails. The whole dress was lime green and very bright.

*

Sitting right on the edge of her mother's bed, her legs look too long for her body. Under her eyes she can see dark shadows, almost like bruises in the corners. She watches her reflection get up – stretching and yawning – stand on one leg, resting the toes of her left foot on the right, heel against shin.

'Pelican,' she says, staring herself in the eye. She looks at the rest of her reflection. 'Cake.' She stomps across the wooden floor and picks up the mobile phone left on top of the drawers.

'Jane,' she says, in a low voice. 'It's me. I'm in big trouble. You've got to help me. Mum's got me this awful dress. Lend me something will you?'

'Like what?' says Jane.

'Anything. Anything's better than this thing. It's making me sick just thinking of anyone seeing me in it.'

'Do you want me to bring something round?'

'Are you kidding? It would hurt her feelings. She's been through Hell, you know.'

'Yes, you said. Well, if Mum sees you she'll only tell your mum, so there's no point getting changed here.'

'We've got to do something. I mean, you won't even want to be seen with me.'

'I know. When I come and pick you up we can sneak round to the lane at the back of our house. Right, now: I need to know something about the dress,' Jane adds in a serious, businesslike tone. Kerry knows that Jane is going to enjoy doing this, organizing it all. She knows she'll make the most of it. 'Like, can you get anything underneath it?'

'Well, maybe a T-shirt.'

'Which one? What colour?'

'Pink. The pink one?'

'Right. I'm going to wear my long denim dress, right? I'll just wear a skirt underneath it. Leave it with me.'

Kerry switches the phone off and remembers hearing Jane's dad talk like that on the phone, when she went round to see her – leave it with me – urgent, but calm. She knows Jane will talk like that right up until they get to the beach.

*

When Kerry opens the front door, Jane is hopping, slowly, from one foot to the other down the steps. She wears a lot of short bunches in her hair – like frozen fountains; white partings zigzag across the back of her head. A pogo jump from the bottom step to the path – a twist in mid-air – brings her face to face with Kerry. She raises her eyebrows and a tight little smile makes the corners of her mouth turn down, giving her a mischievous look. Then her face changes as she looks over Kerry's shoulder.

'Hello, Mrs Stevens,' and Kerry knows she doesn't know what to say next because she just stares right back at the dress again.

'Hello, Jane.'

Today, Jane is wearing her sister's jacket; Lorna's fifteen, but the jacket's meant to be worn tight, so it doesn't matter. It's really plastic, but looks like leather, and it makes Jane look older.

Kerry senses that her mother's eyes are on Jane, and she turns to see her taking everything in: denim dress, jacket, hair. She's glad she's noticed Jane's clothes. That's the kind of stuff I want, she thinks.

'Take the mobile, Kerry. Just in case.'

'In case of what, Mrs Stevens?' says Jane.

'You never know, Jane, do you?' she says in the same hollow tone that Kerry dreads. And she remembers how she once heard her talking to Annie, in another room: 'I really don't like that Jane much,' she said. 'She's a little bossy-boots, and you should see some of the things she wears. Far too old. Far too old for her.'

Jane shoves her hands into the pockets of her baggy denim dress, shrugs, spins on one foot – crunching gravel.

'I hate her,' Kerry mutters as she follows Jane down the path.

'No you don't.'

As Kerry clicks the gate shut Jane jumps off the curb and into the road to face her. She bites her lip, smiles and points, with both thumbs, at her denim dress.

'Let's go round the block.'

*

'See? Right here,' says Jane, pulling loose bricks from the bottom of the wall. 'We'll just pile more bricks in front of it. You couldn't have got much under that dress, but it isn't that bad.'

'It's rubbish.'

'OK, here,' and Jane reveals a long, baggy skirt – hidden beneath her dress. 'It's Lorna's. Sneaked it out of her room. She won't know.'

'You took your sister's skirt?'

'She won't know.'

'Well, if you say so.'

Jane lets the skirt drop down to her ankles, straightens up, giggles, 'And she's fifteen. I had to roll the waist over,' kicks it in the air for Kerry to catch.

'That just makes the dress even worse then, doesn't it? I mean, if you thought I'd get into a skirt belonging to a fifteen-year-old, why didn't Mum?'

'I don't know. Here, give me the dress.' Jane beckons as if scooping something towards her; then she remembers she's seen Jane's dad do that, too.

The skirt has a slight sheen to it, and Kerry likes the way it rustles like paper as she pulls it on. It's just right: baggy, and almost down to her ankles with massive pockets halfway down the legs with chunky silver zips. Black skirt, pink T-shirt. Excellent. And pockets on the hips just big enough for a mobile phone.

Jane holds the dress up by its shoulders, inspecting it. 'You know, you could try things out with it.' Jane's not like anyone else she knows; she buys clothes from charity shops and makes things go together that Kerry would never dream of. Because Lorna is older she knows all the best places, and she's started taking Jane with her. Jane and Kerry talk all the time about the clothes they would make. They invent all kinds of new things, in their minds. 'Anyway, you could wear thick black tights with it. Dunno. Take the hem up?'

'She'd notice,' says Kerry, drawing pink lipstick along her bottom lip. 'She got the dress specially.'

'She won't mind.'

'How do you know that?' and she watches Jane hug the dress to her body, close the jacket over it, and look down at herself. Somehow it looks better with the jacket.

'You're smaller than me. It'd fit you better,' says Kerry. 'But it's still a baby dress.'

'Top bit is,' says Jane, nodding and wrinkling her nose up. She rolls the dress up in a black bin bag, hides it in the wall, and builds the crumbling bricks back over it. When she hears a laugh above them she spins round, looking vicious.

'How long have you been up there?'

'Long enough,' says her brother, grinning down from the wall surrounding the house. 'What are you hiding that for?'

'None of your business.'

'I've seen it now,' he says, scrambling down.

'Come here you little runt!' and Ian screams as Jane runs after him and makes a grab for him. Bent over him, his T-shirt dragged up in a tight fist, she peers into his face, says something and waits. Kerry can see he's nodding like he really means it.

'He won't say anything,' she says. 'We better get going.' A couple of skips in front of her, 'Hang on,' and pulls Kerry's cardigan together, ties it in a loose knot at the waist. 'That's better. And leave it open.'

*

There must be about twenty other kids on the beach. Some have broken away from the main group – sitting on the sand – and are screaming and laughing at the edge of the water. The sun is out, and small white clouds scuttle away from it. Kerry and Jane laugh and scream too, when a gust of wind comes at them from nowhere.

'Gritty food today, then,' Jane shouts over the sudden wind.

Tracy's mother, Mrs Adams is building a hill of sandwiches, the soft white oblongs appearing from the safety of Tupperware;

quick feet kick up sand – a bit too close for comfort. A big pink cake, covered in candles, sits on a trestle table. Tracy sits cross-legged, opening presents.

'Stay cool, stay cool,' Jane says because there are two girls looking at them who don't like them much.

The skirt feels good as Kerry crouches down to give Tracy her present. She feels older in it. Now they're out in the sun she can see it's not just plain black, but the colour of slate.

'I love this skirt,' she says, brushing the sand off the knees and walking barefoot with Jane towards the water. 'It makes me feel sick to think it's not mine,' and she nods back at the girls up on soft sand, 'because they don't know that I'm just pretending it's mine. They don't know that my real dress is stuck in a hole.'

Jane cups her eyes with both hands, and blinks up at Kerry. The frown makes her eyebrows look corrugated. After a long silence she shakes her head and says, 'I dunno. Shall we go over to the castle? And anyway,' she says, looking relieved to have thought of something, 'the other dress is pretend because it's not yours either. It's your cousin's, so there.'

*

The smooth, dark rock is warm and full of puddles. Jane squints at the bridge that stretches miles across river.

'A man fell off that bridge when they were building it. Fell off with his bulldozer – into the water. Happened when Mum was a girl.'

Kerry imagines the man still sitting on the bulldozer, lying sideways in deep wet sand when the tide goes out. The silent cars are glinting in the sun, and never ever stop. You aren't meant to stop on the bridge; you just have to keep on going until you get to land. On a less windy day she could have heard the cars. But today they move silently along, and all she can hear is the sound of the wind and the waves rushing.

The shocks of hair, jutting from Jane's head, shudder in the wind like cartoon palm trees. Kerry fixes her mind on their funny movement to stop herself thinking of cars travelling on a skeleton bridge; giant rib cage or backbone plunging into the river and stretching away across miles of water. Her eyes follow the zigzag paths between hair. But even the paths just look like skin. Pale skin, growing pink on the crown where the sun is burning it.

'I wish today wouldn't end.'

'Good fun, eh?'

'No. I wish I didn't have to go to bed tonight.'

'Why not?'

'I dunno,' says Kerry, feeling her mouth distort and the words shiver in her throat. She didn't know she was going to cry. She turns away from Jane and the bridge, pressing her fingers into her eyes. She cries so hard that the sun's warmth turns prickly through the cardigan. But with her eyes squeezed shut, the blackness in her mind is too much the way she imagined – when she lay awake at night – how being dead would be: a black nothingness – with hair and nails and everything still growing. So she opens her eyes and cries at the sand and the wobbly, screaming children further along the beach. She feels like a stupid baby.

'It's all right. It's all right,' Jane says, awkwardly and pats her on the back. She keeps on doing it until it's all Kerry can think about, and she wipes her eyes and sniffs.

'Thanks, I'm fine,' twisting away.

'I was just trying to help,' says Jane sulkily, pursing her mouth and folding her arms over the too big jacket. 'And why were you crying?'

'Don't know.'

Kerry juggles, in her mind, all the things she doesn't like: the dark, her legs hurting, and the sound of her beating heart through the pillow. But she can't think what to say about it all. Then she stares at the sand for a while and says, 'Do you believe in ghosts?'

Jane keeps her arms folded and looks as if she's thinking hard about it.

'I think so.'

Kerry begins to feel better. 'I think I do, too.'

'Have you seen one?'

'No, have you?'

'Yeah,' says Jane. 'I saw our old dog sitting at the top of the stairs once. I was going to the toilet, and it was dark and he was just there. Kind of lying on his front with his paws out, like he did when he was alive. He just turned and looked at me.'

'Were you scared?'

'Nah . . . no. I don't know. I just stepped over him, the way I always did.'

They look at each other for a moment and laugh. Neither of them say a word, just laugh. Dimples appear on either side of Jane's mouth. Kerry had forgotten about the dimples when she laughed, and with the hair trees and the mauve eye shadow round the eyes, she looks like an elf. Even the laugh belongs to an elf and it makes her keep on laughing until her sides hurt.

Further along the beach something has changed, and the girls grow quiet as they try to figure out what it is. Some of the others, by the water's edge have stopped paddling and jumping about. They're watching some activity on the road above the picnic. On the pavement a boy is marching, up and down. Kerry thinks, for a second, that she has recognized some horrible goblin she'd met in her dreams a long time ago. She knows instantly the shape of the head and the walk. Will Hardy. Lives in the next road along from her and turns up in funny places, like on a high wall – spitting on people below. He's marching towards the castle, shouldering a high flag, left arm swinging. Marching away from the castle and beginning a song – as he turns his head to salute the beach. They can hardly hear a sound until he turns to face the castle again, and then meaningless, snipped words are carried off on the short wind. But she knows the flag; it flaps – cream, brown, red. She hears Jane say, 'Oh! It's your dress!' And Ian is running across the road, catching up with Will Hardy, eyes searching the beach for Jane. They can see he's trying to drag the boy away because the boy's jumper sleeve stretches when he pulls, flicks back when he loses his grip.

'He's for it now,' says Jane, when Ian spots her, and she turns to Kerry, 'It's all right, they don't know it's yours. Stay cool. Stay cool. I don't believe he showed that jerk my hiding place!'

'Let's hide,' says Kerry. 'Go round the other side of the castle.'

'Yeah! He'll get bored and go away. Let's stay there till he goes away,' and Jane is already walking over the rock. But the unfamiliar sound of screeching car tyres makes her turn, and for the first time Kerry sees her looking confused. 'It's your mum! How could that happen?'

Her mother's car – their car – bumps up on the pavement and stops; the car still juts out halfway across the road when Annie and Diane jump out, leaving doors wide open – and run along the pavement towards the boy and stop, eyes wide and disbelieving. Kerry can see her say something to the boy, can see him ignore her; can see him march – three steps to the right, three steps to the left – right there in front of her. Then her face is all distorted and angry looking as she yells at the boy. He turns, and all they can see is his back and the long flagpole. The wind blows the dress, and they can see that it's tied to the pole by the arms. The dress struggles on the wind as her mother pushes the boy back and shakes him by the arm.

Kerry and Jane stagger, on slow sand, towards the strange scene. The look on her mother's face is the worst thing she's ever seen. It's like watching a film where the sound has broken down, and only bits of jagged words cut in – making no sense at all. And all the others on the beach look from the boy and Diane, to the girls walking.

'What's he telling her?' says Kerry, and sees Diane let go Will Hardy's arm, look over the beach, and say something to Mrs Adams. Sees Mrs Adams point in their direction. Her mother spots them as they get up close to the group. Jane says, 'Blame me. It's my fault. My fault.' Kerry thinks of brave people in films; brave people say things like that. Her mother's eyes are wide, and her mouth hanging open. Some hair blows across her face. She doesn't even pull it away and long strands stick to her bottom lip. Annie is there, next to her, looking at the dress – as the wind lifts – then at Kerry. It's a long tree branch the sleeves are tied to; from tight knots they spring out – white and frilly edged – like shocked hands.

'So there you are,' says Annie. She leans in towards her sister and says, 'Tell her off, Diane. Go on, it's good for you.' It looks to Kerry as if Annie's just amused by it all, but her mother is just looking right at the skirt and saying nothing; the vague look has gone and she seems shocked now. Then Annie starts.

'You could have said something, Kerry. Why didn't you just say something? You should have just said you didn't like the dress.'

Kerry keeps her eyes on the sand and waits for it all to be over. She slips her hands into the skirt pockets, and is pleased by the cool papery sound it makes. But then she starts to think of what all the other girls might be thinking. Maybe the best thing is to behave like this is nothing, like it's a misunderstanding. She can sense all the other girls watching, trying to figure it out. If they stop now she could still tell the others a story, make something up. She pulls the mobile phone from her pocket. She can feel the skirt brush against her legs, and she squeezes her left hand into one of the back pockets. She decides to keep her eyes on the mobile phone. She's taller than any girl here and wishing she wasn't, so that she could hide behind Jane – away from all those staring eyes. Pretending to read a message, and pressing buttons, she leans her arm on Jane's shoulder and lets her right leg go slack. She runs her eyes over the numbers, examines the on off button and her varnished blue thumbnail as she presses – randomly – one or two numbers.

'Kerry,' she hears Annie say. 'Kerry!'

She gives her aunt what she hopes is a daggered look.

'Why didn't you say something?' Dunno, she thinks.

'Look!' says Diane. 'I've had enough of this! You've hardly spoken a word for months! And who are you trying to dial on that thing – God? Need a little pow wow with God all bloody mighty? You just hang around the damn kitchen, saying nothing, an apparition of your dead father. Hang around like a know it all little ghost!'

'Jesus!' says Annie, staring at her sister. But Diane keeps on going – screaming and shouting, some words cut off in sudden gusts of wind, hair flying across her face, and then away from it. She's feeling relieved – even if it *is* her mother shouting at her; it's the most she's said to her in all the seven months. 'Do you know what you've done? Thought I'd lost you . . . that was it! Gone!' she waves her hand vaguely at the sky. She seems to stop and catch her breath, but she's looking at the skirt, T-shirt, Kerry's face and hair as if she's seeing it all for the first time. Then she starts shouting all over again – 'I tried to phone you . . . I wanted to talk to you! *Only* wanted to tell you I might come down. You had the phone switched off; what was I supposed to think? And then how do you think I felt sitting at a red light, and seeing that boy running down the road with your dress on a stick!'

Kerry's feeling lighter now, almost happy; it's like the sound has come back, but louder. She thinks, It's all right. Ma, it's all right; I'm here, just let it all out. Things are going to be different from now on. I'm going to be good and talk to you, Ma. Only, I'm not doing it with this lot listening; can't do it, Ma: they'd make a big deal out of it. We'll be all right, Ma. It's time we talked. We're going to talk so much from now on; if you only knew how much. I'm going to tell you about my fear of bones, about the dark, about the sound of my heart beating through the pillow. If you only knew all the things I'm going to tell you.

Francis Gilbert

First Moves

[from a novel in progress]

Her warm breath smells of that curd, *zsendice*, made from sheep's milk. She's been nibbling in the kitchen again. Naughty girl. She's whispering something in my ear. 'Look what I've got for you, Zoltán!'

I lift my head off the pillow, trying to banish my dreamy sleep, and look at her rosy hand holding out a large, ripe peach. The sunlight filters through the nursery window and dapples the fruit. Anna presses its downy flesh against my cheek and I savour its coolness while sinking back into the bed and shutting my eyes. I'm so sleepy.

'Come on, sleepy head, get up!' Anna insists. 'Take a bite.'

She stuffs the peach into my mouth and I find that I'm sinking my teeth into its sweet flesh. Juice dribbles out of my mouth and I can feel Anna's hands cupping the flow of it and wiping away the stickiness with the sides of her hands. Her small fingers are warm.

'Get up. You're dribbling, Zoltika,' she says, tickling me under the bed clothes. 'I'll give you a piggy back.'

I open my eyes and kick away the blankets, wheezing slightly as I stand up suddenly on the bed. I sniffle. A little bubble of snot blinks out of my nose and I feel my passageways clearing. I can breathe properly. I smile and leap onto Anna's back.

(Why are these happy memories the most painful? I could tell you the nasty stuff without a tear in my eye but this memory makes me want to dissolve into the earth.)

I immerse my cheeks in the silky texture of her thick, black hair. I listen to her vibrant breathing as she carries me out of the nursery and into the hallway. I'm already panting but her breath is steady and true. I can hear the pendulum clock ticking behind us in its ebony case as Anna thumps across the shiny floor and bashes through a door studded with milky glass. We flap through and laugh at the sight of the empty kitchen. Not a maid in sight! Where are they?

A large cast-iron cauldron, a *bogrács*, is bubbling on the big, white stove. From the vantage point of my sister's back I can see what's going on inside it. It's pretty disgusting. There are lots of eggs shells tussling around in a scummy, brown froth. Little bits of carrots and celery, and other vegetables that I haven't learnt the names of yet, keep bobbing up to the surface.

'Yuk. What is that, Annuska?' I ask.

'Don't look at that,' my sister says. She hitches me up higher on her back and takes a final run towards the window, letting me drop down onto the wide brim of the sill. She undoes the catch and opens the window. We can hear our maids screeching down below. But it's very odd because there's nothing to be seen; it's as if invisible people are causing a commotion in the courtyard.

Anna hitches me up on her back again and she rushes through a small door in the kitchen. We pass through a cramped room that has two mattresses lying forlornly on the floor, another small room, and then find ourselves at the top of a flight of stairs that look nothing like the main staircase of the apartment building. They are very narrow and dingy, the banisters don't have the fancy ornaments that adorn the other stairs, and there's a horrid smell of mould and bird droppings.

'Look,' Anna says, pointing down at the dark courtyard.

I peer over her shoulders, down through the maze of the buckled banisters and gnarled steps but I can't see anything. But when I really screw up my eyes, I can make out what is happening. At the base of the stairs, Teresa and Margaret, our two waddling maids, are beating the hell out of a pretty rug with their cane carpet beaters. Dust billows up out of the shadows and dances when it hits the slanted sunbeams that are pouring into the stairwell from the courtyard.

It's difficult to hear what the two maids are saying but I can see they are enjoying hitting the carpet with their *prakkers* and they seem to be laughing. I've never heard them laugh. The idea that they're not wearing their usual morose, silent faces seems inconceivable to me.

I lean further over the banisters and catch their words echoing up the stairwell.

'And this one's for the old crow! And this one's for his son, mewling, puling thing!' I hear Teresa saying.

Her greying, thinning hair is tied up in a knot. Margaret is hooting so much that she has to blow her nose on her ragged handkerchief. Before I can listen to any more, Anna's hands press against my ears and yank me away from the stairs, back through the tiny room and into the kitchen.

'Don't listen to them,' Anna says, obviously worried about what I might have heard. 'They're just big hens.'

I gasp. Calling a woman a 'big hen' is a great insult in Hungarian. It makes me think that perhaps the maids were referring to me when they were thrashing the carpet. When Anna squeezes my hand and whispers, 'I'll protect you,' my confusion only deepens.

I never feel entirely safe with Teresa and Margaret again after that. I won't even let them give me my nightly medicine. Only Anna is allowed to do that.

My sister grips my wrist. The spirit lamp throws billowing shadows against the roses climbing up the wallpaper. Darkness enfolds the big dolls' house that stands tall on the mahogany table: its tower, gingerbread trimming, jutting balconies and gothic windows cast spiky silhouettes onto the icy floor. I can hear the ebony clock ticking in the hallway and the hum of air in Anna's throat as she lets go of my wrist and pours the red liquid from a moulded brown bottle onto the tablespoon. She tells me to open wide. I shut my eyes as I swallow the horrid medicine, which tastes of old beetroot, and try to absorb the warmth of her body and smell the apricot scent that always seems to linger on her, and forget the wretched medicine.

'It will make you sleep better, Zoltika,' she always says as she places the brown bottle on my bedside cabinet and then climbs into her own bed that is situated in the far corner of the nursery.

Back then I wasn't convinced of the medicinal powers of that beetroot medicine. I thought that the elixir made it even harder for me to sleep, as it wended its way through my addled passageways and settled in my gut, making me gurgle and fart all night long. But I didn't worry. I always knew that I would sleep because Anna was in the room with me. When I heard the sound of her deep inhalations I knew that it was safe to shut my eyes and that soon the ache in my belly would disappear.

*

Our parents did not hurry to move with us to Budapest. They went motoring around Europe and judged us too young to go with them. As if to compensate for such negligence they left express instructions that we shouldn't be allowed outside of our huge, elevated apartment unless accompanied by our butler, János.

Although I had no inclination to venture abroad as long as Anna entertained me in the nursery, she was endlessly curious about the vast, golden avenue that sang outside our window. She was just tall enough to peep over the windowsill and peer down at the treetops that lined it. Every now and then she would heave me onto her back – against the wishes of Teresa and Margaret who were obviously worried I might fall through the glass – and show me the street below. The rich green leaves of the treetops obscured my view but I did see the occasional bonnet of an automobile or a horse's bridle flashing in the sun.

These fleeting glimpses of a totally alien world were enough for me – after my fateful trip to the kitchen even the shortest of piggyback rides tended to exhaust me – but Anna was not content. I would hear her arguing with Teresa and Margaret that she wanted to go to the zoo, that Papa had promised to take her there, and that he would have them beaten with their own *prakkers* if they didn't escort her.

'His Excellency told us that you must not go out until János comes back,' Teresa would reply in a meek voice – so unlike the vicious screech that she had hurled at the Persian rug that I wondered whether there were two separate Teresas.

After receiving this patient reply a few times, Anna would slam the nursery door behind her and return to playing doctors and nurses with me – our main recreation. You see, we had a wonderful dolls' house and a number of beautifully attired dolls to play with. Unknown to me at the time, the house was actually a valuable antique that Anna had retrieved, against our mother's express orders, from the library. It was an incredible object; I can see it as vividly as daylight even now. It was three storeys high, and had windows projecting from its sloping roof that allowed the light to flood into the attic where several black-suited servants slept in iron-framed beds. There were four narrow chimneys and something that Anna explained to me was a belvedere, or lookout tower.

'The belvedere makes this more than a dolls' house, it makes it actually a castle,' she confided to me once. 'This is a very important dolls' house.'

The tower provided the model with a simultaneously monumental and mystical aura. But the carved gingerbread trimming around the windows, balconies and the roof offset the haughty severity of the belvedere wonderfully well, evoking a contrasting cosy atmosphere.

Each window was pointed, smaller than a child's hand and held patterned glass, making access into the house nearly impossible from the outside. However, it was easy to open because it was divided in half by hinges and was mounted on wheels so that it swung open when you unhooked it at the sides. The interior was a real revelation. Despite its Gothic exterior, it was decked out like a proper English country house inside. There were five main rooms: a dining-room, a parlour, two bedrooms and a music room, all of which contained scaled-down furniture, including a tiny grand piano and brass handrails.

The dolls themselves, who were all girls apart from the dull-coloured servants, were dressed in colours of sugar almonds: primrose, lilac, pistachio and white. Each of their silk dresses was overdraped in transparent muslin, bustled and looped and trained. Of course this meant that one of the servants had to double up as a doctor while the white-dressed doll posed as a nurse when we played our interminable medical games. Usually, the format of these games was very simple. One of the dolls would fall out of the tower after being chased by a *prakker-*

wielding servant. Then the doctor and nurse would arrive and take the injured person to the parlour for a major operation.

I had absolutely no idea where my parents were and I didn't care. I didn't understand the concept of having parents. I automatically assumed that every boy had a sister who played with him and gave him medicine, two friendly maids who fed them and two sinister maids, looking just like the friendly ones, who beat rugs with their *prakkers* down in the stairwell in the early morning.

But I suppose my butler was much more of a parent to me than my actual ones. When I first encountered him I felt that I had never seen such a fine man as János before. His polished shoes patted across the varnished floor of the nursery with a crisp rhythm that seemed utterly thrilling when I compared his perfect tread to the irregular waddle of the maids. Only Anna's twinkling, feathery steps were more refined than János's walk. But I've never come across a more musical male gait than János's.

Those shiny shoes halted before me. He didn't deign to look at Anna but addressed me by bowing decorously before me. Then he ruffled and straightened his tail-coat, took my hand in his strong, weathered palm and kissed the back of my fingers. I can still remember the sensation of his whiskery moustache bristling against my hand, the smell of his freshly laundered shirt and the slight tang of his sweat unblocking my nasal passageways.

(Sometimes I wonder whether I was as sick as Anna claimed I was then. She was always telling me that I suffered from a terrible head cold for most of my childhood but the most vivid memories of my childhood are of smells: her sugary warmth, János's sweat, the maid's goulash, the coffee breath of Andrássy Avenue.)

'Your Excellency, noble son of the Count Pongrácz, I am for this one day, entirely at your disposal. I will serve you in any way that you see fit,' the butler said, and then with another shorter, more peremptory bow departed.

Anna stopped pushing the nose of the rocking horse with the same aggression that she had been when János had entered and ran over to me, giving me a big hug.

'But don't you see what this means, Zoltika? We can go to the zoo,' she said joyfully.

I remained limp within her grasp because I had actually been thinking that I would like to enlist János in the doctors and nurses game that we had been playing; he would make the perfect patient. So far we had only been able to play the game on lifeless dolls, the effect of which was beginning to wear off. We could operate upon his moustache and see what was underneath that white shirt. When I explained this to Anna, her eyes grew wide with disbelief and then she started to laugh.

'You can't do that. He didn't mean that.'

'He said he was entirely at my disposal,' I whined, my eyes brimming with tears at the thought that we wouldn't be playing doctors and nurses after all and that we would be forced to visit the zoo which sounded more frightening than Bluebeard's castle with all its wild animals. (When my sister lovingly explained the whole concept of the zoo to me, she omitted to mention that the animals were kept behind bars and so I had the impression that we might be attacked by lions and tigers, bitten by snakes and stampeded by elephants.)

When it became clear that I was determined to ask the butler to play doctors and nurses, Anna leaned closer to me and whispered in my ear: 'If we don't go to the zoo, I'll carry you down to the stairwell in the morning and you can get beaten with the rugs, you little monkey.'

It was the first time Anna ever threatened me. Her words had a sobering effect and I actually stopped crying. A little undulation of fear shot through my sickly frame: here was the person I most trusted in the world saying that she would make the necessary arrangements to hurt me. I didn't entirely give credence to her warning but I believed her enough to be thrilled by the fright.

*

Although it was directly outside our window, I had no idea just how majestic Andrássy Avenue was until I actually stood on its pavement. Standing in it for the first time felt like meeting a mighty king all bedecked in his royal finery. The tree-lined promenade islands seemed like the huge coils of jewels that hung around his neck, the great curling arches of its buildings formed his vast forehead, and the sunlit expanse of its roadway was his splendid smile.

I looked back at our apartment and gazed up, open-mouthed, at the enormous sculptures of Hercules that supported the pillars underneath the balconies of our apartment and thought how lucky it was that we lived in a place that was protected by such strong men. I almost wouldn't have believed that we lived in such a well protected domain but I recognized the royal red of the curtains and I could see the tip of the rocking horse's head poking through the gap.

János escorted me, with due decorum, off the pavement and into the automobile that was waiting underneath the shade of a big tree. Anna still lingered on the pavement, looking like a wind-blown rhododendron in her starched pink pinafore. I stood on the leather seat of the car, leaned over its rim and yanked at one of Anna's pink shoulder straps.

'Do we really live there, Annuska?' I asked.

'Of course we do, you silly sparrow. We're important,' Anna said, taking my hand away from her dress and squeezing it. 'And you're the most important person of all because right now you are the master of the house. You don't know what that means, do you?'

I contemplated this and realized that those huge strongmen with stone drapery wrapped around their naughty bits somehow indicated that we were not just anybody. Anna still hadn't got into the car despite János's best efforts.

'That means you can do anything. Even go on the subway if you want to,' she continued.

Anna really wanted to ride on the underground railway that ran underneath Andrássy Avenue. She was always making little tunnels underneath my bed and telling me that subway trains take you to the zoo.

'I'm afraid that the Count has forbidden for the young lady to go there,' Janos said sternly, waiting for the awkward girl to hop into the car.

'But the Count isn't in charge today,' Anna said with a wicked smile. And then pointing at my tiny figure, my head dwarfed by the big door of the car, she said: 'The master is. And he commands us to go on the subway, don't you, Zoltika?'

Ever mindful of her whispered threat about sending me down to the courtyard and leaving me to the mercy of those horrid *prakkers*, I said weakly, without really knowing what I was letting myself in for, 'Yes, I command that.'

János deposited us back in the apartment without a murmur of complaint. He stowed the automobile back in the garage where it had mouldered, unused, for over a year, and then took us both by the hand and led us down to the subway.

What a miserable place that subway was. Yes, I know it is supposed to be one of the nicest subways in the world – indeed it is the oldest in mainland Europe – but I hated it as much as my sister loved it. Before we boarded, she sniffed the singed air – caused by the ozone of the direct current electricity – and ran up and down the empty platform. János watched her with weary patience and held my hand. His fingers felt warm and solid.

When the train arrived, she pushed her way through the crowded carriage and squeezed onto the wooden bench next to a ragged old lady. Anna banged her as she swivelled round and knelt facing the window. The old lady was about to complain but she saw János glaring at her and lowered her eyes as if ashamed. Utterly oblivious to this exchange, Anna pressed her nose against the trembling windowpanes as we rattled through the darkness. She begged me to do it as well.

'You get such a funny feeling in your ears,' she said brightly.

I clung to János. I had never seen so many people. I didn't know that so many people lived underground. Anna kept calling me to look at the tunnel but I couldn't face it. I already wanted to go home and play doctors and nurses with the dolls. Dolls were so much easier to control than all these huge people with their flapping dresses, tatty trousers and scuffed shoes. I even saw several people whose feet were bundled up in newspaper. I wondered why their servants didn't polish their shoes. I shut my eyes and buried my head in János's black coat. It smelt clean and not frowzy like these chewed-up people.

Eventually we emerged from that long hole in the ground and strode into the sunlight. High above us, materializing out of the blue sky like the genie in the Arabian Nights, appeared lots of beautiful sea-green minarets, glittering in the sun. I was so engrossed in watching the interplay of the clouds on their effervescent surface that I didn't notice that a ring of frozen polar bears were peering at me from the top of a large archway. But I leapt back in fright when I did.

'Careful, János, they might eat us!' I screamed.

Anna giggled as János reassured me in his quiet, indefatigable fashion that there was nothing to be scared of because those bears weren't alive. Nevertheless I remained a little nervous of them and the two large, stone elephants who were poking their trunks at me as János bought our tickets.

We lost Anna as soon as János had bought her some candy-floss. She ran laughing – her cheeks all smeared with sticky, pink crystals – into the Elephant House and vanished. János didn't seem overly concerned, but I fretted. Firstly, I wondered if she would get trampled by the elephants or eaten by the lions. Then when János entered the elephant house and I saw the huge concrete ditch that separated us from those thundering feet and snorting trunks, I realized the idea of a zoo without bars I'd got from Anna was wrong. I suddenly began to think Anna knew nothing about zoos and had, contrary to her assertions, never visited one before. She was like one of those silly girls who entered Bluebeard's castle – running off into a place that was totally unknown to her.

By the time we had hurried past the animals and reached the Reptile House, even János seemed a little concerned that we hadn't seen a peek of that pink dress. The muggy air of the Reptile House oppressed me and the sight of lots of dead, white mice lying at the bottom of the cages seemed foreboding. Their little eyes oozed blood. I gazed at their crushed carcasses, pondering what horrible creatures could harm such innocence. And then the ground seemed to move beside them and a large, black snake rose out of the brown undergrowth. I jumped away from the glass and ran out into the yard.

Wheezing from these unexpected exertions, I spent a moment catching my breath and stared up at a knot of children twisted around what I believed to be a tall, misshapen, shaggy-haired man with a big mouth and nostrilless nose. Anna was at the front of these children and was feeding this monstrous humanoid bits of her pink candyfloss. When this 'person' opened his mouth, I realized to my horror that it wasn't a man at all but a terrible monster with a long neck and a scrubby hump on its back. When I saw its big yellow teeth, I automatically assumed that it was intent upon swallowing my sister and storing her inside its hump.

I ran through the crowd, yelling at the top of my voice: 'No, you mustn't touch Anna, you humpy monster!'

My protestations clearly had an effect because the crowd parted and Anna dropped her candyfloss as she turned around to face me. However as I approached, her shock at my outcry quickly turned into mirth.

'Zoltika, come here my little sparrow! It's not a humpy monster, it's just a camel!'

Even when she held me up to the railings and showed me the camel benignly chewing on some straw in the dusty corner of its pen, I still wasn't convinced: I already had a sense that the friendliest-looking creatures were the most dangerous. They lured you into a false sense of security. Ultimately, I was perfectly content to accept that I lived in the same world as vicious animals like snakes, lions, tigers, and tarantulas, but I was very reluctant to tolerate the existence of the camel. I couldn't believe it was really harmless.

I hooked my hand into Anna's and didn't let go of her until we left the zoo and were settled down on the horses of the merry-go-round in the fair. I was never happier than sitting on what I assumed would be a stationary black and white horse. Unfortunately I hadn't reckoned on it moving forward as well as jolting up and down. I screamed for the second time that day and let go of the supporting pole in a desperate effort to reach out for Anna's hand. But the awful waltzing music was too loud for my yells to be heard and besides, she was too busy trying to stand on the saddle of her horse to notice my pleas. I remained stranded. Behind me, angels blew their horns on the front of jingling sleighs and boats rocked about on stormy seas. I covered my ears and shut my eyes, trying to blot out this erupting world of movement and fear.

Eventually, the ride came to a stop and I climbed off, begging János to take me home. However this became difficult when Anna ran off yet again. The butler was compelled to take me in his arms and chase after her. He caught up with her in the courtyard of the Vajdahunyad – the amazing replica of Mátyás Corvinus's Transylvanian castle that is situated by the City Park's boating lake. Anna was gazing up in awe at its myriads of needle-point turrets and rows of arrow-slitted fortifications. Her small pink pinafore was so engulfed by that morass of arching stone and sloping brown towers that she looked like a little puff of candy-floss about to be gobbled up by its dragon's teeth.

Fortunately János was far too tired to entertain her desire to look around the castle, and he dragged her away as she said to me in confidence: 'I think that's where Bluebeard lives, you know.'

János summoned a cab and we trotted through Heroes Square with its giant statues, chariots and columns and down the glorious smile of Andrássy Avenue.

Kee Thuan Chye

A Sense of Home

[from a novel in progress]

Mama died two nights ago. Very quietly. No one expected. We were surprise because she's awways so . . . noisy. Dono wy but I diden cry much. In fac, I tink I feel . . . diffren . . . maybe like more free. Anyway, she never love me much lah. I know because she even tole somebody, in fron of me. 'I only love der boys,' she said. 'Der girl I hate.'

Mama love der younges boy der mose. Everyting Huat. 'Waa, my Huat got firs class in der U . . . my Huat jus back from tour, wen to Englan. You know how much dat cos?' Huat is now working in Kolumpur, seldom come back. Mama sick time, I call him to come and see her, he said got too much work. Now he's crying at der coffin. Wafor wan to cry now? Wen she was alive, nobody cared, now wy cry?

Firs Broder *lagi* worse. He living here in Penang, only take twenty minutes to come from his house, awso never bodered to come. Only wen he wans to borrow money, hnaa he will come lah. So many times he's taken money from Mama, from me, from dono how many people. Until der spinster auntie living opposite said she heard he's awso borrowing from der *chettiar*. Dat one der intres no joke. Every hundred, he got to give intres twenty. So he got no money lef to return us. Mama awways said it's like the river of no return.

Der las time Mama came back from hospital he came wit his wife and son to see her, den he never came again. She phone him, ask him wy, he said der wife woan let. Wy woan let? He said dono. Mama said his wife like three days wind, four days rain. Cannot tell wen her mood will change. But wat was so bad dat

47

she woan let him come for so long? Eight muns he never came. Mama died witout seeing him again. Today he tole me he coulden sleep der whole night las night. I wanted to tell him I wonder wy.

Doctor said Mama died of stroke. Someting like der vein in her head burs. She had very high blood but she never cared one, dat's der trouble wit her. Der spinster auntie, Bor Ee, awways ars her to take care, doan eat dis, doan eat dat, but she still doan care. She said, 'I got my medicine, never mind.' Firs Broder awso got high blood but he so young awso scared, dare not even eat outside. Little bit of salt cannot. But she – 'I *hentam* anyting lah. Big prawn awso I eat. Mutton. *Chhar koay teow*, my favourite. Anyting.'

Mama awways said she like steel. 'Sometimes my heart pain wen I carry der basket going marketing. Wokking from der market to my car hnaa pain lah but still I go.' She said she very clever woman. How if not for her, we would all be nowair. Some more looking young for a woman orready sixty-eight. She got married young actually, not yet eighteen. Dat time wartime and der Jappenees were looking for virgin girls to rape, so Grampa matchmake her to one of der Quek family in Pekan Buluh. Der town was very small and her husban very timid one. Mama awways call him idiot. One time, Mama said, he wen for interview for a job but he got so nervous he coulden tok, because the manager was an *ang moh*. He turn pale, said he wanted to vomit and got out of der room. He was shaking all over – aiya, you should see how Mama make like him wen she tole us about it. Funny lah. She real joker sometimes.

So, of course he diden get der job lah. Finally, got some frien help him to get Gahmen job in der Healt Departmen as . . . dono clerk or jus go aroun to check for mosquitoes, Mama said like labourer's job but I never ars him. Actually, he's not my real fader.

Mama met my real fader in Penang a few years after she gave birt to Firs Broder. He was very rich, multi-millionaire, Mama said, got big house in Nortam Road we can only look at wen we pass by. He was much older dan Mama and he awready got wife and chiren, but of course he never let dem know. Quite fierce lah, even at dat time got people doing dat kind of ting. And some more awready married. Mama was still living in Pekan Buluh. I dono how her husban took it. I tink some people knew den she mus have a boyfrien. After I was born and den Huat, Papa bought Mama a house in Penang, far from town so no one will know. Mama just lef her husban behind in Pekan Buluh and move into der house wit all us chiren.

Den Papa died wen I was only fourteen years old. Mama was very los. She cried a lot. I cried awso. But Huat diden cry at all, he never had any feeling for Papa. Mama was awso very sad because she coulden go to der funeral, afraid Papa's family will find out he was keeping her. Papa lef us nutting excep der house, der Austin car Mama was driving, and an insuran policy wort about $7,000. Suddenly, Mama had no income and she had to take care of us. She kep digging her saving until in de en, she had no choice, she had to sell der house. 'I had to bite my teet and do it,' Mama awways said. It was like losing someting very precious. She sold der house for $18,000, but now it is wort maybe ten times.

But wat to do? We move to stay wit Gramma and Grampa and Mama became like a servan to dem, cooking, taking care of der house, looking after dem. She diden feel comfortable like in her own house. Some more, her sisters were jealous because dey were scared she would take over der house wen Gramma and Grampa died. But Mama was awways dreaming of getting her own house one day. She let Huat go to der U, hoping dat wen he come out, he can get a good job and make a lot of money and buy a house. And she and me can move in and stay wit him.

Dat never happen. He got a good job, den he got married, he got chiren. Two years ago, he bought a house in Kolumpur. You tink he call us in? Las time, before he got married, he bought insuran and put in girlfrien's name. Wafor put in her name? She was not even married to him. Put lah in my name. I put mine in his name waat. But he doan care one lah. Der night Gramma died, he wen out dancing. Quietly took out a green shirt, shiny one you know, and change at a phone boot, like Superman! Mama knew waat but she never stop him. She let him do everyting he wanted but she awways stop me from doing wat I wan. Because Mama was saving money for him to go to U, I coulden go to Form Six. Mama said no point for a girl to study so high, better go and get a job. Den wen I was awready working, she said I cannot go out late at night, afterds *kena* rape. 'See *chhow lok*,' she scolded me all der time, 'you doan know ah you cannot trus men nowadays! If dey put someting in your drink, den you know lah. If anyting happens to you, doan come back, I woan accep you as my daughter.' Look at me now. I'm more dan forty and still not married. 'You become a spinster better still lah,' Mama use to say. 'You can look after me wen I'm old.' But I doewan to become a spinster.

She had a bad mout lah. Sometimes I wonder wat's der poin for her to be so religious, saying Buddis prayers every morning. Like dat time she call Firs Broder's wife Carol a low-class girl and somebody reported to Carol. Waa, nex day, Carol came to *tooi chee*. 'What do you mean I am a low-class girl?' she shouted and all der neighbours came out. It was so loud. 'How can you call me dat, hnuh? Waa, in fron of me, you act so good but behind my back you say all kinds of tings. Somebody tole me you got ole man keeping you las time, your chiren got diffren fader, so you got more class or I got more class? If you tink I am so cheap, wy you let me marry your son? Wy not we get a divorce? Come lah, tomorrow we go to court and get a divorce!'

Shameful lah, dat quarrel. After dat, Carol never tok to Mama. Den she got pregnan and she was losing blood a lot and she had to be admitted. But Broder had no money to admit so Mama had to come to der rescue. So later, Carol realise lah and she tok wit Mama again. And wen der baby came out, Mama gave Carol *ang pow* and boil strengtening herbs for her to drink. I wonder how Mama can forgive dat bitch after all der bad tings she said. But I suppose Mama is like dat. She say tings and later regret. It mus be her temper lah. Very bad. Wen Firs Broder was a baby, he cried a lot, and one time Mama got irritated she press a pillow over his face and nearly kill him.

'*Ee m chai see ah*,' Mama awways said wen she got angry wit Firs Broder for letting Carol control him. But he awso one kind lah, so scared of his wife. Dey are staying wit his moder-in-law because Carol prefer it. It really broke Mama's heart because der son mus awways bring back der wife to stay, not go and belong to der wife's family. It's disgraceful. So Mama awways scole him and say how hard she took care of him wen he was a baby. Dat time, he use to *tarik* a lot and she had to wok miles into der coconut estate to look for a medium to cure der fit. He tole her she had to catch cockroaches and take out deir intestine and boil in water, den let Broder drink. She did dis everyday for a few weeks, den only he was cured.

Mama died wit little money lef. A bit of jewelry. A seventeen-year-old *lor cho'* car. Dere's enough for a decen funeral. She awways wanted dat. Die awso mus be gran. Good ting der place to keep her bones at der Buddis temple is paid for awready. Der problem now is maybe her sisters will come and take over der house so dat means I'll have to move out. Only las week, Mama was saying she wish she had money to buy a house, small one awso never mind. 'I wan to die in my own house,' she said. It was as if she knew.

I tink for her funeral we mus arrange for her coffin to pass by our ole house. Mama might wan to see it again, for der las time.

Atima Srivastava

Stanley

There she is, she walks. Little girl. Bones. That blue nylon dress. What did they used to call it? Crimplene. The bodice is fitted. Although there are no curves on her, the skirt flares carelessly, the material can't fall properly because she's not a woman yet. Her hair is black and brushed out. My mother didn't like me doing that. Wanton. Thought I was trying to be like a film star.

Now my hair is streaked with grey and I use a dye on it. I wear it loose around my shoulders. I've done that ever since I haven't lived in my mother's house. A marriage makes you old. Tired. When I think about the work I used to do I wonder why I was never tired then. My husband says I'm obsessed with keeping a clean house, that I use the housework to evade his conversations. He never asked me to do all this, he didn't believe that women should stay in the kitchen. He says I hide behind the drudgery when we should be having fun, we're so young still. We should be playing squash on Friday nights and go for a pizza later and have friends over, his colleagues from the council accounts department. He wants promotion, he doesn't want a wife who stays in the kitchen, he wants me to make interesting conversation.

Most of all he wants to make babies.

She's walking, nearly skipping, there's almost a skip in her step. It's a dull afternoon full of grey clouds and weak sunshine but she's going to the Brook. It's a little clearing, about ten minutes' walk from her mother's house. A secret, right in the heart of London. Of course they don't live in the real heart of London, they live on the outskirts, the 0181 area, where it is cheaper, where you have to wait ages at Camden Town to catch the connection which only comes three times an hour. Nothing happens there. But the Brook is a place she has found for herself.

She came upon it one day when there was a bus strike. She had to walk the distance from the supermarket, there was no question of getting a taxi, it would have defeated the purpose of saving money. She heard it before she saw it. Beneath the road, by the disused viaduct, a clearing. Clear water running in rivulets, a private world, moist and dark, a little wooden bridge, a smell of moss, clear and fresh. A forgotten place. And there, by the edge, she saw him. Stanley. Quietly eating sandwiches from a white paper bag.

He was an old man. Even now I see him in my memory and even though I'm grown up now, he's still old. He must have been about seventy. He had white hair and rosy cheeks and fine threaded veins underneath. He looked like all English people, his nose a little snub, his skin pale and pudgy. He gave me the rest of his sandwiches to throw to the ducks. We sat side by side in silence.

I was a strange girl. I wasn't envious of white girls who skipped unselfconsciously down the road. I didn't want to go to Girl Guides or the youth centre to meet boys and dance to disco. I didn't mind not being like them, the other girls at school. To me, they were like the men on the moon.

Anyway, I didn't have the time.

My mother went to the factory at five thirty in the morning, so I had to get my dad's breakfast and then prepare the vegetables for the evening meal. Then I made sandwiches for myself and put them into the Tupperware box. I told everyone that I didn't like school dinners but they all knew the truth was that we couldn't afford it. My mother taught me to do savings wherever possible. It was necessary. My dad couldn't work, he had to go to physio-therapy to learn how to use his arms and legs again.

He'd been very active before the fall. In Kenya, he had been in the local cricket team. He used to like playing cricket with my brother, diving across the park to field the ball. No one at the Post Office knew he'd fallen down on the slippery floor. He had lain there for hours before the supervisor found him, moaning to himself in agony. The hospital didn't like talking to us and couldn't understand my mum's English. The doctor got irritated when she didn't understand what a stroke was. He explained that my dad couldn't use his limbs any more and his speech would be slurred. She was suspicious. She thought they'd done something to him in hospital, how could a fall, a simple fall from a step ladder do all this damage? But it had. My dad came home a vegetable.

He used to cry all the time. After making up my Tupperware box, I would prepare lunch for him to heat up: two rotis and a dry bean curry. It wasn't a hardship, he couldn't eat much, it took so long to get the food in his mouth. I had to go to school. After school, I would make us both a cup of tea and start cooking the evening meal. Sometimes, my dad would sit at the formica kitchen table and watch me fry up cumin seeds, careful not to burn myself. My mother had warned me. No one else would be able to run the house if I was careless and burnt myself and got myself into hospital. Other times, he would walk himself slowly into the other room and sit in front of the television watching the repeats from the morning. There was a limit to what he could talk to a twelve-year-old about, even if he could talk. He went to physiotherapy twice a week, the bus came to collect him, but those days he seemed more depressed. He couldn't do it. He was ashamed at having to go. He didn't like the therapy, it made him realize how helpless he was. White people were different, being independent was in their blood, they were brought up like that. Us Indians, he'd say, we were fatalistic. God had meant it to happen, there was no point in trying to change your destiny.

Although my mum had a little shrine in her bedroom where she prayed every morning after her bath and lit incense, she wasn't the kind of woman to let God have his way. She asked for the hardest shifts at work, did the longest hours, saved every penny, shrunk her face into a skeleton. It was a few months before she realized she could have claimed compensation but the English forms told her it was too late now. She slapped me across the face when I put too much salt in the dahl and we had to throw it away. We had to manage, she knew we had to manage. She told him to swallow his pride and queue up at the social security office to claim his disability benefit. At night, I could hear her fighting with him when he could hardly speak, she told him this was no time for pride, we were entitled to the money, he could not provide any more. No one was going to help us. The Post Office, all those friends he'd had there, none of them had told us about the compensation. The supervisor sent a little basket of flowers with a get well soon card stuck in it.

They used to call my dad Jay there, they wouldn't pronounce Jaideep. It was a common name in India, especially in the Gujerat where he came from. He had gone to Kenya to work as a clerk in the railways as a young man and married there. My mother's family couldn't afford to support them when I came along and I was brought over to India as a baby, to live in my grandparents' house. I explained to Stanley how it wasn't a terrible thing to do, it happened to a lot of kids. Grandparents in Indian society weren't considered outsiders. In any case, I knew nothing of genealogy. My ancestral home was like a heaven. I spent my childhood playing on the swings in the backyard, being pampered by everybody who all thought I was something special with my big eyes. The women of the house would sit on the verandah, one after the other as if we were in a canoe. Each checking the other's head for lice and rubbing jasmine oil into the scalp. I was at the end of the row and would wriggle away, running about gleefully, but although they scolded me, no one could contain my exuberance. The man I assumed to be my father would offer me his hand, make me promise to hold on tight as we weaved around the open-air vegetable market full of yellow, red and brown spice hills on flattened hessian sacks. The hollering vendors gave respectful salaams to my guardian. All of them seemed to know where we lived. It was a big house with trees and goats and chickens and as far as I knew we were as rich as kings. The day my mother arrived to take me back was the worst day of my life.

I can't complain about my husband. He is a good man. He knows all about me, about why I never put on any weight after the age of sixteen. He knows about every broom handle, every saucepan, every hairbrush she hit me with. He knows about how she pulled my hair out once, a thick clump in her fist. He's educated, he's got five CSEs, he could have gone to college if he'd wanted. He says that medically that couldn't be the reason that I never put on any weight, but he believed me, he was the first person that I ever told and he believed me and I was grateful to him. He said we would get married and he would wash away all the past.

We live in a different area now and although it is far from my mother's house, it is the same type of dull tree-lined street where neighbours do not become friends. At the beginning I thought I would make a clean break and never have to see my mum again, I would show her that I had survived, that I had made a life for myself. But my husband is a good man. He said I was safe now and turning away from my mother would mean turning my back on my brother and father. It wasn't my dad's fault, he couldn't have done anything about it, he couldn't have defended me, he was too helpless. It had all happened so very long ago.

When my mum offered us two thousand pounds to help towards the deposit for the house, my husband said we should take it. I made him promise it was a loan and that we would pay it back within three years because we hadn't to be beholden to her. He didn't mind eating rotis and dry lentil curry and not going out or on holiday, he didn't mind me taking his salary and putting half in the building society account with the highest interest. We were happy he said, and his family was large and loving and they came to our house every weekend with food and news and we were all right. Over the five years we've been married, after paying my mum back, after that, he even helped my parents. He would read over complicated forms for them, advise them on the kind of insurance to take, dig the garden for weeds. He said to forgive was a virtue.

He drives us over there every other weekend and gets them out two Hindi films from the grocery store, because it's important that we all sit as a family and do what other families do. He sits and talks to my dad about this and that, mainly about his family and his expected promotion that the Council's been promising him for the last three years. Sometimes they talk about how stupid English people are because they don't understand about family values. My dad's almost normal now. His speech is still a bit slurred but he's almost back to his old self, it's been fifteen years, they've passed by us and we've lived through them. Now he mows the lawn and initiates conversations and he's even got a part-time job back at the Post Office. The therapy did work, he's right as rain, everyone says so. Everyone knows it's all due to my mum. Everyone says: Taraben you are my *heeeeroooeeeene*; Taraben you are a *marvel*, look how you've managed your family; hats *off* to you Taraben.

The day my mother arrived to take me back, I was in the backyard playing on my tricycle. The woman who I thought was my sister came and scooped me up in her arms, told me my mother had come for me. I giggled at the joke. I knew who my mother was, the lady with the salt and pepper hair who admonished me for eating too many chillies. I didn't understand, but it was quite simple. The stranger in the doorway, with the long oiled plaits in the blue sari holding a baby at her side was my real mother. The woman I had known to be my sister was my aunt; the couple I had regarded to be my parents were in fact my grandparents. I began screaming the place down. My aunt cuddled me and explained that my parents had got the opportunity of going to England, a place across the seas, a wonderful place. We were entitled to go there because my mother had been given a British passport in Kenya by the British government and now I had a little brother our life would be full and beyond my dreams. They were adults, they knew about what was right. I would be part of my rightful family and have access to education and who knew what, which the West could provide. My baby brother clamped to her sari, my mother's eyes watched the proceedings from the arched doorway, big almond eyes, no dark circles, no skeleton face yet, a handsome woman with her life ahead of her, twisted gold earrings, impatience on her brow. My grandparents' faces loomed above me, hands touching my hair, clicking tongues chiding my tears. I was surrendered, given up. My mother towered above me, blue against the blue. She raised her arm and slapped me across the face. 'What a cry-baby my daughter has turned out to be. Don't you know how lucky you are?'

When we go for the weekend, my mum purses her lips as I make tea in her house, in that kitchen that used to be mine. She tells me I've been married for five years now, what's the big idea? If I'm not careful my good husband will leave me. I tell her we're trying. She tells me there's something wrong and I should get some more tests. My husband says the same thing. He's been to the specialist, there's nothing wrong with him. I can't complain. I chose him. He was my choice. I didn't have an arranged marriage. Stanley used to say, you choose, it's your life.

All kinds of people go to the Brook. Entwined lovers strolling through autumn leaves, schoolkids throwing crisp packets and playing with spiders, joggers bypassing the main road. It's dark there, even when the sun's floating overhead, it's like an underworld. Stanley's face lights up as she scrabbles down the side, twigs crackling, she's too impatient to use the muddy steps. She slips in beside him, crouches next to the little fold-up stool he sits on. They don't need to talk, touch, they look into the water. Stanley's fishing line cuts into the stillness. Stanley likes oranges. He tells her things he remembers. The end of the Second World War, his aunties humming out of tune with clothes pegs in their mouth, evaporated milk for the first time on tinned peaches. Stanley's old, she likes to listen to him, sometimes his nose runs and he doesn't realize it, then pulls out a large hanky. He consults his watch, the little steel links make indentations around his pink wrist, the mottled glass face sparkles its numbers in the sunshine. Time to reel 'em in, he says.

Stanley never catches any real fish, because there aren't any real fish in the Brook, not ones you can hold up and weigh. Sometimes he hooks a few tiddlers and he shows them to her. They wriggle about in the palm of his big puffy hand, they jump and twitch. She gingerly touches their scales, so soft, so unexpected. He winks and throws them back into the water and they watch the rippling circles till the water's still again.

My mum's done all right for herself. She's got a car now, she passed her test after failing six times, even though she still can't park. She's the kind of woman who doesn't give up. She looks down her nose at the English people she works with who haven't got a pot to piss in. Managing her family's never stopped my mum from having fun. At the weekends when I was still there, even when my dad couldn't use his arms and legs, she would invite her friends to the house on Saturday afternoons. Other women from Kenya, their kids and husbands, some who worked in the factory alongside, others from surrounding streets. All the women would spend the day cooking together just like I do with the women from my husband's family, and the house would be noisy with gossip. They talked about the new season of saris and who was getting married or having an extension built. My mum would put on her good sari and lipstick. Everyone would watch Amitabh and Rekha on the video, speculating about their off-screen romance. The husbands would sit and talk in low voices with my dad who couldn't speak. It didn't bother them, they just carried on the conversation: the petrol was two pence cheaper at Hendon quadrant, 10-kilogram bags of Tilda basmati were available in Cost Cutters now, electrical goods were discounted in Patelbhai's shop in Edgware, my brother's wedding must be arranged soon – he had been seen loafing with bad company outside Finchley Gaumont, someone's daughter-in-law hadn't got through customs at Heathrow after waiting one full year – the shameless officials gave her a virginity test, the Shah's newsagent got broken into, blacks of course.

My mum made sure that my dad wasn't left out, everyone overlooked his disability, and talked to him like normal. They weren't embarrassed when he had to slurp his tea. If he spilt something, someone would wipe it off; when he tried to join in the conversation, they'd wait, help. They were good people. Indian families knew about community. Not like white people. Stanley has a house like my mum's, but there's no shimmering picture of Ganesh on the wall, there's no plastic covers on the three piece suite. His house is quiet. He's invited her back there for a cup of tea. She watches him put the kettle on, telling her to sit, he can do everything. His kitchen's different. There's no jars full of lentils and rice and flour. How does he cook, she wonders, there's nothing there. In the fridge, she sees bacon and a bottle of milk, a dozen eggs. She only gets to eat an omelette on Sundays, her mother says eggs are an expensive luxury. There are no bowls covered with clingfilm with yesterdays leftovers. He doesn't boil the tea in a saucepan like she's been taught to do.

'Haven't you got any friends?' he asks her earnestly, as he unclips his watch and lays it flat on the check tablecloth. They sit opposite each other at the kitchen table, their hands around the steaming mugs. His white eyebrows are shaggy over his eyes, but his eyes are bright blue as they stare at her. He offers her a ginger nut but she refuses, suddenly aware that she is in a strange white man's house drinking tea. She can hear the slow deliberate ticking of the watch.

'Haven't got time for friends,' she says cheerily.

He looks at her curiously and sips his tea.

'Tea all right?' he says.

'Yes fanks,' she says.

'You've got a right London accent on you,' he says.

I was twelve when I met Stanley at the Brook and I knew him till I got married, twelve years later. My mum and dad thought they knew all about me but they never knew about Stanley. He was my friend. He was white. He was who I talked to about choosing my subjects at school. He said I had to talk to the careers adviser, even though I tried to tell him I wasn't the type of person to have what they called a career, the school was too busy with the top streamers. I didn't understand about making plans for the future, I thought life was only a question of living. My mum and dad came to the school meeting, but my mum didn't ask any questions, she thought it was up to the teachers to decide. She didn't know what to say. Stanley reckoned I should try with English and Art. He said he'd always liked the idea of writing stories, but they put him in the bottom stream because he couldn't read. They found out later he was dyslexic, but by then it was too late, he couldn't catch up. My mum looked at me slyly when I said I wanted to do Art, as though I had something up my sleeve.

My grandmother was artistic. When the auspicious time before a festival came and the fronts of houses were decorated with rangoli, my grandmother didn't make the usual geometric patterns and simple flowers. She had skills. Squatting for hours, she worked her fingertips through the bags of red and yellow powders, pouring them from her fist to create a fantastic Ganesh on the verandah. She let me add little circles of flour alongside the trunk. My grandfather invited the neighbours who came and gasped at her expertise. I always knew they would not survive each other. After my sixteenth birthday, my mother admitted the telegram had arrived weeks earlier telling of the funerals. I knew then, that I was on my own. She said she hadn't wanted to upset me. My dad looked sad. It was all a pack of lies. They had stopped me from writing letters years ago. When I was twelve I had written to my grandmother about how unhappy I was, how much I hated my mum and wanted to go back and live in India, because I had forgiven her for not being my mother. A blue aerogramme addressed to my parents had arrived on the doormat some months later. They never read it out to me. My dad put his hand on my shoulder one day as I was preparing the vegetables, his eyes glazed, his speech slow and painful. He said it was better to not upset them back home, they had their own troubles and silly childish letters could be misinterpreted. We had real troubles to contend with such as his accident and now my mum had become the sole breadwinner, I had to take my responsibilities seriously. I knew he was afraid. My mum had a fit. She closed the kitchen door and twisted my arm behind my back and yanked a chunk of hair out of my scalp.

All of Stanley's kids lived far away, they'd never been any good at school. His son lived in Milton Keynes and his daughter in New Zealand. Stanley didn't seem to mind that they only ever sent Christmas cards. He showed me pictures of his wife, he kept them all in an album underneath the dresser in the hall. They'd had a fine life together until she had died suddenly in a road accident, just when they were ready to enjoy their retirement. There were photos of them on Whitley Bay eating fish and chips on their honeymoon. He didn't know anything about Indian people and asked me what we ate. I said we weren't really Indians, I'd never been to India, neither had my mum and dad. I'd been born in Kenya but all I knew was North London. I don't know why I lied to Stanley other than I felt that any connections I had with India had now gone, been severed. Stanley asked if I'd like to go to India one day and I said yes, it sounded lovely. There was the Taj Mahal, and the mangoes and the sunshine, and people had verandahs and everyone was happy. I'd seen it in the Indian films, the dancing girls with swirling skirts, the jokes, the fights, the tears, the hero. These lists I reeled off to Stanley, but I knew

I would never return to India. There was nothing left for me there.

Stanley asked me questions no one asked. He seemed to think I had an opinion of things. I would go over to his house after school, whenever I could manage it, just for a half-hour, before running home to make the evening meal. Sometimes three weeks went by. He didn't mind, he was always happy to see me. Beaming, he'd consult his watch at the door, as though he was marking the auspicious time of my visits. There was no one else I wanted to tell if I got a good mark in class, other than Stanley. I'd save it up. He looked so pleased, as if he'd got the mark himself. The woman who lived next door used to look at me suspiciously. She stopped me one day, demanding to know why I came to see the old man.

'Are you bob-a-job?' she said. 'I've got some ironing needs doing. Why should he get all the benefit, he already gets Meals on Wheels.'

'Mind your own business,' shouted Stanley. 'She's come to visit me. She's my friend.'

The woman was pegging out her clothes. 'All right grandad, keep your hair on.'

It would be a different story today. No one carries on like that today. If I had met Stanley today, she would have called the social services because there would be something funny, something indecent about an old man entertaining a young girl. It's a different world today. Stanley's been dead for years. I can't ask him things any more. I can't seek his counsel. I can only remember. He's dead and I have to go on living. No one can help me now as he helped me. I have no one to ask what to do.

I didn't get many qualifications when I left school, but Stanley asked me what I was going to do with my life now, and I had no idea. I supposed I would get a job in the factory making soft toys like my mother, but she had bigger ideas for me. She told me there would be more money in the Council. It was miles away and I didn't want to work in an office surrounded by files and forms but I was lucky to get a job there. At the end of the week, I gave my pay packet to my mother, so she could run the house. I explained it to Stanley. We don't believe in the individual I said, we believe in units, money was pooled, everyone was taken care of, that's how it worked with us. It was a different way of living.

I used to go to the library in my lunch hour. Stanley gave me the idea. He told me how he'd worked on the docks, it was hard labour and his wife used to take washing in and they lived in rented accommodation in Wapping. She'd taught him how to read. He'd thought he was illiterate, but she didn't believe it. She'd go to the mobile library every Thursday and get out novels with big print. She'd read to him at night, as they sat in the front room of their two up two down. He said he got the hang of it gradually, started reading for himself. It was a whole new world. He told me that proper libraries, not little mobile trailers, but proper solid buildings were stood all over the place, wonderfully situated within easy access. Full of silence and millions of books all catalogued and free. You could go and read and no one could stop you. You could read what you liked. I went and took hardback books off the shelf randomly, turned the pages. My heart skipped beats. Sometimes I'd sit there all through the lunch hour, just looking out of the window, gazing at all the books around me, so warm and cosy. It felt like something was happening in my life.

My mother says Western medicine doesn't know everything. She doesn't trust hospitals, they keep secrets. She says she knows better cures. She's told a pundit about my problem and he's given her a poultice to give me. I've got to pray and fast and drink it twice a week, and soon I'll be blessed. He's got a 100 per cent success rate, he's made many couples happy. I'm angry, but I don't say anything. My husband's telling my dad something that happened at work. I can hear their muted laughter slipping out of the front room, leaking into the kitchen. I bet he knows. I bet she's discussed it with him. She's discussed my infertility with my husband and the pundit and her friends. She's supposed to ask how I feel about it first. But what's the point, you can't say things like that to Indian people. They don't know what you're on about. They think you've become Westernized. My mother would laugh if I said I wanted to talk about my feelings. Talk about what. You have a life and you have a duty to go on living till it's over. You get married, you have babies, you look after your husband, your family, his family and you get by. Everyone has to. And what's the shame, she asks, guessing at my anger. Babies are natural, why shouldn't she help? Babies are important to a marriage.

It was Stanley who first talked to me about sex.

We used to go to the park sometimes during my lunch hour. He was a pensioner, so he used his free pass on the bus to Hendon and we'd walk about. I was in a routine. My dad was getting better, my brother had got married to a girl from India and she helped in the house, my mum didn't have to do double shifts any more. We had a colour TV and a new carpet. My sister-in-law was a blessing to the house, she was very smart. I'd thought my brother had chosen some village bumpkin who I would have to show the ropes to, but when she arrived at Heathrow, confident with her six suitcases, I was horror-struck. She could cook and clean, she could chat easily with my mother's friends. While waiting for her Visa, she had enrolled in a computer course so that she could work in England and contribute towards the household expenses. Everyone thought she was a gem. She could tell you funny stories while putting intricate henna patterns on your palm. She was finally the daughter that my mother really wanted. Stanley asked why they hadn't arranged a marriage for me and I said I thought they had forgotten about me. My brother had been good at school, they were banking on him. But surely you've got a boyfriend, said Stanley. I was embarrassed. But you're a lovely girl, there must be men queuing up for you, he smiled.

'You're eighteen now, it's such a lovely age.'

She's still a girl. She looks at him and suddenly tears well up in her. It's the park and the open and everyone can see but she can't stop. Stanley looks taken aback, gives her his hanky, the soft cotton soaking against her cheek.

'Why tears?' he says. 'Don't spoil your looks. What on earth's the matter?'

'I don't know about anything, Stanley,' she says. 'I don't know what's to become of me.'

'You should have a boyfriend,' he says, full of concern. 'Won't they like it, your mum and dad, if he's not coloured I mean?'

She wants to laugh through her tears because he understands so little and yet he cares for her. She matters to him.

'It's no good,' she says. 'None of it. I wouldn't know what to say.'

'You have a lovely conversation, my dear,' he says. 'Of course you know what to say. You just haven't the confidence. Don't worry. It'll happen. Sex is a good thing. It's healthy.'

She looks at him, horror in her eyes.

'Sex?'

He smiles and pats her hand. 'You choose,' he says. 'It's your life. You choose a boy for yourself. Don't worry about what they all say.'

We sat in silence watching the park. I never had to say anything to Stanley, his gentleness was always around us. Suddenly he asked me why I didn't have a watch, everyone had watches nowadays. He'd seen digital watches in the market for knockdown prices. I looked at my bare wrist. I didn't need a watch because my life itself was clockwork. I left the house in the morning at the same time and left the office by the clock on the wall. I always got the ten-to bus and arrived home thirty-five minutes later. I got changed, had a cup of tea, started helping my sister-in-law with the dinner. The TV was always on in the front room and the music let me know it was an hour before we sat down together to eat, a half-hour before my mum came home from work. We all went to bed early, after dark in the summer, when the heating went off in the winter.

Stanley suggested we take a different route back from the park. He was smiling to himself. He stopped at a jewellers on the High Street. He took off his heavy watch and told the jeweller to size it to my wrist. My mouth fell open. He told the man to keep the extra links in an envelope.

'I don't want any discussion. You put them back when you get married, dear,' he said to me. 'You can give the watch to your young man to wear.'

No one had ever given me a present before. I could hardly speak.

'I'm never giving that watch to anyone, Stanley,' I said.

At Christmas, Stanley had no visitors. He said he didn't mind because his children had their own lives. I couldn't understand it. I told him to sit while I made the tea. He would smile and describe the Meals on Wheels Christmas dinner, the paper hat out of the cracker and the glass of sherry he had with the Queen at 3 p.m. 'You mustn't worry about me,' he said, 'I'm all right. You worry about yourself. You make something of yourself dear. You've got it in you. You just need the confidence.' I had to hide the watch in my room but I wore it every day at work, the heaviness weighing down my wrist. During the day I'd compare the time with the big clock on the wall, checking to see the minutes ticking by.

It was as though an era had passed, a sweep of time, the past had gone. My mum had changed once my sister-in-law came to live with us. I felt like a ghost in the house, wondering how I had lived through the beatings, staring at myself in the mirror to make sure I was still there. Because of Stanley, somehow I knew I existed, was real, undamaged. The scars of the past had gone away, like a dream I had been pulled from, and yet the world was spinning away. I didn't feel afraid, I didn't feel lonely, I didn't feel anything and I liked it. No one could do anything to me any more because I had an invisible cloak that deterred whatever came towards me. When I thought of Stanley the world seemed still and it was like entering a garden full of sweet flowers and the air let you breathe. It never occurred to me to tell Stanley about the things that had happened to me. You couldn't talk to a stranger, a white man about the goings-on inside your house. It wasn't decent.

My sister-in-law was thick as thieves with my mum, they were always discussing how to keep my brother on the straight and narrow. My mother was very proud of herself for having chosen a bride from India, even though generally she didn't have two good words to say about Indians from India. She declared they were cunning and clever, users, unlike the East African Asians who were a gentler people, loyal, friendly. Our trouble, she would say holding court amongst her friends, was that we were too gullible. Mind you, she loved my sister-in-law, because in her own way, my mum deferred to India and all it represented in her mind. The home of her ancestors. Sometimes they would leave me to get on with the meal while they sat upstairs like schoolgirls looking at the dowry my sister-in-law had brought in six suitcases. There were suits for my brother and my dad, saris for me and my mum, shawls, jewellery, all between white tissue paper. I knew it wasn't that they didn't love me, Indian people just don't show it like English people. Not that Stanley ever hugged me or anything. Yet I knew. I knew I mattered to him. I told him all about the man I chose to marry.

It was like fate meeting my husband. I knew that whatever happened, I was not going to let my mother choose a husband for me. Not that she ever mentioned it. I wanted her to say it, dress me up, take a full-length colour photograph to send to boys' families as other parents did. Yet, I was ready with my refusal, my stubbornness against any sort of care that she dared to show towards me.

I met a man who was the same colour as me, the same caste. His family even came from the same village as my ancestors, it was as though he was already my family, and there he was working in the Council Accounts Department. One day he came and sat on my desk and took me to the pub and bought me shepherd's pie and Coke. His family was different to mine, they could eat whatever they liked, even the girls. He said his sisters were doing secretarial courses because his mum wanted them to be educated before being married.

There she is. She should look different, there should be an aura of love around her, she's getting married to the man of her choice, the man she has met through her own volition. Stanley nods his head as she speaks, tells him the facts and arrangements and rituals of an Indian marriage, that she too has recently learnt. Her marriage is not to be the grand affair of Indian films, but everything is to be done properly. She tells him how her husband squeezes her hand and says they will be all right together, they will help each other. He knows she has suffered, he will be her future, they will bury the past. She is so thankful, so grateful, so relieved that she can leave her mother's house within protocol, but she doesn't know what to say when Stanley asks if she loves this perfect man.

'Yes,' she says, at a loss. 'We will be good for each other.'

Of all people, it was my brother who understood about the marriage. He had been there, all those years, watching from doorways, listening behind doors. At the wedding, I caught him looking at me through the crowd. There was a strange look on his face, it was full of dread. In that moment I felt closer to him than I had ever done. I chose my moment. It was once we were living in another area in our own house and my sister-in-law organized a picnic for the four of us at Virginia Water. She chattered while she lay out the chappatis and pickles under the willow tree, flirting affectionately with my husband as all sisters-in-law should do, chiding him for ruining his health with cigarettes. I walked with my brother to the small shop for bottles of water, pulling the tail of my sari around myself, shaking my hair free in the breeze.

'So, I'm going to be an auntie?' I smiled at him.

'Does he make you happy?' he asked suddenly, urgently.

'Yes, of course,' I said.

'It's been only six months. How can you be sure?' he said, the same look across his face that I had seen at my wedding.

'What's the matter?' I said.

My brother sank to the grass and began to cry, strange hollow uncontrollable sobs, kept shaking his head to throw the tears away.

'All those years. I did nothing. I knew how she treated you. I let you take it. I did nothing. You had no one. It was unforgivable of me.'

I held my brother's head in my arms.

'Don't you see? I survived. I married a good man. I never blamed you. There's nothing to forgive. I'm happy now. Everything is good. And there was someone. There was someone.'

My brother was the only person I ever told about Stanley. About the Brook and the fishing and the walks in the park. He looked at me with a queer expression.

'Dirty old man,' he said and I knew he hadn't understood at all. He had just wanted me to forgive him.

'Not that bloke who died? The son came and took up the garden. Rented the house out to students. Not that bloke? I think

I remember him. I thought he was some sort of spastic. What could you have been thinking of?'

When we came back from the honeymoon, I had taken my husband to meet Stanley. Just as I had been unable to explain to Stanley my love for my husband, so I had not known how to frame my relationship with Stanley. He was an old man who lived a few streets away. It seemed as good a definition as any. The woman next door told us Stanley had gone into a hospice. A cold terror had run down my back, because I knew people only went to those places to die. My husband offered to drive to the address but I didn't want to go. I wanted to grab my new life and live. I didn't want to think about Stanley any more. He didn't have a place in my future. He had been part of the life that was now over. I wanted to live like other human beings in a world of affection. I was determined to manage my life. So Stanley had died while I had been busy with my new life. I had thought of going to see him in the hospice but I didn't want to say goodbye. Things just happen, people just slip away without you noticing. Things just change without you realizing. I accepted Stanley's death as casually as my brother had mentioned it. The sun was shining brightly overhead. We had all moved on with our lives.

After paying back the debt to my mother, three years into the marriage, my husband spoke gravely to me. He said he had done his best to be a friend and a husband to me but it was impossible to be close to a dead person. He said he felt sorry for me but he could not understand how anyone could be as cold as I was. He said it kept him awake at nights. He said holding me was like putting his arms around a tree stump, there was no humanity in me, no warmth. My husband didn't want to live that way and he asked me if I wanted him to go away so that I could be happy. I didn't know what he was talking about. I had nowhere to go. I was dumbfounded, all I could hear inside my head was a kind of white noise. I could hear him telling me that he could not fault my duties as a wife, as a housekeeper. It was something else. Something was missing. He was tired. He couldn't do it any more. There was something missing in me. I did not have the ability to love anyone. Perhaps I was more like my mother than I knew. His words tumbled out and out into an ocean that filled the room. Because my husband is a good man he did not leave me. He started to sleep in the spare room and said we should continue our married life for all to see. Perhaps things would get better.

Things became worse. I felt like a stranger in my own house, a ghost again flitting through the walls, and snippets of the past kept zooming around the days. He had killed something inside the very core of me. It was not something that I could talk of. I simply grew away from him.

My infertility has given my husband a subject. He is obsessed with making a baby, because he is human and he wants to love me, he thinks we will be able to love each other if we produce the proof of our love. We have continued for two years and perhaps we could have continued for longer if we hadn't been burgled.

Last week, we came back from my mother's house, driving in silence to our house. The back window had been forced open and the front room completely ransacked. The television, video, hi-fi, even the glass ornaments from the sideboard had gone. The settee had been slashed with a knife. As my husband stalked around the front room, his hand pushing his hair back, searching for the phone, my heart began to beat. I raced upstairs, hardly able to breathe. I didn't notice anything. Not the wardrobe thrown open, not the bathroom in disarray, not the chest of drawers thrown around the floor. I started scrabbling inside the drawer underneath the double bed where the sheets and towels were kept. It was difficult to get a breath. I reached into the far corner of the swaddled drawer, stretching my fingers into the recesses. I could feel it. The small paper bag. I scrunched it in my hand, and even before I had pulled it out, I knew it was empty. Stanley's old watch and the remaining links were gone.

She's crouching on the floor, holding the paper bag in her hands. She cannot move. She cannot see her husband coming into the room because she is howling so loudly she cannot breathe. She cannot stop the flood of tears, her body shakes uncontrollably. Her husband is at her side. He puts his arms about her, buries his head into her hair.

'I've been a fool,' he says. 'Nothing matters. Only that we're all right. I love you. They're just things. Don't worry, don't cry.

I've never seen you like this. I'm going to take care of you. Nothing will ever tear us apart again. Just you and me.'

I realize he doesn't understand anything. He doesn't know that it doesn't matter to me. However deep I search inside myself, it doesn't matter and black is the same as white, love is the same as pain. It's a strange feeling, different to feeling invisible. It feels like not being present. I look at the paper bag and the only thing I can remember is Stanley fishing at the Brook, in that private underworld where we met. Perhaps I loved Stanley, perhaps I was loving him all the time but I didn't know, will never know. I watch my husband on his knees, professing love for me, making plans. The house, the world outside seems so small, and both of us in this room, crouching. So much smaller.

Khan Singh Kumar

The Indian Who Thought
He Was English

Just for a minute I was in with the English,
thick with their skin
or thick with just their words
and no one asked in the local:
where is it you really come from
you sojourner from a strange land
from a childhood of bud-bud
who has forgotten his own pubs
and tries to be part of the picture?

I was one of us, at ease,
welcoming late-comers when all my mates
were there supping for the great game
on an ends-of-the-earth nostalgia.
We were taking on foreigners,
shouting at the screen
as though our nation would live or die by it.

I tucked my voice into theirs
without splitting to a guilt-word from a turban'd
               ghost
or shame or feeling of estrangeness to a single voice.
I wasn't black or latin or half anything,
I was unconscious of a home
living its Indian life in my name,
or the need to keep that secret-self
from my friends, to still this smiling face
as I went back to the frame
of my tear-filled wife to hear:

Those shrubby people . . .
where you go . . .?
They colouring our wall . . .
Why still we here . . .?

Shrubby = drunk

Tim Liardet

The Wasps' Nest

'The hole through which everything poured, beneath
        the rug . . .'
wrote Liu Hsün, but we had a wasps' nest.
Almost as if our great room of desk and clock and
        wing-chair had begun to sag

and sink, where some keep cash, we had a wasps'
        nest. And board after board
blocked the view. So did the rug.
Beneath castors and claw-feet – though its towers and
        ladders were crude –

it began to draw at the whole house, bowed the long
        joist beneath us
like the weight of the afterlife.
It toiled in its place like an engine softly burning gas

on the wick of itself, dipped deep. And this was
        strange. We feared
the flame of it. Not that
it seemed to threaten us but the heads we heard gently
        butting the boards

that traversed the pit far below, made us afraid. We
        feared the swarm.
It was our thoughts though,
not Council steam, went down beneath the floor of
        the towering room

and the water lilies of the Chinese rug floated in light
into the furnace of stumbling wasps

to sense something that might make us welcome at a
        later date

burning out a gulf through the cracks and knot-holes,
        beneath the lid.
At times, it seemed innocuous,
a glue pot, a piecrust slapped on pocked timbers, a
        pat of swallow mud,

but at others, forgive me, we grew uncertain if the
        nest was glued to the house
or the house was glued to the nest.
At such times, it seemed the house was perched above
        a precipice

as if all its roots and foundations were suddenly flying
        out over it,
just hanging there, while
the wind of twenty thousand wings beneath it took
        its whole weight.

It was a summer of drought, and I stepped into the
        rug's radiance where
the great bay printed its shape
and I sensed the nest massage the soles of my bare
        feet like a jacuzzi of fire

and we wondered if perhaps it was a symbol of wealth
        sent to us,
or of bankruptcy, or both? There below
was it the windfall, or the bailiff's notice slapped on
        the dusty window?

Or was it a gateway? Again and again we dreamed
        the multitudes
of wasps, each one
among the many like a fizz in a helmet or an
        armourplated ohm

crumbling the breach, until the din filled our heads,
        rose above tape-hiss

and kettle, Mozart and the mains.
And we traced the vaguer image of ourselves in
            earphones

in the lens of the television once we had switched it
            off, seated as if
at one with the room's
curvaceous perspectives, in caps, unable to drown out
            the hum.

Was it some sort of centre, beneath our feet? It seemed
            to coincide
exactly with the balancing stem
of the rug's huge floppy lily. It seemed almost as if the
            stem led

further down into the heart of things, as if such solace
            depended
on such combustion,
perhaps, or as if somehow such depths of turbulence
            were required

to hold the petals so, stock still. The pit of crawling
            coals,
we dreamed, seemed to draw in
everything to itself like a cistern that fills and fills and
            fills

and melts the wax walls of its sides like smelting
            gold and dissolves
our shape and overflows
though the Chinese lily does not for a moment
            tremble. Nor change its pose.

Clare Wigfall

When the Wasps Drowned

suggested musical accompaniment:

The Wasps – Aristophanic Suite, Ralph Vaughan Williams
The Flight of the Bumblebee, Nikolay Andreevich Rimsky-Korsakov
Be(e)bop

That was the summer Therese stepped on the wasps' nest, and put an end to our barefoot wanderings; the summer when the sun shone every day and everybody commented upon it, old ladies breathing heavily on park benches, fanning themselves with well-thumbed issues of *Woman's Own*. 'Oh, isn't it hot?' they'd sigh, and I, desperate for conversation, would agree and smile and sit high on the wooden seat and imagine myself as old as they were. It was all anyone seemed to speak of that summer, the heat, and I knew that when the weather changed we'd still be talking of the same thing, only then we'd be blowing at our hands and complaining of the cold.

That was the summer the garden walls seemed suddenly confining, when finally I was tall enough to peer over their mossy tops and look across the line of gardens and see sheets, dried out in the heat, listless in the still air, and hear the tinny music of distant transistor radios, and the ache of cars moving slowly in the hot sun, their windows wide as if that might change anything.

That was the summer they dug up Mr Mordecai's garden.

We heard her screams from inside. I was standing at the sink, barefoot on the lino, washing up the breakfast dishes, soaping them lazily, watching the light play on the bubbles. Tyler was curled under the kitchen table pushing a toy truck back and forth, smiling at the rattle of its metal wheels. Hearing her scream, I dropped a glass which smashed against the tap and fell in jagged pieces into the dishwater below. She was running in circles round the garden, shrieking, a halo of angry wasps blurring her shape, her pigtails dancing.

For the first few moments I just stood, mouth agape, watching her through the grime of the kitchen window. I didn't want to go anywhere near Therese or all those wasps. As I ran to the back door, Tyler rose and toddled after me. I remember him laughing as I turned the hose on her, he thought it all a joke. Dripping with water, her sundress clinging to a polka-dot of red welts, Therese continued to scream into the afternoon. Around her on the grass, wasps lay dark on their backs, legs kicking, wings too sodden to fly.

Mum was out at work all day. She left us to our own devices. Sometimes I'd take them out, Therese picking at her scabs, Tyler strapped in the buggy. We'd walk down to the park and I'd sit by the swings and watch the boys. They'd stand in a huddle by the public loos, puffing on cigarettes and coughing. They never spoke to me.

Other days we'd just lie out back in the heat. I'd fashioned a bikini from a pair of pink knickers and an old vest which I'd cropped just below my nipples. I had a pair of green plastic sunglasses I'd bought at the corner shop and the yellow flipflops Mum now insisted we wear. I'd sunbathe while Therese scoured the grass for wasp corpses. When she found one she'd place it on a paving slab and, using a stone, pound its body to dust. Tyler would squat sagely beside her. I'd watch them idly, lift an arm perhaps to point out another dead wasp lodged between blades of grass.

It was maybe early August when she and Tyler started to dig under the garden wall. Sitting in its shadow, they scratched away with sticks, collecting the dry earth in a plastic bucket. 'Help us, Eveline,' they'd say, 'we're digging to Australia,' but I'd just roll my eyes and turn the page of my magazine. The task would occupy them for a while and then they'd come and loll next to me. Tyler flat out on his stomach, snuffling as the grass tickled his nostrils, Therese plaiting together thin strands of my hair.

So we'd lie and wait for Mum to come home, her uniform sweaty round the edges. Then she'd sit, her legs up on one of the kitchen chairs, complaining how her feet were swollen, watching as we prepared the fish fingers or chicken nuggets.

I never felt like moving in all that heat, everything seemed an effort. There was a day I remember; I was lying on my side, eyes closed. Therese, finished her digging, was flopped next to me. One plump arm was curled in a damp embrace around my knee. She was breathing hotly against my hip. I opened my eyes in a slow squint against the sun. Therese's other arm was flung out above her head.

It was the glint that caught my eye. I only saw it as she jerked her hand at the buzz of a fly. Wedged on her thumb was a thin gold ring, studded with small diamonds. There was dirt lodged between the stones, but still they caught the sunlight and glimmered. At first I didn't react. I just lay there, watching.

'Therese,' I questioned finally, 'where did you get that ring?'

'Found it,' she sighed.

I heaved myself up by one elbow and took her hand in mine to look more closely at the small piece of jewellery. 'Where?' I asked.

Therese yawned before rolling onto one side and up. She walked me to the hole they'd been digging. It was deep and long now, tunnelling under our wall and into Mr Mordecai's garden. We knelt down and peered into its depths. It was too dark to see much. Therese took my hand and guided it into the hole. I knew straight away what it was I could feel, but I told Therese to run in and find the torch. She came back a moment later and we angled the light. At the end of the tunnel a pale hand reached towards us.

We said nothing as we looked. The skin was mauve in places, the fingernails chipped and clogged with soil. Suddenly the day around us seemed unbearably quiet, as if everything was holding its breath.

'I think we'd better fill up the hole, Therese.'

Scrunching her lips, she nodded. We collected the plastic bucket, and shook the earth into the hole, patted it flat with our hands.

Leaning across to her, I took the ring from Therese's thumb and slipped it onto my right index finger. She didn't protest.

And so the digging stopped. We ignored the bald patch of earth by the fence – the mark of the aborted Australia project. Sometimes I wore the ring, but only while Mum was at work.

The long days continued to melt into one another. Mum would put us to bed and it would still be light outside. Beyond the curtained windows the world continued and we could hear it all, ever clearer than winter nights when it was dark. Tyler and Therese were too hot and tired to feel they might be missing anything but I would lie awake under the sheets, listening to the street and the muffle of Mum's radio downstairs.

One night Therese woke crying from a bad dream. She padded through to Mum's room and I could hear them across the landing, Mum's voice comforting and sleepy, Therese's diluted by her tears, 'and I was watering the garden, Mum, with a blue watering can, and it started to grow . . .'

'Sleep now, my love, shhh.' I wanted Mum's gentle shush in my own ear. When I closed my eyes I could see Therese's dream, the arm growing up through the soil like a plant.

The holidays began to roll to a close. The days were still stifled by the heat and we were running out of ways to fill them. By that point we'd even begun to miss going to school. Very occasionally, Mum would leave sweet money. Then we would buy Smarties, lick the shells of the red ones, and rub swathes of scarlet food colouring across our lips. That's what we were doing when we heard the door bell ring. I flipflopped through the cool of the house to open the front door. A man and a woman stood on the step.

'Is Mum or Dad in, love?' As she asked the question, he peered over our shoulders into the hallway.

I blinked up at them through my sunglasses. Therese and Tyler were both clinging to my bare legs, Tyler fingering the elastic of my bikini bottoms. Pouting Smartie-red lips, I told them Mum was at work, wouldn't be home until six. I held my right hand behind my back.

She bent towards us and smiled. I tried to stand taller. 'Maybe you can help us then. We're from the police department, just want to ask a couple of questions.' She held out a photograph of a late-teenage girl. A holiday pic, the girl was sunbrowned, smiling at something beyond the camera lens. 'Do you think you might have seen this girl?'

We all looked, then shook our heads.

'Are you sure?' she held the photo closer. 'You wouldn't have seen her on the street or anything?'

We all shook our heads again. The man loosened his collar, wiped a trickle of perspiration from his forehead. He caught my glance and smiled. I didn't smile back.

'Well, that's all then,' said the woman, lowering the picture to her side. 'You've been very helpful, thank you.' She stretched out a hand to ruffle Tyler's curls. He pressed closer against my leg.

I shut the door and we waited a while, heard them walking down our garden path and unlatching Mr Mordecai's gate next door. My fingers, fiddling unconsciously, played with the ring for a moment as we stood together in the dark hallway. None of us said anything. Taking Therese and Tyler by the hand, we stepped back out into the sunlight of the garden.

Caitríona O'Reilly

Anxiety

Something had made a killing.
A few small bones by the wall
were sticky with dark blood
but no parts of wing or skull

survived to tell me what it was.
What was it? By afternoon
the petrol-coloured rain had come
and washed it down the drain.

So I wondered if a bird
had ever been killed in a corner
by a wall, and moved off slow
like those pompous burghers

of Oslo do, in *Anxiety*.
But something had made a killing
and the corner worried me
with everything I had, not noticing,

killed. Like those sickish faces
underneath their stovepipe hats,
a yellow shriek of sky behind them
and beyond. It was like that.

Anne Stevenson

Red Hot Sex

Miranda hoists her lips in a grimace.
Her arms are two peeled twigs, her ankles curl.
That dark soft hair and narrow porcelain face?
A sketch, a spoiled first draft of a pretty girl.

She's friendly with Fred, whose electronic chair
(State of the art for men who can't stand up)
Glides around hers, not touching anywhere.
He's spread into his, an egg (soft boiled) in a cup,

So cheerfully disposed he makes a joke of that.
He's been in a chair since childhood. Awful burden.
Parents worn out in their eighties. Misses his cat.
A brother, whose wife can't cope, talks of a Home.

Here he's neither home nor in a Home.
Laughing, he makes Miranda laugh. And me.
A heap among heaps, I glance around the room,
Our island of wheelers in a walking sea.

Thanks to the cash of a caring modern state,
We've space and food. It's institution-dreary,
But OK. When strong enough, I paint.
My helpers set me up in the conservatory,

Paint book, water glass, tray, plates of gouache.
Don't laugh when I tell you, all I paint is flowers.
As long as my Minnie Mouse paw can grip the brush
I forget my melting bones – for those few hours.

And once I can't paint? Never think of it.
No, not true, I do. I look around.

The TV's always on, and there they sit,
So many white-faced zombies. Gets you down.

What can you do? Your mind is seared with pain.
The worse your body, the more it seems to fill
Each tortured fold and cranny of your brain.
I haven't given up yet. I never will.

I pity Pete, for one, and sullen Clive
(Miranda hates it when they stare at her)
Who, half the time, don't seem to be alive.
No jokes, no books, no smirking at the paper,

Unless you count that section of *The Sun*
Stuffed in a plastic sack outside the lockers.
Red Hot Sex. Apologetic porn.
If the cover lovers hadn't both been starkers

They could have stepped right out of the TV.
She might have looked as sexy, selling weather.
And what's he fondling? His own vanity!
I wonder if they'd even met each other

Before they posed? Do actors, acting sex,
Feel anything but numb from the neck up?
X + Y = Zero. Solve for X.
Oh, thinking's hopeless! So I paint a tulip.

That lipstick red corolla is a show,
A lure, a pit where unsheathed pizzle-anthers
Practise the only sexy act they know;
Or mock-perform it – chancers playing nature's

Bingo, mixing the useless with the worthless,
Setting the lifewheel spinning, with no aim.
That's Mother Nature for you! I'm an artist.
Choosing to paint, I'm chosen. That's my game.

Chris Rose

The Shoemaker General of Naples

The Shoemaker General of Naples lives where he works in one small dark room in a tiny alley off a tiny alley that is to be found behind a tiny alley deep in the ancient black heart of the city. The Shoemaker General is so old that he remembers when this tiny alley was just a tiny bit bigger and the tiny alley that it is behind was more like a tiny street, and when the black heart of Naples was only dark grey. His small dark room has no windows and no doors but opens out directly onto the tiny alley. His small dark room is very small and very dark indeed. Thousands of people pass by the Shoemaker General's shop each and every day and none of them suspect for one moment that he is in fact the Shoemaker General. They all think that he is nothing more extraordinary than an ordinary old *calzolaio* who makes his living by gluing, stitching and nailing together other people's worn out and broken old shoes. These people who pass by every day do not even suspect that such a person as the Shoemaker General of Naples exists, let alone that he should be this hunched old man before them, a simple *calzolaio* like any other, in a tiny alley off a tiny alley deep in the ancient black heart of the city.

The Shoemaker General knows all of the twenty-three basic forms of the shoe, their history from times of antiquity through to the modern age, their exact construction, their corresponding numbers in the *Smorfia* and the Torah, their relative constellations and signs astrological and zodiacal (Western and Chinese horoscopes). The Shoemaker General of Naples can accurately predict what size shoe a person takes by looking only at their nose. The Shoemaker General has taught the Shoemakers General of Paris, Lisbon, Prague, Moscow, Cologne, Avignon, Madrid and several other European capitals. Many, many years ago, more years than even he is now able to remember, the Shoemaker

General made shoes, boots, pumps, slippers and sandals for all the Crowned Heads of Europe, but now the Crowned Heads of Europe are but few, and buy their shoes from ordinary shoe-makers, some of whom have, nevertheless, studied under the Shoemaker General himself, or one of his many protégés, at least. The Crowned Heads of Europe are now so very few, thinks the Shoemaker, that they probably wouldn't provide much of an income anyhow.

The Shoemaker General of Naples thinks that people don't think enough about their shoes any more, and are thus subject to any number of woes and ailments, ranging from athlete's foot, bunions, corns and verrucas to muscular and nervous disorders, sciatica, poor eyesight, sweaty armpits, bad breath, indigestion, headaches, sleeplessness and the general malaise. Most of the problems of modern society, says the Shoemaker, if he is ever asked, can be directly attributed to poorly made and ill-fitting footwear. The Shoemaker General of Naples knows that one of the five most important *chakra* (the points of the body where, according to Hindu mysticism, all vital energy is accrued) is situated in the foot and that the shoe is consequently the almost holy site which connects the body to the Earth, and the Earth to the body. Not for nothing does he take his profession seriously.

The Shoemaker General of Naples also, unfortunately, knows how his brethren in India were reduced to being the lowest Chaamar caste, cast out and shunned by members of polite society. The Shoemaker General of Naples has a large bunch of keys hanging outside the doorway of his shop. Since his shop has neither doors nor windows, nobody knows why. The Shoemaker General of Naples often sees old and abandoned shoes left lying in the street, singly, or sometimes in couples. He feels pity for these strays, a feeling akin to that many of us may feel upon seeing a lost animal. He often picks them up and takes them with him, to give these shoes a good home.

Once, many years ago, a friend of mine went to a wedding somewhere in France where he met a man who was also a shoe-maker, albeit a relatively minor one. The French Shoemaker, who was wearing a pair of black winklepickers which matched his angular and uncomfortable personality perfectly, began to tell my friend all about the art and craft of the ancient mystery of shoemaking, and that the most important shoemaker in the world was said to be still alive and living, masquerading as a simple *calzolaio*, in Naples. At this point, my friend became interested, having lived in that very city for some time himself. Upon his next visit to the city, he resolved to himself to find the Shoemaker General.

Unfortunately, due to a long and complex series of circumstances which it would be both unnecessary and uninteresting for the general reader to go into at this present juncture, my friend had to delay his long-intended visit to the capital of the South, that is, the city of Naples, for a good while after his French excursion and his fateful meeting with that angular and unpleasant Gallic cobbler. Several years later, however, for reasons of work, he found himself back in the Parthenopean city, the encounter in France and the story of the mythical Shoemaker by now nothing but a faint memory in the distant past. Stepping off the train in a comfortable but elegant pair of brushed suede desert boots, perfectly adapted to the warm early autumn weather, my friend set off to find his hotel which was conveniently located in the centre of the city. Not wanting to take a taxi, thinking both that his hotel was within easy walking distance and also of the unfortunately less-than-spotless reputation of Neapolitan taxi drivers, my friend set off at a brisk pace across the large and chaotic square that spread out before the central station. Having visited the city on more than one occasion previously, as we have already noted, my friend was not too surprised or taken aback by his first contact with the city, and indeed even stopped off at one of the many little market stalls which line the square which was selling many different kinds of footwear at what seemed to be extremely reasonable prices. Soon discouraged by the apparently poor quality of the shoes on offer however, as well as their somewhat outmoded styles, to say nothing of the unpleasant demeanour of the stallholder (which led my friend, in all honesty, to question himself about the provenance of the goods, which he felt may have been dubious, to put it politely), he was soon off on his way, sauntering along the faded elegance of the Corso Umberto Primo. It was at about this point, noticing the extremely high number of emporia devoted to the selling of shoes on that street and thinking it curious, that the first vague memory of that strange story that he had heard all those years ago began to come back to him.

That night, lying in his bed in his hotel room, he went back over the story in his head, and, on rising the next morning set out to look for the Shoemaker.

Not really having much of a direction, he thought firstly to ask the proprietor of the small hotel where he was staying. The proprietor, a fat, rather sweaty man in an open-necked white shirt and a pair of ill-matched worn-out navy-blue deck shoes, looked askance at my friend when he made his strange request. The hotel keeper claimed to know nothing of any historical shoemaker in the city, which was perhaps unsurprising given the incognito nature of the Shoemaker General's current activities, but was however able to direct my friend in the general direction of a number of other Shoemakers in the vicinity.

And so it was that my friend, armed only with a guidebook to the city, a rudimentary knowledge of the Italian language and his trusty pair of Clark's set out, once again, for definite this time, in search of the Shoemaker General of Naples. His first stop was a small *botteghino* in a very small alley up a flight of steps around a corner off a twisty little street where a short and extremely aged gentleman, helpful if not particularly polite, wearing a handsome pair of kid leather brogues (evidently made by another fellow craftsman, or possibly by this gentleman himself seeing as they were old but had been well repaired and reheeled on several occasions), responded with a certain amount of interest to my friend's request. He replied, somewhat brusquely, that he knew nothing whatsoever of any ancient or legendary shoemaker and, moreover, that he believed my friend to be having his leg pulled. By way of a digression however, he offered up the following story (which I have not recounted using his exact words, not being overly familiar with the Neapolitan dialect in which it would have originally been delivered), in which he supposed that my friend may have had an interest:

There is a part of the city not ever so far away from here, over the other side of the town centre which is known as Piedigrotta.

It is commonly supposed, understandably so, that this area is thus called because it lies at the foot of a long grotto. There is, however, another story. This city, being as ancient and as many-layered and as complex as it is, has given host to any number of cults, sects, divinities and religions over the centuries. Some of these have vanished, others have left their trace by having been incorporated into orthodox Catholicism. There have been, and continue to be a number of maverick voices, shall we say, in the city's religious make-up. Naples, as you no doubt already know, is also known as Parthenope, after the Homeric siren who was reputedly washed up here. According to some myths, the whole city is emblematic of her body, with Piedigrotta being her feet. The mermaid's feet then somehow transmuted into the shoes of the Madonna. Even today, some Neapolitan women conserve a small talisman in the form of a tiny shoe, 'o scarpunciello d' 'a Maronna'. This is said to assist childbirth, or even other stages of procreation, if you catch my drift, he announced with a wink. If you ask me, you could try looking round there for your shoemaker. Good luck.

My friend didn't place too much credence either in the old man's story or his advice, but nevertheless decided to strike out for the northern part of the city. His journey there, undertaken as were all my friend's journeys, on foot, took him across one of the rather more fashionable areas of the city and through some of its wealthier shopping streets. It was while traversing one of such streets (later he believed it to have been the Via Chiaia, though admits that it may well have been the even more salubrious Via Dei Mille, or indeed that his memory is failing him all too much and that the street he remembers is none of these) that his attention began to be distracted by the extremely large number of shoeshops lining the street. (Given the current nature of his quest, it was, we may safely assume, almost inevitable that his attention should have been so drawn.) Shopping for footwear, it seemed to him, must be an extremely popular pastime amongst the Neapolitans. One of these shops in particular held his attention: nominated by a single letter only (the letter 'Q'), the shopfront was entirely white and seemed to be made of marble, no less. One large square window was set into the middle of the otherwise blemish-free façade, illuminated by a few tiny pinpoints of bright silver light set into the frame of the window. This was indeed all very attractive in a very modern, *minimalist*, sense, but the thing that really set my friend to curiousing was the fact that, in all this beautifully lit white and silver and marble space, there was only *one* pair of shoes. There, on a little white plinth at the exact centre of the window space, placed neatly together, as if in the spotlight on an otherwise empty stage at some strange Theatre of the Shoe, was a pair of deep purple velvet pumps. Modest, yet also presumptuous, refined yet daring with a heel slight enough to seem discreet, but large enough to turn the wearer's ankle in just such a way, finished with a wide purple ribbon to tie them, the shoes were quite a creation. The only other thing present in the shop window was a small white card, the size and shape of a visiting card, placed just in front of the shoes. On it, in a script small enough and elegant enough to be almost indecipherable, was written the price. It isn't necessary to distract the present reader with such vulgar details, but the figure inscribed on that card was enough, shall we say, to leave my friend feeling surprised, if not outright shocked. Yet a small question had already formed in his mind: might it just be possible that this incredible work of art and artisanship, this rare jewel of the shoemaker's craft, displayed in one of the most fashionable shops of the city at a price to beggar belief, could it just be possible that those shoes there could be an example of the handiwork of our Shoemaker General?

In order to pique his curiosity, my friend trepidatiously entered the shop. He pushed the heavy door, only to find that someone was pulling it from the inside. It brushed against the floor as it opened, and the opener nodded a nod of welcome with such a formality that for a second my friend feared it was about to become a bow. The young gentleman who had opened the door was tall and thin with a face that seemed a perfect oval, an effect exaggerated by the fact that his hair was cut short to the point of inexistence. He was dressed in an immaculately cut designer suit with lapels that could have doubled as razor blades and a pair of extremely smart, extremely shiny black leather shoes with a neat silver buckle. My friend nodded a good day to the young man and turned round to see the other sales assistant who was dressed in a manner perfectly identical to his colleague – the same haircut, the same suit, the same shoes. The only difference was that whereas his colleague was as tall and as thin as an etiolated rake, this second young man was as short and as round as a nice fat football.

'Good morning, sir. May we . . .'

'. . . be of any assistance?'

Rather taken aback by this odd pair, my friend momentarily forgot quite why he had entered the shop, and not wanting to appear foolish, said that he was looking for a pair of shoes.

'And what kind of shoes . . .'

'. . . would sir be looking for?'

'Well,' hummed my friend, 'what about a fine pair like you yourselves have on?'

'Ah, yes sir, the loafers . . .'

'. . . most fashionable this season, loafers.'

My friend could not quite understand why they were called loafers as he could not ever have imagined doing any loafing whatsoever in such an elegant pair of shoes, in fact he couldn't imagine himself doing anything in them other than attending cocktail parties, and therefore mused that 'cocktail partiers' might be a more appropriate name, and found himself trying a pair on anyhow.

It is strange how one is often unwillingly cajoled into doing things entirely to avoid embarrassment, and such it was on this occasion. My friend found that the shoes he had accidentally tried on were a perfect fit and asked how much they were. The reply, he told me later, hit him rather like a punch in the stomach would have done. However, not wanting to appear cheap, he whisked out his credit card and, within seconds, the deed was done. Reeling somewhat, feeling much lighter, he began to walk out of the shop before remembering the original purpose of his visit.

'The shoes that you sell here,' he began to ask, 'where are they made?'

'Oh, they're all Italian, sir . . .'

'. . . made by the finest stylists . . .'

'. . . and top-name designers.'

'There's nothing made locally? By a local maestro, perchance?'
They looked puzzled.

'Well, sir . . .'

'. . . some of our shoes . . .'

'. . . *are* made locally . . .'

'. . . but I don't know of . . .'

'. . . any local maestro . . .'

'. . . maestro, no.'

Some heated exchange, which my friend unfortunately missed,
followed between them.

'Some of the finest Italian designers . . .'

'. . . are Neapolitan though, sir. We wouldn't want you to
think'

'. . . otherwise.'

My friend bid good day to the two strange young men, and
left.

Feeling rather hungry by this point, after his long morning of
still-fruitless exertions, my friend decided to look for something
to eat and soon found himself in a most amiable little family-run
trattoria, contentedly sitting in front of a large plate of *spaghetti
alla puttanesca*. After having finished all of the pasta and finding
that there was still rather a lot of the tomato, olive, anchovy and
caper sauce left, my friend asked the proprietor of the place (who
was also the only waiter) if he may have a slice of bread in order
to 'mop up' the remaining sauce.

'*Ah, vuole fa' la scarpett'?*' responded the man, 'Oh, you'd
like the "*scarpetta*"?'

My friend, despite a fair knowledge of the Italian language
was perplexed by the expression, and enquired further.

'When you have a little piece of bread, explained the waiter-
owner (elegant but unassuming brown leather brogues), and you
use it to clean up what's left of the sauce on your plate, we call
it the "*scarpetta*", the "little shoe". And no, I'm afraid I've really
no idea why. Now, as a second course, how about a nice plate of
melanzane a' scarpone? Hmmm?'

My friend declined the offer, and trudged wearily on his way
out. He had had, it is now fair to say, enough.

He walked back down the streets tracing the way he had arrived, back towards his hotel, across the old centre of the city. As he walked he couldn't help but notice the footwear of every person he passed, and also stopped to look in the window of every shoe shop that he passed. Feeling himself to be in either a film by Pedro Almodovar or a picture by Hieronymous Bosch he was tired, bewildered and close to giving up his search. When he had all but arrived back at his hotel, he again passed the small little *calzolaio* where he had begun his wanderings earlier that morning. The man saw him and waved.

'Did you find what you were looking for?' he asked.

My friend shook his head despondently.

'Never mind,' replied the shoemaker. 'It's a dirty business, old shoes. You're better off not worrying too much about it. Listen, I remembered a story though, after you'd gone. It might interest you.

'There was a traveller, a long time ago, I'm not sure exactly when, it doesn't really matter, there was a traveller walking along a long open lonely road, somewhere in the middle of nowhere. There's nobody else around, nobody for as far as he can see, only himself and the long open road. Suddenly, he notices that there's a fellow coming towards him. He doesn't understand how this chap can have got there, can have appeared so suddenly without him having seen him earlier. This fellow, who's pulling a large cart, just seemed to have appeared without even so much as a flash of light and a cloud of smoke. Anyway the traveller sees this other fellow pulling his large cart coming closer and closer to him – there's nowhere else to go of course, it's a long straight open road with no turns anywhere, no trees or hedges to disappear behind. They keep on getting closer and closer until they're eventually face to face. The traveller notices that the large cart is piled up with old shoes. Some are single, some in pairs, and they're all old, really old, all broken and worn out, all cracked leather and holes in the bottom. As two people meeting on such a road would do, they say hello to each other, nod to each other. Our friend the traveller, in an effort to be civil, asks the other man, the one with the cart, if he couldn't find a mule or a horse or something to help him pull his cart.

' "It's not a problem really," the cart-puller replies. "They're not heavy. Anyway, I couldn't find any animal to come with me to go where I'm going."

' "Oh, and where's that then?"

' "Well, why don't we liven up our day a bit and have a little bet," suggested the cart puller. "Why don't we see if you can guess where I'm going."

' "OK, but if it's a bet, what do I stand to win if I manage to guess?"

' "Hmmm," said the cart puller, "I could offer you this here cart with all these old shoes, but I don't think you'd really want that, would you?"

' "No, I wouldn't really," replied the traveller. "But talking of shoes, those are a nice pair of leather boots you've got on there. If I manage to guess where you're going, why don't you give me those boots?"

' "It's a deal," replied the cart-puller, without so much as a moment's hesitation. "And if you get it wrong, then you've got to give me your shoes."

'The traveller, who was wearing nothing more than a dusty and fairly worn out pair of ordinary old shoes didn't have to think too hard either. It seemed like a risk worth taking.

' "You've got yourself a deal," he said.

' "All right then," said the cart-puller, "just where do you think I'm going?"

' "Well," said the traveller, feeling fairly smug and pleased with himself. "I think you made a bit of a stupid bet there. Seeing as this is a long straight road that has no turns or junctions anywhere, and seeing as with that cart you can't be going to cross over any of the fields or hills, and seeing as you're going in the opposite direction to me, well then you must be going to the place that I've just come from."

'The traveller smiled contentedly, feeling himself already the owner of a nice shiny new pair of boots.

'The cart-puller, however, was also smiling.

' "I think you'd better start unlacing, friend, for I was coming along this road just to meet you."

'The traveller was never seen again, not in the place where he was going, nor in the place that he had come from, nor anywhere, with shoes or without. Sometimes people still see the cart-puller around though, with a pair of dusty old brown traveller's shoes added to his notable collection, or that's what they say.

'How long are you staying in Naples for?' asked the shoemaker with a friendly smile. 'I'm leaving tonight,' said my friend, 'on the next train,' having just made a quick decision, which would not prove to be hasty.

That night, after having gone back to the hotel to grab his bags, my friend found himself sleeping badly on a train bound north. He had strange dreams about the Devil pulling a cart, and about the soles of the dead.

He hasn't been back to Naples since.

The Shoemaker General of Naples lives where he works in one small dark room in a tiny alley off a tiny alley that is to be found behind a tiny alley deep in the ancient black heart of the city. Many people pass by his little workshop every day, not having the least idea about who he is, nor even suspecting that such a person as the Shoemaker General of Naples even exists. The Shoemaker, though now old and decrepit, still dreams of the day when shoe shops will take over the world. In Midwest shopping malls and rainy Northern high streets, shoe shops already outnumber juice bars and smoky pubs.

The Shoemaker sits there all day, polishing, nailing, stitching, cutting and sewing, and watches all the people who go past. Sometimes, he thinks, he could recognize each and every one of the inhabitants of this city, just by looking at the shoes they are wearing.

Ruth Fainlight

Opera in Holland Park

Raucous peacocks like abandoned babies
counterpoint the final chorus of Tosca, Act I.

Every table in the café is occupied
by drinkers halted in the posture of listeners:
abstracted gaze, alertly lifted head.

The fumy blaze of flowerbeds, smouldering brasiers
in the summer dusk. Vortices of midges
vibrate above the hedges like heat mirages.

To stare at the waterfall in the Japanese garden
for more than a few moments alters the scale:
a thousand-metre plunge down an Andean precipice.

In the interval, the audience eat ice cream, stroll
past the orangery. Violinists tighten their strings.

I have never been so close to a peacock before.
It struts, stops, opens its beak, emits a creaking,
tentative call and makes me jump with fright.

The small blue head swivels, crowned by
                    feather-antennae
searching a signal. Like precious mottled enamel,
precise articulation of spurred legs, clawed feet.

Massed trees darken into carbon-paper silhouettes
against the glassy tension of a paling sky
perfecting its spectrum of yellow, mauve and red.

Scarpia's room in the palace. Magnificence.
I can hear Tosca singing. The anguish starts again.

Tom Pow

Caravaggio in Dumfries

On the first ever day of spring, Caravaggio
strolls over the old stone bridge to market.

There, he orders three pounds of pippins,
two of red delicious, one each of bananas

and of pears. His eye tells him what's ripe,
what's sweet, crisp or tart. Lastly, he points

to a large bunch of inky-blue grapes. *Per favore.*
'Nice ones these,' remarks the vendor –

a tiny lady in a black Bulls cap with one
winking gold tooth. She's noticed how

taken her customer is with the grapes.
Caravaggio thinks he'll paint them later,

include them in his knowing *Little Bacchus* –
that sallow-skinned portrait of his self.

He is twenty or so – fresh from the country –
and what he feels this warming morning

standing before these piled fruit stalls
is not innocence but wide-eyed appetite –

an openness to all fecundity. History
will call him stormy petrel, tempestuous,

libidinous; temper as much as fever
will eventually kill him. But this morning

all that feels so unlikely; impossible even,
as he heads for home, cradling his five bags of fruit.

At the bridge head, one of a pair of swans,
circling its young, raises itself from the river

and lifts up its wings. A slab of white light
hits Caravaggio with a shock of pleasure

like a lover's open thigh, a magnificence
that folds in on itself, as indeed light folds

into darkness. A lesson his eye takes in
before he returns across the sparkling waters.

Patrick McGuinness

A Border Town

This isn't where you'd start by looking:
where big things have tapered down
to feel their way into small lives being led
far away from where you'd think to look,

but where your looking leads. It's where
events have come to hide away, to break,
like light, into those particles of dust that spin
and settle back in layers on what they lit.

Des Dillon

The Blue Hen

In Greenend me and John up the stairs shared a garden. It was the early eighties. Everything was grey. The pavements. People's faces. The buildings. The sky. The future. Nobody had a job. Not one solitary single soul. Men were gathering in bigger and bigger numbers on the corner – passing buckie and dope. Unemployed moulders and turners and puddlers tugging away at joints. It was one big party. But smack was coming onto the scene. Bannan worked beside me and John in the Klondike. A money lender. He took to dealing like a duck.

Things started to change. John noticed it before me. I goes up for him this night – I had a bottle up ma jook. I was anticipating the first slug burning its way down my gullet and hitting my belly like a mother's love.

I chaps his door and he peeks out the letter box. I push the buckie bottle up till the golden cork's poking out ma jumper. But John wasn't going down the corner that night. Or the next night – or any other night. The corner's stepped over the line, he said. There's no way back now. I could see what he was saying. Needles were on the corner. And last week Bannan stabbed a welder from the Whifflet trying to move in on his patch. He's in the Monklands – critical.

If John's not happy with the corner, I'm not happy with the corner. So we sat in his scullery drinking. John says there's corners all over the country like it. Men gathered up. And it's a holocaust – only it's not bodies that's piled up and destroyed but souls. People's spirit. By the turn of the century the whole country'll pay for it. Mark my words, he said.

It was making him angry so I asked what about the garden – what's our plans? He looked out over the garden. Thinking. Then he turns and says – Things're tight and they're not going to get

100

any better. If you want to at least keep your dignity you've got to have goals – long-term plans.

John thought we should get chickens. It was a great idea. I took a swig and handed him the bottle by way of a toast. We figured we could get six or even a dozen eggs a day. That with the carrots and radishes and spuds we were already growing could save us a fortune. Soft-boiled eggs and omelettes were lighting up in my head.

Next day we went round the Whifflet library and researched on chickens and eggs and hutches. The hutch was easy enough to build – we got the wood from the swing-park fence. Bannan's maw was looking out her back window wondering what the sawing was and – hey! – off walks an eight-feet section of council fence. We never thought we were doing any damage cos the swing-park had no swings – just some broke slabs and a universe of smashed glass shrapnel. Sometimes on a clear night if you stared into the particles starlight would be in them. You never knew if you were looking at the heaven or earth.

A week later and four eight-feet lengths of fencing – we've built a chicken run. In the book it says to hang a hundred-watt bulb inside so the chicks can huddle round it. I ran the wire from my house cos I had my powercard meter wired up to run for nothing anyway. John took the bulb out his back room that they never used except if they got visitors – and I've never seen any of them the three years I've lived in the bottom flat. All we needed now was the chicks.

We went down to Bankhead farm where they were doing chicks for fifty pence each. Twenty we bought – a tenner – and that was a lot of money to us. We put them in and watched the wee yellow cartoon characters buzz about searching and pecking and sniffing in their new home. But they're not as daft as they look chicks – soon they were all piling over each other to get below the hundred watt bulb. The cheeping and the smell of sawdust and all them chicks squeezing into the light made me feel good. A wee yellow ball of life. Me and John smiled at each other. It was a great feeling and we both looked forward to omelettes and soft-boiled eggs. I know that because we talked about it all the time.

At night I'd sit at the window looking at the slither of warm light beaming across the garden. I'd imagine the quiet burble of the chicks pressing round the bulb. Snoring maybe – if that's what they do. And then – now and then – one of them falls out the bundle and scutters round the other side and launches itself into the pile looking for a place nearer to the heat of the great bulb sun god.

The spuds and the other stuff were doing fine in the garden. We'd even took up some radishes and made pieces on margarine with a bit of salt. The way they crunch when your teeth arrive through the soft bread – mm!

Well – the chicks soon passed that wee lovely stage and turned into these pre-historic monsters. Their crazed gaze said they'd tear the eye out your head if you gave them half the chance. Sometimes – if John wasn't there – and they were all staring at me I'd get a bit scared and have to shut the lid. But if he was there I'd not mention it and try to see if I could see it in his eyes. You can't mention fear in Greenend.

On and on it went and they got bigger and uglier. Then one morning in winter I went out and there was one lying dead. I chipped a few stones up at John's and out he came with his maw's slippers squeezed onto his feet and her housecoat wrapped round him. We held it up by the claw and looked at the white slither of death over the ball of its eye. We were really worried that it could be some chicken disease and we'd lose the whole lot.

In the library there wasn't much about chicken diseases. It was mostly all good news about chickens – how to get the best eggs and stuff. We convinced ourselves it was natural causes and erased one soft-boiled egg each from the future menu in our heads.

But when we got home and lifted the lid there was another one dead. Eye pecked out. Bloodied stalks hanging out the socket like fibre optics. So that's it. Fights. These chicks were now teen-agers. When we looked about to see who was responsible every eye was evil – every eye intense. Like when I got my video knocked – every guy grinning on the corner the next day – I thought it was him. It's not easy to spot evil.

We talk about separating them into two groups and see what

group's got a dead one the next day – but John makes an intelli-
gent point – what if they're all killers! And there's no getting by
that – if they're all killers we'd need to put them in solitary
confinement and I don't think the burgh fence could take another
hit. We went to bed that night a bit subdued but took the curse
off it with a bottle of Buckfast between us.

Although John hardly ever got out his bed before twelve I
wasn't surprised to meet him in the close at half nine the next
morning. He'd been up all night same as me – worrying.

We opened the lid together. Looked. Two dead. The rest chattering on the corner like Bannan and his mob. John shakes his
head and leaves me to close the lid. He walks to the other end
of the garden and kicks this old shed. He puts a hole right
through it in fact. But that's nothing cos it's all rotted away. Just
like this whole place – disintegrating. And he never says much
John but when he does it makes a difference. Men don't lay eggs!
What? I goes. Men don't lay eggs, he says with his palms firing
out the meaning. I get it. I go and have a boot at the old shed
myself. He's right – we got all them chicks but we never checked
to see what ones were hens. For all we know it's all cockerels
we've got.

What to do? The book wasn't much help – we looked for
dicks and stuff between their big rubbery claws. But there was
nothing to see. Then John came up with a great idea. His best
yet. He's a bit of a psychologist. What applies to human beings
applies just as well to chickens, he says. The ones that've already
died are probably male. All this territorial shite that goes on
down the corner. Like Bannan and his drug-dealing. The cockerels
are probably killing each other for control of the hens. It's a sex
thing. Great! he says. And I give him a how's that great look
when he explains it to me. Well – how many of the corner team
d'ye know that attack lassies?

None!

Exactly – so if we let things take their course we'll be left
with one male and the rest'll be hens!

That makes a lot of sense. For the first time in ages the whole
thing takes on a happy glow. And something else John says too
– the male that's left – that'll be the Bannan of the chicken run.

If we start a breeding programme we'll have the best genes in the pool. Christ – things were getting better by the minute. Half of me wanted the weak chickens to be dead already.

By the end of January the happiness of that day had faded. There was only one chicken left. And it was a big Rhode Island Red. Male. Me and John couldn't believe how unlucky we'd been – we'd bought twenty chickens and they'd all been male. The very last omelette went pop in both our heads at the same time.

Then it started cock-a-doodle-dooing at four in the morning. There was nothing you could do. People were starting to make comments. Not bad stuff – Is that your chicken I heard this morning? – stuff like that. I discussed it with John but he seemed to have washed his hands of the situation. I knew he'd finally let go when the bulb went on the blink. Even though my electricity was stole it was still me that was providing it for the chicken hutch. I felt it was morally right that John should provide the bulb. When I asked him he never said no – he just said that his maw had asked where the bulb was in the visitors' bedroom and he'd to go and nick one out the doctor's. I looked at him. He looked back. There was no bulb coming out of him so I used the one out my toilet although I felt a bit resentful at the whole thing by now. And it's hard to shake off a resentment when you're getting woke up at four every morning by a big red rooster.

I decided not to fall out with John. So we chewed the fat as if the chickens had never happened. And we carried on drinking in his scullery cos by now the corner was a no-go area. The red rooster ruled the garden.

That's why I was surprised when my door goes at half nine this morning. It's John – and he's got the *Advertiser*. Wait till you see this, he goes. And he lays it out on the floor. We crouch down and he points to a wee advert. Blue Hen – three pounds. Apply Headrigg Farm Plains. I took in a big happy breath! John was back on the breeding programme – and we had the top dog male out there ready to go to town. And – and this is important – and! – we know this one's going to be a hen.

Plains is six miles from Greenend. Six there and six back. I chipped in two quid and John chipped in a quid he stole out his maw's purse. And just to show me he was serious he brung a bulb down – he hands me it – Spare! Is all he says. I put it in my toilet and he waited in the close. We had to act fast – there's no telling that a blue hen won't get snapped up.

It was freezing. One of them days when your shoulders rub off your ears. Our words were muffled by the fog they came out in. On the corner everything was arranged around Bannan. Like he's the hub of a wheel. Power – that's what it was. A few of the boys looked over. Some nodded but Bannan was staring us out. Don't look, says John, keep walking. Bannan shouted a few things but we kept going.

Once we cleared the corner I felt at ease. And so did John cos his head came back up out of his jacket. We strode out towards Plains. The snowflakes were coming down now and then like miniature saw-blades – they were cutting into our skin. But that's nothing. With a wee bit of imagination you can think yourself back into the Klondike at the furnace – me and John and big Bannan – having a laugh and a couple of cans – and the snow biting your face becomes furnace heat. That cheered me up and I imagined a year from now – hutches all over the garden and me and John out with trays collecting eggs. Selling them round Greenend. All these boiled eggs and omelettes rushed back into my head. I glanced at John and his thoughts were the same. We smiled. I mind the exact moment John smiled a wee snowflake landed on the end of his nose and he licked it off. Going cross-eyed at the same time. And we laughed. And he put his arm round me and gave me a wee hug. And I gave him one back. It was the happiest time of my life. We smiled on through the thickening snow. Two lights in the darkness of March.

When we got to Plains we paid three quid to a thirteen-year-old laddie. We told him all about our bad luck and our new breeding plans. He gave us a couple of tips and wished us all the best. The walk down the road was a lot quicker. The snow had took the sting out the air and we kept swapping the blue hen. I'd have her up my jumper for a mile then John'd have her up his. Chances each at being pregnant with the future. The whole world was that warm hen. I love the way snow effects sound – it was like beyond me and John and the Blue Hen nothing existed. The place was white and our feetprints behind were driving us into the promise of uncharted lands of snow.

We were back at the corner in no time. Bannan was strutting about giving orders.

Cross over, John said.

We crossed over. But Bannan seen us. Hey what's that you've got! he shouts. Ignore him, John says. We marched faster. Bannan kept on shouting. Stop! he shouts. We kept going. Out the side of my eye I could see him struggling in his jacket for something. Some of the corner boys were scattering. Others grinned – black holes for mouths. Stop!! Bannan had a gun. John – he's got a gun! But John pressed the Blue Hen into his belly. Keep going, he said. This is your last chance! shouts Bannan. That was the moment I seen what dignity was. It was John. It was the Blue Hen up his jook. The palms of his hands pressing her soft feathers. Dignity was John keeping on walking with that gun pointing.

The shot rang out the exact same time as this groove made its way under the snow. A line like a pipe appeared between me and John. A pipe of snow bursting open at the seam. And a starburst of slush exploded at the kerb. I could feel the corner boys walking away from Bannan. I turned a bit as we walked. John never even broke his stride. Bannan pointed the gun again. John – I'm telling you – Stop! he shouted. We turned the corner as the shot went off.

When we walked into the back garden John was shaking. That's when I realized so was I. We never said nothing about the gun. It was like it never happened. The red rooster swung its head round but it stood well back. By this time it was pretty adept at getting up onto the roof and that's where it went. There wasn't another bird up there. We put the Blue Hen in the hutch and watched. But the red rooster stayed on the roof. Outwaited us. Watching. Glaring. We decided it was as shy as we'd be if somebody brought us home a woman to marry. It might be bold and tough but – as John pointed out – It's still a virgin and that's why it's bashful. Probably be all right in the morning.

I woke up the next morning about eight with this racket – a squawking like I've never heard. I ran out the back and there's John and he's just pulled the head off the red rooster. Murdering bastard – murdering bastard, he's shouting. The claws of the red rooster are still twitching but the blood's spurting out its neck. Onto John's hands – dripping into the snow. I look in the hutch and there's the Blue Hen lying stiff and dead beneath the ghostly daylight glow of the hundred-watt bulb. Both her eyes are pecked out.

Deryn Rees – Jones

L

Some mysteries are never solved: the tongue of flame,
the rolled back stone, the body's weight
when it walks on water; or even the tale
of the Capuchin priest who for fifty years
wore the wounds of Christ, was drenched in the odour
of holy blood, his body healed at his last confession:
Maria! he whispered, bowing his head,
dying the death of a little bird
as he stood before the gates of heaven.

Which takes me back to that night in San Andreas
and the barbell I found, caught like a thorn
between mattress and sheet. Or was it a dream –
the blue of her skin between ligament and bone,
her arm bent like the letter L, as she washed your feet
with her hennaed hair? The blemish on your palm
between headline and heartline, a faultline,
like her name, or the scent she wore,
the line of a song you won't remember.

Patricia Debney

Friday

[from a novel in progress]

This extract is taken from midway through the first half of the novel, which is narrated by Marilyn, a counsellor. She and Doug are American, living in Britain with their son Louis. Hilary, Adam and their son Aaron are becoming close family friends. Marilyn's father lived near her and has recently died. The setting is his wake.

By the time I am on my way back to the house after the service, the world seems to have contracted and contracted. I look out the window of the special car I have been assigned by the undertaker, the car that declares I am grieving, I am grieving – and everything seems miniaturized, almost, moving as if speeded up, moving away from me like I'm in a tunnel.

Doug holds my hand next to me, and Louis sits, still as a stone, next to him. My little man.

Doug's hand is sweating. Or is it mine. He spoke beautifully at the funeral, shaking slightly at the podium. My father had been like his own, he said, like the one he never had. He left it there but the whole story rushed back to me as I sat there, trying to find my father's face in my memory. Instead I saw Doug's home town, his own peculiar parents who left him and his sister on their own much of the time. The absolutely disgusting house, the pathological inattention to hygiene, routine. I only ever visited it twice – and the first time we washed up two plates and two cups to use for dinner. Well, they weren't plates. They were baking trays.

Poor Doug, my god. His folks were nice enough, just entirely useless. I looked at him by the podium and thought that all this has made him a brilliant father – obsessive, yes, in the opposite direction to his parents – but loving, solid, affectionate. Much like, in fact, my father.

My father was the last relative of sorts Doug too had in this world, except his sister and her family, far away in California. I must remember that, I thought, in the midst of this; his parents died when he was really quite young, within two years of each other, when he was in his late twenties. I was with him when he heard about his mother. His sister rang at about six o'clock one morning. He thanked her, hung up, then turned to me, and we made love. He did not, as far as I remember, go to either of his parents' funerals.

All of this came back to me in quick succession, and as I sat there listening to him, I was surprised by the force of the memories. Especially by the way we responded to grief then – the sex, the mess of it, the intense drinking and eating. There was a time when families formed the core of our conversation together – their troubles, the attendant battles, the recognition of ourselves in our parents.

But no more. Like the intensity, the sex, we lose track of things perhaps.

I tried once again to remember my father's face, but I could only catch it for a moment as I last saw him: dead, yellow-lit. I saw my mother instead, whose close-up face, peering at me, testing me for truthfulness just through a look, is never as far away.

Now as we pull up to the house I can see several cars already there. I don't even know who's coming except for Hilary and Adam. I think Doug has invited a few people we know. I again feel sick. Of course, none of them will have known Daddy.

As I enter the house, John, my boss, approaches me with his arms out. Everything else recedes as he reaches for me, and catches me in what he no doubt thinks of as a fatherly hug. 'Marilyn, you poor thing,' he says, 'and so soon. I'm glad I could be here.' He pulls away and leads me towards the drinks. 'I almost had to be in Scotland for that conference – meditation and mediation, I think, or some such nonsense. But thank goodness I didn't.' His hand wavers over the bottles. 'Whisky, please,' I say. 'Lovely.' He pours me a drink and squeezes my elbow as he gives it to me. 'Jacqui will be here later. She sends her apologies and love.'

Hilary joins us. 'Marilyn,' she says, 'you should eat something.' She takes my arm and leads me into the kitchen.

'Thank you.'

'That's OK. You looked like you needed saving. Who's that?'

'My boss John. He means well, he's just . . .'

'Overpowering.'

'Yes, and I must admit a bit of a bore. Apparently we have the pleasure of his wife's company later. Now she's a piece of work.'

Hilary sighs. 'God, all you need. Now—' She hands me a plate. 'I was actually serious. You should try to eat.'

Doug finds me in the middle of my sausage roll. 'Thanks Hilary.' She tactfully leaves.

I look at Doug and try to smile. He looks worn out already. 'I see John made it,' he says.

'Yes. And apparently we are to expect his wife later.'

'Oh. Jacqui.'

'That's right. She is forever making me feel stupid and ugly – it's awful how some women do that . . .'

'I won't give you your own advice and tell you that only you can make yourself feel that way, she can't – ' I glare at him. ' – but I will say that Charles and Suzanne should be around some time, and you can count on them to save you, anyway.'

'Oh good.' The sausage roll is fuzzing up my mouth, but I mean it. I like them enormously. Suzanne worked with Doug – another electrical engineer. We'd been to their house once for dinner soon after we'd arrived here from London. They'd been back to us once at the old house, and we'd enjoyed it. I kept wanting to get them over again but there seemed to be something in the way – perhaps just too much reservation, too much business. I suspected, however, that it was something else, something not mentioned: that they desperately wanted, but could not have, children. I can see them now in the split second of Louis waking up while they were at ours, him walking into the dining-room behind me, their faces caught quite bare as if from the flash of a camera, one instant. Especially Suzanne. I couldn't identify the look, didn't know at first that Louis was there, thought it was Doug, somehow coming in from the kitchen. It was almost greed, the look on her face, or even more primal, hunger – then something else slipped over, and she said, 'Hello there, young man.' She was another American, although altogether more Southern, being from Virginia. Charles was her perfect complement – smooth, charming, devastatingly handsome and modest, British.

I finish my sausage roll. 'It's been ages since we've seen them. I'm glad they're coming.'

'Yes.' Doug comes over and wraps his arms around me. 'You're doing brilliantly,' he says. I put my arms around him and rest my head on his chest.

'Thank you. You too. I thought you did just great at the service.'

'Thanks.'

We stand there a moment. I find that there's something inside me scrabbling around, something trying to protect itself. From what? I think for a second about it. From not feeling anything for Doug right now, from being numb. Again I remember the sex we had after his mother died. I want it, I realize, I want that release. But not with him, and I don't know when this happened or why.

He squeezes me and I squeeze back, then we pull away from each other. 'We better be sociable,' he whispers, and kisses me on the forehead. 'I'll go first.'

He leaves, and I continue to stand with my back to the window. The sun comes through onto the floors and wall above the cooker; it's very yellow now, later in the day, and I look at it striking the robin's egg blue we painted the kitchen, the first room in the house we did. My stomach turns, just a little. I can't think why we chose such an insipid, passionless colour.

*

Back in the throes of the so-called party, someone pours me another whisky. I've never been much of a whisky drinker, but my father was, and the feeling of drinking like him is quite pleasant. Added to this is the feeling that no one knows I am drinking his drink, and it feels like my own private accolade.

I sit down on the sofa. I wish I could say I sank or reclined or thudded down, but I didn't do anything so dramatic. Just sat, like everything in my life. Placed myself. Never carried away, never tortured or, for that matter, ecstatic. My wedding day. The birth of Louis. Even grief doesn't seem to disturb the graph of me, the peaks not so high, the troughs barely existent. Poor Dad. He did always say that there was something cold about me, something too analytical. That made me go on to do what I do, but also made me, he would say, hold back. Like your mother, he would go on, God rest her.

Not a wholly bad thing, then, I think now. The whisky, oddly, is strangely conducive to this kind of distance. There is a mellow-ness, but also a kind of control with it, a sharpness. Or perhaps it is an illusion associated with this particular kind of drunkenness, I wouldn't know.

What I do know, even in this state, is that somewhere all this will come out, probably in my dreams. I feel myself smile and hope no one sees. Someone – I should know who but don't – is talking to me. I try to focus on her. Good God, is it really a neighbour? The feeling I have that Doug has called in the troops, so we won't be alone, is reinforced. Yes, I think it's Margaret from two doors down. Her voice carries on rather melodiously; we are both aware she isn't saying anything important. Mean-while, I wonder about what's happening inside me, think, my father has always been right about me, always: I determine every-thing, and allow few surprises. Which comes first, I wonder, the emotion or the reason, the reason or the emotion. Just exactly which one needs to be at the helm?

I can see Doug across the room doing a much better job of mixing this party than I could ever hope to do, even when sober and comparatively untroubled. He looks contemplatively jovial, restrained yet kind, as he is. John's Jacqui has arrived, and I can see Adam's back, head slightly forward, listening to her. No doubt his attention is well taken by her extreme animation. She always seems to have something right at the top of her mind which simply must spill out. In my inebriated state I allow myself the thought that John should have counselled her out of her incessant talking and extroversion long ago; it's so obvious she is desperate for validation – surely this can't be attractive to live with? Unless, like so many other couples . . . I find that I sigh right in Margaret's face, then apologize. I can't even follow through the thought. Who knows what happens in private.

I glance again towards Jacqui and Adam, the back of his head. The nape of his neck is olive, dark like he's been in the sun, and his dark hair spreads in sparse outcrops down the prominent muscles of his neck. The twin indentations on either side of these remind me of a child's head, his own boy's perhaps, or Louis's when he was a toddler.

I take a stinging sip of my drink, and rest my head on the back of the sofa. A wave of tenderness passes through me. I realize that I don't know what Louis will be, a giver like Doug, or a holder-back like me. I don't even know what it is best to be, what I would wish upon him.

Louis. I make my excuses to Margaret and slip out of the sitting room; it's in a bit of a bustle, people loosening up, laughter – and make my way upstairs. For some reason I need to see Louis, his face. Yet another downfall of an only child, as if we needed any more: the constant worry over his welfare, his happiness and health. But, alarmingly, he seems to know more than I do in some way; even he knows that everyone must die. It's just that I sometimes find myself overtaken by fear, the fear of him dying before me, before his time. My only blood relative. Then I really would be alone, completely alone. I don't think there could be a feeling worse than that.

As I walk, the floor dips like I'm on a boat. I can't remember the last time I was so drunk in the daytime. Hilary will tell me off. A sausage roll is not enough.

As I approach his room I can hear them talking, he and Aaron, I think. There is the clatter of vehicles running into each other, and the high cries of pretend people in trouble. 'Oh no-o-o-o-o!' Louis moans, and as I round the corner I see a miniature man dive-bomb a truck and struggle with it. 'Dead,' Louis says with finality.

He looks up at me. 'We're just doing this, Mom,' he says, 'aren't we, Aaron.'

'Yeah.' Aaron looks around. 'Look, Marilyn, there's a huge pile-up, and everyone might be dead.'

'Yeah,' Louis continues, and they are back in their own game. He reaches for his fire engine. 'And there might be a fire . . . nee-naw, nee-naw, nee-naw . . .' Both boys bend their heads together and start negotiating a path for the fire engine.

I take a step backwards out of the room. They are fine, of course, I knew they would be. It's an irrational feeling, an irrational worry, his sudden disappearance. I feel tears coming into my eyes again, and back further around the corner, lean on the wall. Bloody hell. I put my hand over my mouth so they can't hear me. I must be drunk.

I glance over to the stairs and see someone's head ascending. It won't be Doug, I know, he wouldn't leave the party when I'm not there. It's Adam, and when he sees me, he quickens his pace, comes up and puts his hand on my shoulder. Although I barely know him, I put my head down and lean into him. I am extraordinarily tired, exhausted. I really just need to rest.

He moves his hand up to the back of my head, my neck, rubbing gently. Close as I am to him, I can smell his deodorant, or what I take to be part deodorant, part him. It smells wonderful, sexy, and at the absolute second I register this, he leans over and kisses me on the lips. Something happens, and I seem to lose all will; I fall against him – I can feel, briefly, lightly, the outline of his thighs, his erection, and the imprint my breasts make on his chest.

The next second though, I have put my hands up and pushed gently away. I am still dizzy. Adam moves his hands along my arms and takes my hands. We squeeze.

'That was a bit silly of me, wasn't it?' he says. 'I'm sorry. My fault. Bad timing – ' He pauses. 'Or perhaps there's nothing to be timed . . .' He lets the sentence hang, waiting, no doubt, for some sort of response. The truth is, I recognize even in my state, that an affair with him had never even occurred to me. So the question of timing, as he guesses, is indeed irrelevant.

But I can't deny the charge. It is a charge, I assume, that any stranger kissing me would have created, but it's there. So, I think wryly, I am still alive.

To him I say, 'Never mind,' and realize almost immediately my mistake. Belittling, to say the least. 'I'm flattered,' I add, 'but it's not a good idea, really, is it?'

He lets go of my hands and pushes my hair back, quickly, gently. 'I'm sure you're right,' he says. Then, 'The boys OK?'

'Yes, in there,' I say, gesturing around the corner. 'Playing wonderfully together. They're good mates, aren't they?'

Adam smiles, I wonder if it's a little wistfully, but again I feel drunk enough to think anything. He holds out his arm and I take it. 'Good then,' he says, 'shall we go downstairs?'

Somewhat jarringly, Hilary is coming up just as we are going down. I let go of Adam's arm – too quickly, I think, too late – and move a step down from him.

Her voice, however, is bright enough. 'There you are,' she says, 'how are the boys?'

'Fine,' Adam and I say together.

'That's good.' Hilary doesn't look at Adam, but reaches for my hand. 'Marilyn, Doug's been looking for you. People called Suzanne and . . .'

'Charles.'

'Charles, right, are here and want to see you.'

'Oh good,' I say, 'I was hoping they'd make it soon.'

We go down and walk across the sitting-room, Hilary still holding my hand. It feels quite odd, to be holding hands with someone of my own size. For years that space has been occupied by baby / toddler / child, enclosed by mine. Or held by Doug's, my fingers pushed a little too far apart for comfort. Now – but I don't have time to think about it properly, as I am soon safely delivered to Doug.

As soon as I join them, Suzanne turns her rather beautiful face to me and stops the conversation. Doug touches the small of my back. Suzanne reaches for me and hugs me, her bobbed dark hair pressing against my cheek. And, to my surprise, an unmistakable bump presents itself.

I step back. 'You're pregnant,' I blurt out, 'congratulations!'

She flushes. 'Yes. Thank you.' She glances at Doug. 'Only sixteen weeks. Nobody at work knows . . .'

'My lips are sealed,' Doug says, and he pulls his finger across his mouth as if zipping it up. 'Great news,' he adds.

'Yes.' Suzanne nods. 'And we never . . .' She tears up, then shakes her head a little. 'Sorry. It's not important, all over now.' She touches my elbow. 'But it's you,' she says, 'we need to be thinking about now, how are you?'

'Oh . . .' Suzanne looks so radiant, so open. She's older than I am but I feel like an old hag – cloudy face, soft neck. I smile. She would die if she knew what I was thinking. It is part of her charm, her complete modesty.

Suzanne's face has a look of concern. 'Doug, get her a drink and something to eat,' she says, a little sharply. 'Poor thing.' She leads me over to the sofa and pulls the small table over. 'Damn men, can't see what's right in front of their faces.'

Doug arrives, for some reason a little flustered, and Suzanne spreads the food out on the plate. I take a bite of quiche and it's fantastic – who made this? I wonder – and a bit of potato salad.

Doug is still standing. 'Can I get you something, Suzanne?' She looks up at him, and I am struck by how familiar they are with each other, how well they seem to know one another. 'Yes please, Doug. Something to eat and apple juice.' She doesn't even say another 'please'. Not obsequious at all. Of course they see each other every day, hour for hour more time together than Doug and I have.

Her hand is resting on her tummy. She follows my eyes down. 'I keep thinking I feel something,' she says, 'I know it's silly.'

'No, it's not.' Before I can stop myself I reach out and put a hand on top of hers. 'I started feeling Louis at fourteen weeks. Like little bubbles, I remember it clearly.'

We take our hands away, but I continue looking at her stomach, the small rounding out of it, like a planet, one side of the moon. Being pregnant with Louis seems a lifetime away now, as of course this life would have seemed then. As Dad dying would have seemed.

I sigh. The reinfusion of a little whisky begins to take effect and that, combined with the food, improves my spirits in general.

Doug comes back with Suzanne's food and drink, and he sits down next to her, probably for the first time in hours judging by his groan as he stretches out.

It's a small sofa, but we sit wordlessly on it. I look up at the clock – late afternoon. What have people been doing? The noise level has diminished, but even so I am amazed at people's stamina for a party. And a wake at that. There's Charles charming Hilary, who looks more animated than I've seen her in the short time I've known her. Charles is gorgeous, this cannot be denied: tall, blonde, elegant, womanly almost, with a dry sense of humour and perfect white teeth. He too must be delighted with their good news.

After a minute they seem to reach a lull in their conversation, and they turn their heads toward us. I catch Hilary's eye; she raises an eyebrow, and touches Charles's elbow. They move in our direction.

'Hi, Charles,' I say, and reach up for his arm. 'Great news.'

'Yes.' He glances at Suzanne. 'We're looking forward to it.'

I look at Suzanne, too. She has turned her head slightly away, looking at I don't know what, over the high arm of the sofa. There follows the kind of moment I remember experiencing only a few times in my life – an odd gap, a sort of emptiness, yet it is tremendously full of something, something no one knows, perhaps a secret – a space where no one will jump in, and any movement, any word, feels like it might change the course of something, of life maybe, for ever. Somehow, we just need to wait for it to pass, hardly daring do anything, and yet each second is magnified, glossy, frozen into frames.

My brain, however, continues its predictable ticking and analysing. Of course these sorts of sea-changes don't really happen, they can't. Cells and momentum – the motion of things – can't change direction that fast, can't change direction at all really. Rather, they do a slow, wide turn, like a ship negotiating wind and current.

Nevertheless, in that moment, I wonder if the feeling I have is right, that something opens up, something perhaps closes. And could it be happening for everyone? I look around, feel the hairs on my neck. Slowly, slowly, we bump over, we leap together.

Then Charles moves, squats down next to me: 'How are you, Marilyn?' and Hilary, I see out of the corner of my eye, picks up my empty glass, makes off with it and hers towards the drinks.

Doug turns to talk to Suzanne. His whole body turns away from me in fact, just slightly sideways, and as I take notice of this, Charles reaches for my hand. I look at him. I do not remember his eyes as so – serious? beautiful? Or perhaps I've just never looked at them.

The room still has the remains of something unusual, like an echo or a summer storm approaching. Hilary comes back with my drink and slips it into my other hand. Charles's mouth is moving. I can't make out what he's saying. But I have the feeling that whatever it is, it won't matter until tomorrow, or even, much later.

*

That night, I lie in bed and think of all the countries and peoples in trouble. I don't know why this happens, but it is like a channel which sometimes opens, the swirl of a ham radio. I imagine the darkness overhanging half the earth, the satellites up there passing messages. The conversations people are having, long-distance loves, like a soppy movie, the man and the woman, woman and woman, man and man, hanging on to a piece of plastic, for every word through the crackle and delay. Or indeed the arguments, the phone left hanging there, the misunderstood sentiment, the phone slammed down. Or the conversation that never really begins, but instead runs over and over the same tracks.

And beyond that, there is a quieter hum, one I've experienced all my life, that only comes with my head on the pillow, awake, and only when I'm very tired. I hear voices, people talking, a sort of murmur, some in English, some in languages I don't even understand. Whole exchanges, or just a word. As I grew older and trained, read all my books, I wondered if it was just an expression of my own subconscious, sorting things out. But there's no rhyme or reason to it, nothing changes. It's like I am a conductor for something, a way for people to talk, a receptor. Or it's just a way for me to listen. It is always very calming, comforting, although I long for some piece of clear information, something

I can use and gain from to come to light. It never comes of course; the voices bubble on, talking almost without words, and I'm just on that frequency, picking up a few of the crossings and mis-crossings and single messages that go up like flares, a quick burning, *help me*.

I remember again a half-conversation with my father about this phenomenon. I suspect that for all his jolly manner, he was fundamentally contemplative, but this never showed itself much, I don't know why. We very rarely seemed to finish a discussion. He certainly, however, had the air of someone who didn't quite manage to do what he'd intended.

We were on the front porch, the place where most of the exchanges with my father happened. At that time of day. I believe it was between high school and college, deep summer. The cicadas were warming up to their racket, and he almost had to raise his voice to be heard. 'Like people,' he said, 'all talking at once!'

I smiled. He would know. His lifetime career, starting soon after he settled with my mother, was working for the phone company, Bell Telephone, or 'Ma Bell' as he called it. 'Do you ever think about all those lines, all those people and what they're saying?' I said.

'Sure.' He put his drink down on the side table. He gestured with his hands – 'You open that box, it swings open like this, and inside are wires and wires of all different colours, each one of them carrying someone talking to someone – or each one of them might be doing that, could be.' He glanced at me. 'Because it's unlikely they'd all be in use at once, of course – the system'd probably collapse! Anyway,' he went on, 'it's the idea that there is ever that much to say, and that I could just plug in and listen to any one of them. Not that I ever did, and the kind of trouble you'd get into if anyone ever found out . . .' He shook his head. 'But I often thought about what this kind of communication could do to people's minds, how different people seemed to be from when I was growing up. Their expectations and such.' He stopped, abruptly.

'But you don't really do that kind of stuff any more, do you?' I said, eager to keep him going.

'No,' he sighed. 'I'm more in the office now, which I don't

like as much to tell the truth. But, as your mother would say, needs must.' He smiled at me. 'Anyway, I had my time, and it was hard work, out and about in all weathers.'

'I can imagine,' I said. Then I don't know why I said it, but I did. 'I have this thing sometimes,' I said, 'it's weird. When I hear voices at night, just talking away . . .' I looked over at him. For a second he stared at me quite intently, then he turned his head back towards the street, where just at that moment a kid on a bicycle rode by.

'I used to have that,' he said, matter of factly. 'I think I know what you're talking about. And this was even before there were lots of telephones, these big exchanges. There were radios, ship's radios, police talking to each other—'

'But it's more than that,' I interrupted.

'Yeah, it is.' He locked his fingers together and sat back. 'It is. I know what you mean.' He shrugged. 'I really don't know what to tell you, I've never known what it is. For a while there was something about it that made me want to do something different, make something of myself.'

'But you have,' I said.

He put his hand up and laughed a little. 'Thanks, but I know I'm doing OK. It's just that at first I wanted to do something really big – I used to be an inventor of sorts, I bet you didn't know that.'

I shook my head.

'I wanted to make something that would change the world.'

'Like what?'

'Well.' He laughed again. 'That was the problem. It seemed like everything I thought of had problems, didn't do what I wanted, wasn't enough. This was before the war, you know, when I was even younger than you. Anything seemed possible then. Then I met your mother, and life took over. In a nice way, mind you, it wasn't bad.' He looked over at me again. 'We had you, and a good job seemed the most important . . .'

'Do you regret it?'

He shook his head. 'No, no. You can't have regrets in life, serious regrets. We are lucky to be in this world at this time, so much is happening. We're just running to keep up with progress, with all the new things. I'm getting up there, but I think I do all right. I've had a good life, so far.' He held up his crossed fingers.

We both smiled. 'Well, I think you've done great.' I meant it. He seemed to believe in the future more than I did, even then. 'I just hope I do as well and am as happy as you are.'

'You will,' he said. 'Believe me. You'll do better.' He waved away my objections. 'The point is, sweetie, you should do better, it's the way of the world. Children should always better their parents. And you're a good kid. You will.'

It was the end of the longest and most profound conversation I ever had with my father. Soon after, my mother called us in for dinner, and we went in without another word.

*

My father's face. He was right about so many things, about progress, about almost everything becoming possible. What he ended up being wrong about was something I could never even mention to him, and now of course, never would. And that is, that one generation does not necessarily improve upon the other, that the great forward motion of his parents and of his own pursuits have more or less stopped with me. My own happiness does not exceed his; indeed, I doubt if it even matches what his was. And for this, as well as for many other things, I know I've gone all wrong. Not so as many people would notice, but enough to feel it tonight, Doug snoring next to me. Enough so that I can't help but think of Suzanne, her beatific face and a new start. Hilary's offer of friendship I don't know what to do with. Whatever it is that keeps me from just seducing my husband. And most importantly, what I know already I won't be able to give Louis, the sense that anything is possible.

I can't think too much about this now. Not after today. The big thing's been gained – at least I've located my father's face as I want to remember it: healthy, smiling, his lovely hands moving, his hair just turning white, touching his collar, the points of his casual slacks lined up with the toes of his home shoes. At last I have something to hold on to. And so I hold it, push the voices out and out of my head, turn over, and let myself fall asleep.

Rayda Jacobs

The Guilt

Lilian Thurgood was busy picking guavas at the side of the house when she heard the growling of the Alsatians on the stoep. Just a low growl telling her that someone had stopped at the gate. Perhaps it was the postman, she thought, dropping something into her box. She looked about her for a moment. They were at the end of winter, the morning fresh with the footprints of rain. She marvelled at the brightly coloured new tips of trees, the pots of purple and pink geraniums with cellophane drops glistening on the leaves, the cluster of basil and oregano sprouting near the lemon tree. She liked the mornings, when God's breath was hot on the earth and steam rose from it in easy surrender. Then she heard the growling again. Still low, but more intense. Someone had stopped at the gate and wasn't going away. She put down the basket with the guavas, and reached for her cane.

She reached the front of the house and saw Tembi and Tor like sentinels at the gate. Fierce and powerful dogs, they had been trained by her late husband to follow specific commands. It was the man's calmness that held them back.

'Can I help you?' Lilian asked.

'I am looking for work, madam.'

'I don't have any work.'

He reached into a brown envelope and lifted out a plastic-wrapped sheet of paper. 'I am from the Transkei, madam. I have here a letter.'

Lilian Thurgood looked at him. He was young, persistent, wore dark pants and a jacket that had seen darning and letting out, but was clean. She'd seen these letters before, but took it from him anyway. As she suspected, a letter on a home-made letterhead – the paper dirty, water-stained, dog-eared – saying William Sidlayi was collecting donations on behalf of some organization. The man was doubly prepared. If he couldn't find work, he would ask for a handout. The letter made it easier to beg.

She handed the letter back through the grille of the gate. The gate was locked, the wall round the property ten feet high.

'Wait here,' she said.

'Thank you, madam.'

Lilian left him at the gate and started to walk to the house, listening for the renewed growls of the dogs.

In the house, she looked for change in her purse. She knew it was a mistake. She should've been hardened by now. Every day people knocked on her door for food, old clothes, money, and work. Most days she didn't answer. They took merciless advantage, especially since the new government. There was a boldness not seen before.

She remembered the African woman who'd knocked at her door one night at nine. Lilian didn't want to go out. It was raining, a long walk to the gate, but there was the woman, with a child on her back and one at her side. Did the madam have garbage bags, she called. An unusual request, especially at that time of night. And Lilian couldn't see well in the dark. What if there was a second person waiting behind the wall with a knife or a gun? The papers were full of stories of people getting killed in their own gardens and houses, and she'd heard of husband-and-wife crime waves.

She went to the gate. There was no one but the woman and her children, but it irked her that she should be afraid in her own home, that they thought it all right to knock on your door any time of the day or night. Was it racist if you were afraid and didn't want to open your door to strangers? But, of course, she knew what it was. It was making good on the guilt, the guilt they were accused of having. As benefactors of the old regime, whites were shot through with guilt. And where there was guilt there was opportunity. Like the woman who saw her sit on the stoep the other day and begged Lilian to buy four geranium plants for two rand. Her garden was overcrowded with flowers, but the woman insisted. If the madam would buy eight plants for four rand, she would even plant them. Lilian had felt sorry for the woman and opened the gate. The woman threw herself to the ground with her grocery bags in which she kept the plants individually wrapped in wet newspaper, and asked for water so she could wet the ground. Lilian went round the side of the house for the hose and when she returned, there was the woman with thirty plants in the soil. How she'd managed to plant so many in a few minutes, Lilian didn't know. 'Please madam,' the woman begged, 'it's almost five o'clock. I karn go home with these last few plants. Madam won' regret it, madam will see. I'll even give madam a special price, twelve rand.' Lilian gave the woman the twelve rand.

Then there was the man who'd rung persistently at her gate, and when Lilian came out, he asked for money for the bus as he didn't know how he was going to get home. When Lilian told him she had no money, he asked for clothes, and when she said she had none, he asked for food. But not brown bread, he added. Could he please have a tin of fish.

Lilian's thoughts returned to the young man waiting at the gate, and she fished around in her purse for loose change. There was only a five-rand coin and twenty-three cents. Five rand was a lot of money for a pensioner to give away, but she couldn't give him twenty-three cents. What could a grown man do with twenty-three cents? He couldn't even buy a cigarette. She was suddenly angry. Angry that she should be standing there examining her conscience. That she should feel guilt for his circumstances, and shame for the forged letter in his hand, for having to beg, for raising these emotions in her. She was a pensioner. What money did she have? If her husband had been alive, he would've ordered the man off the grounds.

Lilian went outside and found him still at the gate trying to be friendly to the dogs. She gave him the five-rand coin. He took the money, then vigorously nodded his head.

'I can't take this five rand.'

'What do you mean?' Lilian asked, not understanding him.

'I can't just take madam's five rand. Let me do some work for it. I see madam has many leaves from the trees on the grass. I can clean it up for madam. I want to work for it.'

'It's all right. Take it. It's a donation, isn't it?'

'Yes, madam, but it's five rand. I can clean madam's garden.'

'It's quite all right. Please.'

'No, madam, I insist. Look over there, look at all those leaves.'

Lilian looked at the carpet of leaves covering half of the garden. She didn't have the stamina to argue. 'All right,' she said, knowing herself to be foolish to open the gate.

William stepped in, and the dogs moved forward, pink tongues idling in readiness. Lilian made a signal and they relaxed.

'Your name is William?' She remembered the name on the letter.

'Yes, madam.'

'William, just those leaves over there.'

'Does madam think I'm a *skelm*? That I want money for nothing? Those leaves are not even two rand.'

'Well, just do five rand's worth, then. Really, you don't have to do anything. I gave you the money. Just those leaves over there. I've got to go out in a few minutes.'

'Don't worry, madam. I'll be finished now, now.'

Lilian remained at the gate and watched him remove his coat as if he was going to tackle the whole garden. She knew he knew that she wasn't going anywhere, that opening the gate was more a show of trust than a display of fearlessness.

The rake was under the guava tree and she watched him fetch it and sweep up the fruit, sorting the good ones from the pile. He would take them, he said, if she had no use for them. She said it was all right and watched him collect curled fig leaves and other debris, and stuff them into the bin.

'That's enough, William. Thank you. I really appreciate it.'

'No, madam.'

'Really, it's all right. You've done enough.'

The telephone rang and Lilian excused herself. The dogs followed her into the house. She wouldn't lock the door behind her, she told herself. She trusted him. She would show him that she did. She wouldn't make him feel like a criminal. Black people knew that white people were afraid of them. She would show by her actions that she wasn't one of them. But what if she was wrong? What if he came in after her into the house? The old revolver was in a box at the back of the wardrobe, she wouldn't even know what to do with it.

Lilian reached the phone, but the caller had hung up. She became aware of her pulse. Racing. Frantic. She stood for a minute to calm down. The dogs growled. She turned. William was at the door.

'Madam?' he said nervously.

'Yes?'

'I've raked the leaves and cleaned up the guavas.'

'Thank you, William. I'll unlock the gate for you now.'

'I've worked one hour, madam. That's ten rand.'

The effrontery shocked her, but lasted only seconds. Lilian did something with her hand, and the dogs rose. 'I'll ask my husband for the money,' she said.

'There's no husband, madam,' he said in a calm voice. 'Madam lives alone. Why's madam so afraid? I'm not a thief. Madam will give me the money?'

Lilian's purse was on the mantelpiece and she reached for it. In front of him she took out a ten-rand note. The tone of his voice had changed, and somewhere deep inside her, she felt a terrible chill. She was painfully aware that the only thing between her safety and his will, was the dogs.

'I only have this ten-rand note. You can give me back the five rand I gave you.'

'Madam wants change? I thought the five rand was a donation. Madam owes me ten rand for the work I did.'

Lilian looked at him. The smile on his face told her that he thought her a stupid old woman. That she had no choice. Still, she could not get herself to give him the money. 'Leave my house, please,' she said.

'The ten rand, madam.'

'Now, or I'll call the police.'

He came forward.

'Sa!' Lilian commanded the dogs.

The bitches leapt – Tembi at William's wrist, Tor at his collar – and knocked him to the floor. William screamed at the top of his lungs as the dogs ripped at his clothes and nipped with their sharp teeth at his hands and arms.

Lilian looked at him squirming under the canines. The Alsatians had their snapping mouths dangerously close to his face, slopping saliva all over him. They would terrorize, but not draw blood, not until the other command. Lilian had never had to try that out on them yet. She didn't know what the dogs might do if she gave the last signal.

'Please, madam, please!' William shouted. 'I'll leave!'

Lilian left him struggling under the dogs and went to her bedroom. In the wardrobe, she found the little brown box behind Jock's army paraphernalia, and drew out the revolver wrapped in a piece of green felt. It was heavy, smooth, and she stroked it with her fingers, strangely calmed, aware of the screams in the front room. She couldn't remember whether Jock had said it was the revolver or a pistol that had a safety, and couldn't remember how to check if the chamber was loaded, there were no bullets in the box. Gripping her hand tightly about the weapon, she limped out. There was a tremendous surge of something pumping through her veins. She wasn't Lilian Thurgood. She was a woman possessed of only one thought: to come out of the situation alive. In that moment she understood that it took very little to pull a trigger, and that the distance between rational thought and insanity was no distance at all.

'The law says I can shoot if you trespass on my property,' she pointed the gun down at him.

William's eyes danced around in his head like cherries in a slot machine. His jacket was in shreds, the front of his shirt and face wet with snot and dog spit.

'Please, Madam,' he begged, 'don't shoot!'

She tightened her finger on the trigger.

'It would be good for some old woman who's afraid to sleep with her windows open, to read what I've done.'

'No, Madam!!'

Lilian Thurgood loomed over him. She couldn't separate fear from insanity, her trigger finger acting independently of her thoughts. For a few seconds she felt trapped in a vacuum and couldn't move. The moment passed and she stared down at the gun trembling in her hand. She snapped a command, and the dogs took their paws off his chest.

'Get up, and put the five rand I gave you on the table,' she said.

William struggled up on his feet. He felt his jacket, but there was no pocket left.

'It's in your pants,' Lilian said.

He slipped his hand into his trousers and took out a handful of silver.

'Just what is mine. Put it on the table.'

William did as he was told.

'Now walk backwards out the door so I don't have to shoot you in the back.'

With the dogs nipping at his knees, William reversed gingerly out the door, tiptoeing backwards down the stone path to the gate. Lilian had the gun pointed at him the whole time, her eyes never leaving his face.

'I'm going to report you to the police, William. I'm going to give them your description and tell them about the scar under your left ear, about the letter you walk around with, about your evil little scheme to get yourself on someone's premises. I'm going to report you not because I think they're going to catch you, but because I'm going to shoot you if you come here again.'

Lilian unlocked the gate and watched him edge nervously out. William was wide-eyed, still expecting her to pull the trigger. Without a backward glance, he ran down to the main road where he turned the corner and vanished from sight.

Lilian Thurgood stood very still. Her heart was racing, but the pain in her leg had disappeared. She was stunned. She couldn't believe what had just happened. A flash of madness. That was the only way she could describe it. She couldn't believe that it had happened to her, an old woman minding her own business. In sixty-six years, she and Jock had experienced nothing like this. Her hand shook and she put her left hand over her right to still the trembling. She wouldn't think about it. She couldn't. It would finish her to dwell on what might've happened without the dogs or the gun. What might've happened if she'd been forced to pull the trigger.

She took a deep breath, then went inside, forgetting all about the basket of guavas sitting under the tree. She didn't immediately put away the gun, and didn't rush to the medicine chest for one of her pills. She made a cup of okra tea and sat down at the kitchen table listening to the laughter and shouting of the children in the school yard across the road. The voices were reassuring. It told her that there was life outside the ten-foot walls, that there was hope.

At three that afternoon, Margaret and Ruth and Ethel May came over to play bridge and commented on the high colour in her cheeks. Lilian said she'd been raking up the leaves. That night in bed, the gun in its new place under the pillow where Jock's head used to be, she cried softly into her hands.

Erica Wagner

The Woman Who Was Afraid of Fire

I thought I would be afraid.
It had come in my dreams:
A second sleep stealing over me,
Fingers curling over a window-ledge,
Love note shoved under a door,
Hot breath on my neck.

When my eyes were open
Things were different.
Minutes melt and flow,
Wax from a wick,
The crack of the hour: this is what it's like.
Smoke-scarf muffles. Shhh. It was easy.

Newspaper reports mention
My unusual dental work.
No flowers, please.
Donations to the New York City
Fire Department: I loved a man with an axe.
The box was light and small.

Then, to burn again.
Here's the man in black, his tie:
I couldn't hear his words
Over the judder of cogs
And the silver, gasjet hiss.
'The dear departed,' I think. We never met.

Ash feels no fear. Warm vase.
Pale silt, scentless, light as smiling.
So no surprise when you

Slip me in the pocket of your coat
And walk that autumn night
Up Primrose Hill. Ablaze.

We stood for a while, the heat
Pressing a palm against your chest,
Drawing blood to your skin, fire with fire.
A Catherine wheel.
A Roman candle.
A fuse under your thumb.

At the last moment
I didn't want to go.
I clung to your hand –
I fit you like a glove again – remember?
But then it was over – again –
And I fled to my home in the flame.

Andrea Holland

Specimen Days part 2 (And All Along, You are my Mother)

In the revealings of such light, such exceptional hour,
one does not wonder at the old story fables of people
falling into love-sickness with trees, seized ecstatic with
the resistless silent strength in them – strength, which
after all is perhaps the last, completest, highest beauty.

– Whitman, *Specimen Days*

Under the giant oak a girl tatters a daisy
to shreds, thinks of her father's hand,
the breath of her mother, her mother's

whisper that morning, *he is sorry.*
Noon light blasts through the leaves
like the end of the reel at the Saturday

pictures. She remembers a book
in her grandfather's library, a book
of trees: beeches, birches, ash and pine.

The greatest of all is this oak, its stern
column as tall as God. Transparent
leaves letting the sun rush through,

a reckless charm that stuns like a fist
then warms you with love, with light.
The small girl leans into the bark

humming some child's song about
the ocean. She can't imagine how big
is the sea. The only thing greater must be

this tree and the voice of her mother: it is always
       there,
it is quieter than God. It promises nothing
short of heaven.

Eva Salzman

The Ice Cream Lady

Mrs Kovsky was immensely popular with the local school children. She had beautiful auburn hair with bangs, but her face was shockingly weathered in contrast, even though she was only about forty. It was said that her family had died in the Second World War. Her husband was a tall, gaunt fisherman with an unfriendly look on his face. He never seemed to say anything and no one had ever ever, not once, seen him talking with his own wife. Still, stranger things happened in Ponquattuck.

Part of Mrs Kovsky's appeal was that under her joking exterior, which was somehow part and parcel of her Ice Cream Lady persona, she seemed world-weary – or maybe it was battle-weary. She had a tough, earthy way of talking which she didn't modify in the presence of the young. She treated children like adults, saying just the right thing to flatter, so each one thought they had a special relationship with her. Her ice cream truck had the words 'Good Humor' emblazoned down the side, because that was the most famous brand of ice cream around the town of Ponquattuck.

June liked Mrs Kovsky because she made her feel better about her outsize breasts which she loathed, not being old enough yet to understand breasts as a good thing.

She hated the boys knocking into her, and hated her mother for not buying her a bra, so that in the school production she had to play Chicken-Little (as in The-Sky-is-Falling-In) bounding about the stage with her arms crooked like wings, her hands clawed and curled in, trying to hold still those accursed bouncing breasts. Breasts! Such dreadful things. Her sister Helen, on the other hand, was slender with small firm swellings – infinitely preferable, as far as she could see, neat and contained, like June would never be, in any way.

'You mark my words, young lady,' said Mrs Kovsky handing her her double chocolate Good Humor cone. 'You'll be just right – *just* right – and your sister's little nippers will inflate like blow-fish.' (She was right.) But that pleasing realization was still in the future. For now, she suffered her giant breasts.

The rest of the gang had their reasons to like Mrs Kovsky too. Silly Billy was ecstatic about the old bullet from the Second World War which Mrs Kovsky gave him one day with his cone. It was the neatest thing he could imagine. (It wasn't really from the war, but the lie kept him happy.) He showed it to his father, who'd been in the Marines, thinking it would earn him brownie (or cub scout) points, but his father just gave him the usual friendly whack on his head, which was always kept shaved according to his father's trendy military fashion, even though Silly Billy was only eleven years old.

'Don't be so dumb, kid. That's for ducks, not men.'

As for Mary, one day, she was waiting for her Good Humor Rocket icicle and rummaging around in the basket of her bicycle trying to find her money. All she could come up with was a large rusty screw.

'I guess you wouldn't want a screw,' said Mary.

'No thanks, this isn't my day for girls,' replied Mrs Kovsky quick-fire.

Also, she'd put up a swing in her yard, where all the kids could come and play. The day her own son Jimmy was bullying poor fat June, she came outside and grabbed him by the scruff of the neck and dragged him inside.

'You've got a real talent for being a bastard, haven't you? Wonder where you get it from.'

June didn't wonder at all. Although the other kids all secretly liked for June to be bullied (by someone else of course) they appreciated Mrs Kovsky not taking her own kid's side. As she dragged her son inside, they could all see the long, tall figure of Mr Kovsky behind the screen of the porch, standing there like a Modigliani painting.

'Have you ever talked to Mr Kovsky?' Mary asked Allen, whose dental braces she felt drawn to with a fascinated revulsion. Tough, gawky in the extreme, he wasn't quite as thick as Silly

Billy, but couldn't find girls to kiss because they came away with bloody lips.

'Nope.'

'Me neither,' said Billy.

Sometimes Mrs Kovsky seemed to go into hibernation, not coming out for ages. They'd still come over to play and see the ice cream van sitting in the drive at rest looking puffed out with all its exertions at delivery and cheerfulness. It was old-fashioned in shape, a chubby and friendly thing, with two round headlights like puppy's eyes. Its bell unfailingly got everyone excited, even the adults, before they remembered again that they were adults.

During the hibernation times, Jimmy would come out to play with his little sister Susy, who he was very protective about. The dog would bark from the house. Sometimes his mother's voice would screech out from the depths of the rancho house.

'Jimmy! Get your butt inside. Now!'

'Maybe she's run out of ice cream,' whispered someone.

'Hey, Jimmy, your dog wants his breakfast,' Allen yelped, as he grabbed June and pushed her towards the house.

'Hey Jimmy, where's your ma? Ain't she comin' out to play?' asked Mary who was on her knees on the swing.

'Shaddup. Susy's turn on the swing.'

Mary rolled her eyes, but got off. Jimmy lifted his little sister like she was a china doll, and settled her on the swing. No one could object. It was his house, his swing, his sister, after all.

Then Mrs Kovsky would suddenly appear again on her ice cream rounds, maybe a little quieter, not quite so friendly for a while, her thin mouth ground down to an almost invisible line. She seemed such a strong woman, you couldn't imagine . . .

'I ain't got no cones today, and I won't have any cones tomorrow neither. So what'll it be now? Make up yer mind. Or the world'll melt.'

Mary was craning her head to see inside the fridge, which Mrs Kovsky had half her body inside.

'Gimme a popsicle then. Rasberry.'

'Rasberry,' came the muffled automatic response from the depths of the fridge.

Mrs Kovsky emerged and slammed shut the door, twisting the

metal lever handle to seal it. It seemed to give a deep sigh, like the posthumous breath of a corpse. Mrs Kovsky took change from the pouch around her waist and then, maybe to make up for her bad mood, winked at Billy which made him blush.

'Good Humor, my ass,' she said as she hauled herself into the driver's seat, like a real man, revved the engine, also like a man and took off, most like a man, yelling at some beach buggy type thing (driven by a man) which had cut in front, forcing Billy to jump back off the road. They all looked after her admiringly.

'Hey asshole,' said Mary to Allen conversationally. 'Is she limping?'

'Nah,' answered Allen.

'Yes, she is,' said June, always agreeing with Mary who she loved and hated in equal measure. (Talk about neat and compact, Mary was the ultimate in that department.)

'She's always limped,' said Billy. 'It's in 'er family. They all had short legs, or short arms, or somethin' missing.'

Of course, he'd never met a member of her family in his life, but in a place like Ponquattuck, the perfectly natural and explicable had to be rewritten into something fantastic to be understood. Ex-city kids like June and Helen and their friend Petra, had the most amazing stories built around them, which involved guns and knives and strange rituals in the woods, with groups of people and their binoculars. It was Petra's parents who had the binoculars; this alone made them weird in the eyes of the locals; and, frankly, Petra was inclined to agree. (She had a country-hick reputation to cultivate.)

'*You've* got something missing,' said Petra. 'She's never limped before.'

Plus she noticed what looked like a bruise on her inner arm, a five-finger bruise.

One night they'd all sneaked out, as usual, to tramp around the town in a gang for no particular reason. On this occasion no particular reason wasn't good enough and so they decided that stealing road signs would be fun. The boys crept back to their houses to get some screwdrivers and hammers and saws, which they didn't really need but wanted to carry around anyway.

Then they started the business, standing on each other's

shoulders, as they unscrewed a Yield sign, a Stop sign, a No Trespassing sign and the road sign for Joe Halsey's road which he was particularly keen to do, since it was called Halsey Avenue, after his ancestors (whose ghosts apparently, according to Joe, lived in a burnt-out barn at the end of town and came out to party at midnight . . . 'Yeah right,' said Petra, rolling her eyes).

It was after midnight now. While the boys worked, the girls stood around cracking their jawbreaker bubble gum, feeling important, like little country-hick molls.

When they had all their signs, they didn't know what to do with them.

'The Halsey barn!' said Petra. She was going to show that Joe just what she was made of, not scared by boys or boys' stories. There was so much worse to be scared of!

But wouldn't you know it, the boys were keen and the girls shivered, which kept everyone erotically happy for a few moments, though still undecided about what to do.

'The clearing by the Kovskys',' suggested Billy. So they all trucked on over, laden with signs, ducking into the undergrowth by the side of the road every time a car went by. They felt like spies on a mission, like thieves, like members of gang united in their job. It felt good.

But when they'd dumped their signs, they got greedy. They were looking over to the Kovskys', to the ice-cream truck, to the pretty sign along its side, the words 'Good Humor' lit up by the outside porch light. The letters were bright red and swirly and had exclamation marks.

Mary didn't want to do it. June didn't want to do it. They liked Mrs Kovsky. But Joe Halsey and Silly Billy were made to feel like wimps, and June did what Mary said, if not did, and, well, all that group teenage stuff that goes on was going on. Petra criticized everyone and everything, then went along with the group, not wanting to miss out on anything.

So they all crept over – except Mary and Helen who waited behind as sentries – and crouched by the side of the van, out of sight of the house. Joe put a foot on the running board and the suspension creaked. They all gasped and waited. The dog barked once. June was ready to bolt, but Petra had her claws in her.

'Don't move,' she hissed.

After silence descended again, Joe began to climb up the hood and stretched his arm around sideways.

'Can't reach,' he whispered. 'Gimme a shoulder Allen.'

Allen half stood and braced himself as Joe stepped on.

'Fuck's sake,' Allen groaned.

'Shut up,' said Joe. He began to apply the screwdriver, but it was taking a long time. Petra and Mary and June were jammed in near his ass, giggling about that, while Allen started off with jokes about 'no farts' and hilarity along that line.

'I can't hold it,' said Allen.

'Hold what?' asked June innocently and they all broke up in hysterics.

'You wimp.' Mary giggled.

'Git off!' Allen said more urgently.

'Just another . . .' started Joe, but it was too late. Allen gave way and Joe slid down, the screwdriver hitting against the van, metal on metal.

The dog broke into mad barking as they all charged off in different directions. June heard the screen door of the house bang and turning her head in full flight, she could make out the gleaming fangs of a huge German Shepherd.

'Why is it always me?' she was thinking, though all that came out of her mouth was a wail diminishing into the distance. The others laughed for years just at the thought of it. 'Why Meeeee?!' she wailed as the animal sank its fangs into her fat, racing bottom.

Collapsed in a cowering heap, she waited, but just before it could take its final bound onto her, someone called it off. It veered sideways, began to rush in crazy circles, still barking. She felt him standing there – it was Mr Kovsky for sure – but all he said was: 'That'll learn ya,' before disappearing into the house.

It took her an hour to get the nerve to crawl home in the dark, she was crying so hard with fear. You'd have thought that by this time in her life, with all her past experience of these good pals of hers, that she'd be used to being left alone in a heap on the ground. Anyway, that's what the others thought after they left her. There was no point going back.

*

For several weeks there was no ice-cream truck. They were all hanging out at the town dock one day when they heard the bell ringing. June's hand was in a bandage. So was her ass, but no one could see that, as she habitually wore loose clothing which covered up her fat body.

'I'm getting out of here,' she said standing up.

'Don't be such an asshole. You always look like you've done something wrong,' said Mary disdainfully.

'I have. We have.' Her guilt and principles were part of what annoyed everybody else and as soon as she said this she regretted it. She longed to do wrong and not care just like the others. Should she stay or go? Which would be more impressive? She stayed put as the van pulled up.

But no one got out. It just sat there, the engine rattling. The sun was reflecting on the windscreen in a great blaze of fire, so they couldn't see Mrs Kovksy.

'I'm scared,' said June, unable to help herself. She looked round wildly.

Joe jumped down from the dock's pillar he'd been straddling.

'I'm getting an ice cream,' he said coolly. 'You want one Mary?'

'Yeah,' she said, following him. The others reluctantly trailed along. Silly Billy was whistling inanely and Mary was chewing her gum with feigned indifference. Petra and Helen grabbed June and dragged her along.

Still, no one got out of the truck, and all they could see as they approached was the sun on glass like bright steel, the engine motor growing louder. They approached the driver's side, shaded their eyes as they peered in.

'Would you like an ice cream?' asked Mr Kovksy, his long drawn, unsmiling face looking somewhere over their heads. A cigarette drooped from his mouth and he had his blue baseball cap on, backwards.

Nobody said a word. This was a new one. Mr Kovksy had never been the ice-cream man before.

'I've got some of them Carn-e-val ones for ya special. The ones that stain your tongues all red and purple.'

He swung his long spidery legs to the ground and jerked open the handle of the fridge door. They all peered in. It was June whose shoulders he put a friendly arm around.

'See for yourselves.'

And it was June who went running the only way down to the water's edge, splashing in with all her clothes on until she could go no further. That was all that happened. But it was enough.

Alan Brownjohn

The Sweeter Fool

Although aware that she was mysteriously setting limits to our meeting by preferring to see me at the Horizon, I had been longing for my date with Rachel so much that I had forced myself to do other things (go to the jazz at the Constant Hope, for example) to take my mind off the slow passing of time.

And this was awful. On the Friday afternoon I had taken a bath so as to look and smell my best for an evening beside her in a warm theatre, and while cooling off had fallen asleep in one of the cavernous and grubby lounge armchairs in front of the electric fire. I had also dreamt of Lucy, something about Air Hostess thighs activating an X-ray portal at Stansted . . .

Given the clear and mild weather, I'd intended to stroll down early, assembling my thoughts about my prospects with Rachel as I went. But as it was now late, I had to drive down, at speed, arriving with only a minute to spare.

I had purchased two tickets on the edge of a small side row of seats, thinking we might be more private there. But in the foyer Rachel was waiting for me with two of her own in her hand (holding in the other a Consumerama plastic bag). It shamed me.

'You've paid for these already?'

'They're comps,' Rachel said, motioning me towards the entrance.

I didn't understand.

'*Complimentaries.*'

We entered the small, worse-for-wear auditorium circumspectly, passing the poster suggesting we 'Get in the mood for the festive season with SID AND BERYL BURGESS: A SONG, A DANCE, A SMILE.' It was not warm but vaguely chilly, the arms of the seats cold to the touch. Very quiet background muzak came over on a tape that occasionally jumped. No doubt to save energy, few of the house lights were on, so it was hard to tell whether I might recognize any of the twelve or so other persons scattered across the stalls. Rachel rested her plastic bag on the empty seat beside her. There were still no more than twenty of us when, several minutes late, the muzak stopped and live music (piano and drums) struck up in the orchestra pit. Why on earth had Rachel insisted on this venue for a clandestine transfer to me of her ongoing manuscript?

I wished I could have picked my parents' brains for information about Sid and Beryl. My father would have remembered their names. My mother, who was the political activist in the household (I had gravely disappointed her by becoming just a lecturer in politics instead of a member of parliament) – my mother could have recalled and placed their kind of entertainment. On the wide and intricate social scale of comedians they stood, I seemed to think, not for the resilient working class, Cockney or Lancashire, nor for the suave-suited troupers who worked on the fringe of cabaret or in the genteel English musical. The Burgesses were the archetypally bland and amiable happy middle-class couple whose 'light comedy' would offend no one and appeal to any undemanding audience in any place except the roughest inner city halls. My oldest readers might like to think of them as a Jack Hulbert and Cicely Courtneidge with rougher edges.

They had long fallen off the TV screen, where they had not been very comfortable, and there was no route back to the radio given their age and the advent, in the later 1980s, of young 'alternative' comedians. 'Stars of stage, radio, TV and film', their publicity went on (what film, and when?)

Onstage, when the curtains pulled jerkily apart, were their 'company', an advance guard of three persons and a wire-haired terrier. The dog took up a sitting position downstage under its own spotlight while the humans went into a dance routine. Two, announced later as 'Dick and Cindy', were unusually young by comparison with Sid and Beryl, probably because they were unemployed; dole jokes were to come, resigned and acquiescent because anything satirical or resentful would not have been in the Burgesses' style. The third person, 'Nobby', was older, tattier, in a tight-fitting, well-worn striped suit, chirpy and agile but looking exactly like a down-on-his-luck performer who had somehow gravitated to this show.

When Sid and Beryl appeared, entering from opposite wings after three minutes' warming up by this trio, only Rachel clapped; the rest of the tiny audience was too slow to give them any hoped-for celebrity applause. The 'stars' gazed out warmly into every corner as if playing to a full house.

I could not tell what Rachel was really thinking of them, as she applauded everything politely in a very kind fashion. I felt sad with embarrassment, almost sick with sadness. The proceedings were terrible, though I admired those people up there with something near to tears of sympathy for their carrying on as if nothing had changed in the world. They had inextinguishable nerve to keep it all up. When they died, few living persons would remember them and they would get only a couple of obituary sentences in the theatre journals.

I dislike dogs, but had to give Nobby's terrier credit (I supposed he was its trainer, they came as a package). Nobby did a juggling turn, conducted a bit of backchat with a non-existent audience member, found a flea in the ticket pocket of his jacket and told it an Irish joke, whistled up the animal. 'Chris' walked up one side of a see-saw plank, barked three times at the top, trotted neatly down the other side, jumped easily through hoops with which Nobby tried to confuse him, ran adroitly between Nobby's legs while he did exercises, leapt onto a high stool handed out to him from the wings and from there jumped onto Nobby's broad head where he balanced for several seconds while the drum rolled in the pit.

The Burgesses did a quick-fire middle-aged-man-and-wife-at-the-seaside sketch, and the lights came up for the interval. Rachel put the plastic bag in my hand.

'This it?' I asked.

'It.'

'Do you want to come back after the interval?' I would go anywhere rather than stay for further passages of pathos on that stage, now that I had Rachel's writings safely in my hand.

'Of course,' she replied.

'You wouldn't prefer to go?'

'*No!*'

'The tickets — you can't treat me.'

'I told you — they were comps. My mum got them.'

'Your mother did?'

'On the piano.'

The two persons on piano and drums in the pit, both women, were standing up. So the older one was Rachel's mother?

And naturally, by the rule that so many things were surprising that surprise itself was becoming *un*surprising, the drummer was Flamingo. As we passed she caught sight of me, and looked. When I looked back she nodded at me, with clear recognition. After feeling excited by that, I felt caught out. By Rachel's wondering how I knew the drummer? Or by Flamingo seeing me with Rachel? Rachel nodded at Flamingo, to add her own greeting to mine, I supposed. We went out for a drink in the silent and deserted bar.

In the second half, after another spell of dancing, Sid and Beryl Burgess talked to each other across the stage on two telephones, busy husband in the office called by his wife on a bad line about a plumbing problem. At last there was laughter from the audience, possibly people remembering an old sketch. Cindy and Dick sang, a passable romantic ballad, and then came a schoolroom scene in which Sid put on glasses and mortar board to teach sums to the rest, Beryl a naughty girl in front, Nobby in short trousers regularly interrupting from the back.

Nobby stripped down to vest and underpants to take a bow and arrow as Cupid for some stand-up comedy, Dick and Cindy reappeared in lime green light as Harlequin and Columbine, a serious bit of ballet which, because it was 'sad', did gain some genuine applause. How much longer could I bear this?

Ultimately Sid appeared in front of the curtain while objects were being removed behind it and thanked us for being so nice to meet. If we had friends in Cromer, or Mablethorpe, or Llandudno, we were to let them know they'd be coming there on their New Year tour. He hoped to see us all again here, when they came back — 'maybe a few more of you?' — but seriously we had been a lovely audience and ours was a lovely town. He'd like to settle down one day in a place like this, perhaps he and Beryl would actually do that. But the busy life of touring entertainers still called... Meanwhile, then, he wished us all a Merry Christmas (why had the show been so lacking in seasonal stuff, I wondered? A trick missed), a Happy New Year, and to end the show tonight—

The curtains parted for a climactic turn which even I recalled — could it be from a live variety show in my childhood? It involved the entire troupe again. Sid Burgess was a posh, endlessly patient men's and women's outfitter. He had to cope with Beryl as a scatty, never-satisfied South Kensington customer, Dick and Cindy as two stylish youngsters in search of fashions he didn't stock, and Nobby as an ordinary working-class bloke who had strayed into the wrong shop. The dog, belonging to the lady, interfered with every transaction, getting under people's feet, barking, begging. Without thinking I began to laugh at the changes and flauntings of unsuitable garments (Nobby in a brassiere), the ancient slang, the timing perfected in a thousand repetitions. I was glad, because I did want the Burgesses to go home happy. I hoped they were receiving a decent fixed fee, not a percentage of box office takings.

Everyone came together in a row for the final song-and-dance, and yes, I recalled their signature tune, which Rachel's mother thumped out on the piano with energy and no doubt relief:

> Sleep well — and wake up to sunshine —
> There's sunshine — tomorrow — for you.

The curtains closed for good and all. Until their second and final performance tomorrow.

'Do you want to say hullo to your mum?' I asked Rachel. If she didn't, I would propose another drink in the theatre bar.

'I'll do that at home,' she said. 'She'll be pleased I've dragged someone along to support her — and my sister will.'

'Your sister?'

'On the drums.'

Peter Scupham

Sleeping Beauty

In the parlours there were pianos,
their music glazed behind gates of ivory,
and lucky tea-sets of best bone china
lay rinsed from the lips' kisses
when lips were still for kissing.
At night, mere echoes of a ghost sonata –
old hands had sloughed away their grace-notes.

Even by day the darkness of cortège:
vault-smells, uneasy among flowers –
narcissi, roses, and the darkest asters –
each sconce of music's coffin white with candles.
Flies died at the windows. In the cold,
light rocked a slow berçeuse
on skins of ebony and rosewood.

Once a year, soft-footed, prim and slow,
princes came with gold-rimmed spectacles
and instruments in cases rich with velvet
to be alone with music in deep coma,
to feel her stammer love,
her waxes, rouge-flush, crotchets,
thrilling again beneath a lover's hands

as they, with bird-brained repetition
struggled to charm away her sleepy-sickness,
screwing the tension up to fever-pitch
and rattling china with arpeggios
before the sweet, cool absences again,
the settled air dusty with minims, crotchets,
freed from their crossed hands.

Used Notes, Plain Envelopes

You could speak truth and shame the devil,
though young and old pretenders throne the darkness
in these ruinous Balkans. Undiluted evil,

the echt, quintessence, premier crû of it,
Elixir of Death, true Philosophic Stone
which deconstructs from shit a purer shit

is hard to come by, scouring to your peril
this world awash with acronyms, dark glasses,
tappers of blood and keyboards, vicars choral,

their visas, access, lettres de cachet
signed Hugs-and-Kisses, Papa, Forkytail:
a simple cartwheel cross or girlish spray

of characters so bread-and-butter plain
that you would put aside your longest spoon
to share and share about such food and wine

as lay there, with your cards, upon the table,
not noticing, in this new-found bonhomie,
things spat upon, words thinning into dribble,

and the flies lording it in the window-pane.
But, as you blurt 'I love you. I'm sincere.
Please be my friend', your own cheeks bare the stain

of that blush by whose light witch-finders tell,
as surely as by pricking in the thumbs,
where the wind sits, which quarterings of hell

your quarters have been pitched in. And what cure,
the compact made, in scrabbling to rub out
the genuine forgery of your signature?

Gerda Mayer

Prague Winter

[from an autobiography in progress]

A Rude Man

People are consulting each other about the imminent invasion of the Sudeten. My father tries to consult another small Jewish shopkeeper in the street of shops. 'How do I know! How am I to know what to do! Why does everyone come to me for advice?' roars that reluctant guru at my father. (Who knows; – perhaps his shop is a smidgen larger, more prosperous, than the other little shops in the street; perhaps in normal times he was a man to be looked up to . . .) Now he fairly dances with self-importance, with assumed exasperation, in the middle of the street. He puffs himself up. – But then, indeed, how is he to know.

Farewell

'The Czechs will throw Hitler out in a week,' my mother predicts. Even so – a week's holiday from school! And, who knows, Hitler might oblige and stay a full fortnight. Perhaps, too, in subterranean consciousness, the lights of Prague beckon, romantic poverty and adventure.

At my Aunt's

In Prague we separate. My parents go to one aunt, I and Waldi, our dachshund, to another. I am allowed to sleep in a drawer on the floor – a thrill and a treat. This is adventure indeed.

My uncle-by-marriage tends to bellow at me; my Aunt Mizzi, in her indolent, good-natured fashion, and with barely a word said, indicates that I am a pain. My handsome, red-headed, gangly cousin Heinz has already entered the land of grown-ups and girls.

(So each table has a telephone and, when a man wants to ask a girl for a dance, he just rings her up at her table and requests the pleasure.) It falls to my cousin Anneliese who is 'good with children' to take me in hand.

Anneliese, sixteen, is pretty and jolly, with bouncy curls and big brown eyes. She is a poet and a teller of stories that sometimes entertain and sometimes horrify. She is a great favourite and much more fun than my own elder sister. Nevertheless . . .

The Refugee Dog

We are at the butcher's, Anneliese and I, to buy Waldi, our dachshund, a sausage. It is his one meal of the day. Anneliese glances – first at the butcher and then – meaningfully – at the dog. As usual, Waldi carries the sausage home, patiently in his mouth. And suddenly I notice things moving in the sausage, white, terrible, filthy things, and realize that the sausage is full of maggots. 'Look, – oh look!' (Oh my poor dear dog.) But my cousin feigns deaf and walks on.

Eventually, my parents, my elder sister and I, move to a couple of rented rooms. Waldi stays behind.

And later, in England, when I pray for my family before falling asleep, I shall be including Waldi in my prayers; and I shall ask about him in my letters back home. Then, one day, my mother, perhaps to reassure me, will draw a picture of our dog in one of her letters. He is a dachshund but she has given him pointed ears. She has not only not seen him for a long time, she has forgotten what he looked like, she has even forgotten what breed of a dog he was . . . And I, in my letters home, shall not be mentioning my dog again.

Ablutions

Our digs in Prague do not run to a bathroom. My sister, Anne, is standing naked at the wash-stand, with her back to my mother and me. Her small waist curves gently outward at the hips. My mother who feels that I never do my elder sister justice exhorts me to admire her.

'Oh Mother, really . . .' says Anne.

On another occasion, with the family assembled, I dance around in the nude.

'Mother, how can you allow Gerti to caper around like this in front of father.' And, in the silence that ensues, there is a sort of embarrassment. For already I am sprouting breasts.

Very soon Prague loses its glamour and I am homesick.

'I wish I were back in Karlsbad,' I confide to my diary. 'If only Hitler weren't there. He's very disagreeable.'

Background

My father made the following entry into the *Baby-Diary* which he had kept up in a desultory fashion since my birth:

> . . . Emigration – suffering for the Jews. Two concepts that determine your fate and ours. We *had* to flee from Karlsbad, although we did so voluntarily and despite the manifold assurances of the good towns-people there that we had nothing to fear. Nevertheless, it was good that we fled in time . . . Now we live here in Prague, since end of September 1938.
>
> There's a continuous hurry and chase from one official department to the next, every week new decrees with their requisite documents, etc., a chaos in which nobody knows what is happening and which, when all seems sorted out, turns out to have been a wild-goose chase. In addition, there is all the running around to be done to the consulates.

The Emigration Game

My mother marches through Prague in shoes that have semi-high thick heels. She is small and overweight and they give her a little added height but they cannot be doing her varicose veins any good. She marches in a brisk yet unhurried way, straight-backed, hands ungloved and balled against the cold, like the brave plump little soldier she is.

We buy chocolate creams. Mother says that if we pick one with a brown filling, we'll go to England; if pink, then to Scotland;

if white we'll have to stay here. I pick a brown (England!), she has the white one. 'Ah well,' she says with subdued cheerfulness. 'Let's try again.' And they do, they do try – again and again and again.

Another Omen

Hanukkah – the festival commemorating the Maccabees. 'The Festival of Little Lights' my cousins Hansi and Susi call it. We three children stand before the lit candles. Hansi is nine, Susi and I eleven. Hans and Susi sing the appropriate Hebrew song, the *Maoz Tzur.* I merely go tra-la-la and feel a fool. The lights are switched off, only the candles are lit and are reflected in the mirror put behind them to enhance their glow. The grown-ups stand back, in the darkness. And, suddenly the mirror behind the candles cracks with the heat, and somebody says in a scared and hasty way: 'Seven years bad luck!' And, true enough, seven years later I was to be the only survivor.

John Burnside

Three Studies of Fungi

1.

I never thought ill
of darkness, or the slow
unfolding of the caps, through days
of rainfall and leaves,

and carried home
like leech-prints, or the taste
of silver in my mouth, each bitter slug
of animus I gathered from its gaze,

the woods infested with a form
of memory, or kinship, and myself
included in the blue
of stinkhorn, or the fade

of drowned men's fingers,
gone from earth to earth
through sweet molasses, rock-salt,
flowers of zinc.

2.

I could tell you the story
of how we climbed the hill
through birch woods
 – how I swear we tasted them,
before we saw the spill
of fly agaric, newborn and exact
amongst the drifts of light
and fallen leaves;

or how it came to us
that it was blood
recovered from a well
of flesh and bone:
that any fall demands
a transformation, one bright cord
become another,
risen from the soil

and reaching
for the standstill of a red
boletus,
where the wood mouse
and the owl
resolve
against the fruitfulness
of spores.

3.

Out in the woods, it isn't déjà vu
that everything seems familiar,

it's just a gap we know
from somewhere else:

the afterlife of bark and flaking leaves
we used to imagine in school, or the cursive space

where one life is abandoned for the next,
the old flesh invested with snow and the taste of
                    currants,

the old regrets and loves becoming
tendons, milk-teeth, misted fingerprints.

If we could draw the hanging fire
of presence from these puffballs, like a veil,

or like the egg-yolk, spilling from the shell
pregnant with weight and light, would it reveal

the fade of spikenard or foreign blood,
or taste a little of ammonia:

a spirit not quite whole, but tuned beyond
all hearing to its own

estrangement,
like a blizzard, or a fall?

Michael Murphy

Thrush

For Merilyn Smith

Late evening in the conservatory.
We're drinking wine,

watching the June light still
and deepen

against the tilted rim
of the horizon.

Heat drains from the breathless soil,
cooling to obsidian –

colourless, opaque, blown.
You reach me another glass

when a sound we guess to be the television
with its now nightly rumours

of emptied villages and towns –

jab deeper you lot with your spades
you others play on for the dance –

switches the garden to standby.

A thrush – a maniacal thrush –
is using a stone in the middle of the pond as an anvil.

Its nervy pneumatic head
cracking the fused enamel

it dislodges a slobber of gristle
then frisks the unaccommodated shell,

dark eyes keeping sentinel.
With a loose shrug

it hops into a sycamore
before sounding the all clear:

a song under whose brittle roof
are rooms enough to house the migrant dead.

The lines in italics are taken from Michael Hamburger's translation of Paul Celan's *Todesfuge*.

MICHAEL MURPHY · 158

Helen Simpson

The Tree

'I'm very worried,' she said. 'Can you come over right away, Derek?'

'Listen, Mum,' I said through gritted teeth. 'I'm on my mobile. I'm sitting in a traffic jam in Chudleigh Road. Is it urgent?'

'It's that dead tree in the back garden,' she said. 'I'm really worried about it. It's a danger to life and limb.'

'Do you know where Chudleigh Road is, Mum?' I said. 'It's in between Catford Greyhound Stadium and Ladywell Cemetery. And you're over in Balham.'

'Never mind that,' she said. Then, 'Ladywell used to be a lovely area. Very what-what.'

'Well, it isn't any more,' I snapped, glaring out of the car window into the November drizzle.

'I'm really worried, Derek,' she said. 'That tree out the back, it's dead and now the wall beside it is shaky and it might fall on someone.'

'That wall is only shaky because you went and got rid of the ivy,' I told her, crawling along in first, trying not to sound irritated.

'Ivy is a *weed*,' she said with surprising force.

I hate ivy too. It makes me shudder. To me it's the shade-loving plant you find in graveyards feeding off the dead.

'You should have left it alone,' I said. 'It was helping hold that wall up. Parasitical symbiosis.'

When I was over in Balham two days ago she took me to look at the tree, which was definitely dead and was at that point covered in strangulating ivy. There were flies and wasps crawling all over the ivy berries when you looked, and also snails lurking under the dark green leaves which smothered the wall.

'I did a good job getting rid of it,' she said down the phone. 'I ripped it all out, it took me the full morning.' Her memory may not be what it was but physically she's still quite strong. I could just imagine the state of the old brickwork after she'd torn away the ivy; the dust and crumbling mortar. No wonder the wall was shaky after that.

'You should have left it to me,' I said tetchily. 'I'd have cut the stems and left it a few weeks. That way all those little aerial roots would have shrivelled up a bit and lost their grip on the brickwork. It would have come away easily if you'd only left it a bit.'

There was a pause, then I heard her start up again.

'I'm really worried, Derek. It's that dead tree in the back garden. Can you come over?'

'Listen, Mum,' I said, and my voice was a bit louder than I meant. 'You keep saying the same thing. I heard you the first time, you know. You're repeating yourself, over and over again, did you know that?'

'Oh dear,' came her voice after another pause. 'I suppose it's true. You've said so before and you wouldn't make it up.'

'Don't worry,' I said, immediately remorseful. 'It's not the end of the world. Me, I'm forgetting names all the time now that I've reached fifty.'

'Are you fifty?' she said, and she sounded quite shocked.

I wasn't making it up about the memory. I go hunting for a word, searching up and down my brain, and just as I think I've got it, it's gone – like a bird flying out of the window.

'It's important to forget things,' I said down the phone. 'We've got too much to remember these days.'

'It's a bit worrying though, isn't it,' she said.

'Well, you can just stop worrying,' I said, seeing the traffic start to move at last. 'Stop worrying about that tree. I can't come now, I've got too much work on my plate, but I'll be over on Saturday. OK?'

I had so much work on that it wasn't funny. I was on my way back to the office in New Cross where there was a pile of stuff to be dealt with, then I had to be over at the house in Bassano Street by three, which would be cutting it fine but I'd have a sandwich in the van on the way. I was going to go round it with Paul the surveyor before starting in on the structural stuff, just for a second opinion. We put business each other's way on a regular basis, so it works quite well.

Now a surveyor really *does* have to worry. That's what he's there for, to worry. He worries for a living. It's up to him to spy the hairline crack in the wall which will lead to underpinning in five years' time. See that damp patch? That's hiding wet rot, which in turn leads to dry rot, and dry rot will spread through a house like cancer. You have to cut the brickwork out if it gets bad enough.

Seeing a house for the first time, you can tell everything about it that you need to know if your eyes are open. It's the same between men and women, the first meeting. You know everything on the first meeting alone, if you're properly awake. And as things go on, it'll be the first cold look, the first small cruelty which lays bare the structural flaws.

Martine would never even consider having my mother to live with us. 'I am not marrying you so that I can be a tower of strength and a refuge to your relatives,' she said. I drop by when I'm passing through Balham, generally once or twice a week, and I tend not to mention it to Martine when I do so. 'I have the right to decline responsibility for other people's problems,' says Martine, and I agree with her. She is the first woman in my life who doesn't lean or cling, and this is a luxury I had not thought possible. She's independent yet she chooses to be with me. I can hardly believe it. Anyway, I left Vicky and the boys for her. I can't talk about selfishness.

Later I had to ring Paul to say I was running late for Bassano Street. I had to track him down on his mobile in the end because he was already there. He started telling me about the dodgy flaunching on the chimney stacks, but far more interesting than that was the news on the Choumert Road house I'd sent him to check out that morning.

'I went down into the cellar and I couldn't believe my eyes,' he said, sounding quite excited for him. 'Asbestos everywhere. I've never needed my mask before in all my years in this job and of course I couldn't find it when I needed it so I had to make do with a piece of kitchen paper . . .'

'You're going a bit over the top, aren't you?' I said, because

I'd liked the look of that house. 'Can't you just case it in and seal it off?'

'Normally I'd say yes,' came his voice. 'But this stuff was crumbling, it was in a dreadful condition. White dust everywhere.'

'Even so,' I said, not wanting to give up on the house, which had looked a nice safe bet to me when I'd seen it the week before.

'More people die of asbestosis every year than die of road accidents,' he said. 'Did you know that? You don't get to hear about it because it's mainly building workers that get it. Like my father.'

'OK,' I said. 'Message received.'

Funny how the picture of a safe solid-looking house can cave in on itself to reveal a cancerous deathtrap, all in a few seconds.

The next day my mother rang me again, and this time I was at the office battling with the VAT returns. She was in a real state, very upset, sounding guilty and at the same time humiliated. It was that tree again, of course.

Gradually I got the story out of her, how she couldn't wait, she'd been so worried about the tree that she couldn't think about anything else so right after my last call she'd dug out a copy of the Yellow Pages and got some tree specialists along.

'You think I'm incapable,' she said at this point in the story. 'You think I can't do anything on my own any more.'

When the men arrived, she told them, 'I only have £825 in my savings account. Will that be enough?'

'That should do it,' they assured her, and I can just imagine them struggling to keep their ugly faces straight.

So she left five men in her house, alone, while she went down to the Abbey National to draw out her entire savings. When she got back she watched them cut the tree down, which took about five minutes. They cleared some of the rubbish, pocketed her money and said they'd be back to deal with the roots. She hadn't seen them since.

'They promised they'd be back right away with some poison for the roots,' she said, and she was almost in tears. 'They haven't finished the job. The roots are the most important bit, aren't they, Derek?'

Of course, I knew it could have been a lot worse. Stories centring round the vulnerability of old ladies, they're what keep the *South London Press* in business, as you'd know if you read that paper. New mothers are notorious for going to pieces over sad news items involving children, and in just the same way I am overcome by tales of helpless elderly women like my mother being robbed blind or beaten up or worse.

I realize Martine might seem hard to some people, but she's just frightened of getting old. Before bed she always rubs hand-cream into her elbows and her upper arms as well as into her hands. She knows how to look after herself. My mother is not like that. Her hands are mine, so is the way she holds herself and the line of her worried brow. She has trouble with her hips, her shoulders, and so do I. She is losing her memory. So will I. There's a phrase I have to describe her to myself. I saw it in one of those poems they stick up now on the underground along with the adverts. When I read the words, I thought, that's her: Ancient Person of my Heart.

'Am I talking sense, Derek?' she said last time I visited. I said, of course she was. She went round the houses sometimes, I said; but that was allowed once you were no spring chicken.

One day she'll look at me and she won't remember me. She won't know anything about me, who I am or what I'm called or the baby I once was in her arms. It happened to her own mother after all, and I daresay it will happen to me. My grandmother's last ten years were spent in a bad dream of not knowing who or where she was, until she fell off the edge at last into the final darkness.

'What's the number, Mum?' I said down the phone, and I kept on at her until I had it. She was sure she'd lost it but then I told her to go and fetch the Yellow Pages and when she came back to the phone with it there sure enough she had circled their name and number in biro.

'Right,' I said, taking down the number. 'Leave this to me, Mum. And you stop worrying, do you hear me?'

I dialled and waited then demanded to speak to the manager. I was reasonably under control at this point, I'm sure

I was, but there must have been something in my voice because the man whistled and said, 'Who are *you*?' Very calm and controlled, I told him how my elderly mother had had his men in to deal with a dead tree in her garden; how I was concerned about the extortionate fee they'd charged her; how they'd not been back as promised to remove the rubbish; and how they hadn't even finished the job. What's the point of cutting down the tree and leaving the roots, I demanded, my voice rising. The roots need to be poisoned and then, later, dug up. Call yourselves tree surgeons?

He listened to my story in silence. He heard me out. Then he flatly denied his men had ever been there.

Of course, I thought. Bastard. I banged the phone down and I was shaking. I sat there and I began to boil with rage. I started to think through what I would like to do to them, that bunch of Del-boy crooks. Smash their windows. Their legs. Then I had an idea. I leafed through my address book and punched in the number of a debt-collector friend of mine. I gave him the story, gave him their address and number. I told him to get the money back whatever way he liked, and he could have half.

When I am old and have the illness my mother is now entering, I will remember this while the rest is slipping away. And Martine no doubt will have come to a just estimate of the situation and of her own needs, and will have arranged suitable care for me. As I will have to, eventually, for my mother. For I cannot look after her indefinitely, I cannot roam the plains of dementia with her, that howling wilderness, hand in hand.

I rang the tree crooks back and went completely ballistic. I threatened them with the strong arm of the law and with all sorts of illegal strongarm stuff too. I moralized at them and told them exactly what scum they were, what vermin, taking advantage of a defenceless widow; how they deserved to rot in hell. I poured a molten screaming lava of vileness into the mouthpiece and then I slammed the phone down.

The noise I'd been making, I must have brought the rest of the office to a standstill. I was completely shaken up, shuddering with indignation. I was exhausted. Plus I had three appointments lined up that afternoon for which I was now running late.

Someone slid a mug of coffee onto my desk, with a message

to ring my mother. I took a few slow deep breaths. I took a sip of the coffee. Then I rang her back.

She told me she was very sorry but she'd given me the wrong number. She hoped she hadn't caused any trouble. After giving me that number she'd circled in the Yellow Pages, she'd wandered off and found a business card on her hall table. It belonged to another firm of tree surgeons altogether, and this lot were definitely the ones who'd been round and done the work. She remembered them leaving the card on the hall table, she remembered them pointing it out to her. She'd tried to ring me back about it right away, but I'd been engaged.

Since that business with the tree, she's been on the blower to me about every little thing. She's totally lost confidence in her own judgement. She rings me at the office, and also at home, which she never used to do. Martine is fast losing patience. She rings me up to ask my advice over every tiny detail. A man has offered to clean her windows for ten pounds – is that too much? Every little thing. It's driving me mad.

Ranjit Bolt

Four translations from the French with a note on translation

Apollinaire *The Aeroplane*

People of France, whatever have you done
With the airman, Ader, who had one –
Yes, just one precious word, and now has none.

Ascesis once assembled, and among
The myriad words that make up the French tongue
Finding for his contraption not one name
He called it 'aeroplane' and so became

A poet. So I say to all of you –
Not just townfolk, country-dwellers too;
Rivers and mountains of our land; to say
Nothing of Paris, Lyon and Marseille:
Flying machines are aeroplanes – OK?

Would Villon not have been quite swept away
By the charm of such a word? Henceforth
Poets will rhyme on it for all they're worth.

There *was* a label, Ader, for your wings:
The fruit of our grammarians' footlings:
A learned coinage, not in the least bit
Aerial – with a horrid gap in it –
A compound as distasteful and absurd
As – yes, I'll say it – as a *German* word.

Now Ariel whispers in the sounds and sighs,
As the machine that takes us to the skies

Deserves. The murmur of a breeze is heard
In those three syllables, or else a bird
Crying on high. And yet it's a French word
And you and I will speak it more and more.

Aeroplane! Aeroplane! Oh, let it soar
Skywards; range over mountains; oceans; or,
As Icarus is fabled to have done,
Undertake a visit to the sun;
Or, venturing still higher, let it trace
An everlasting groove in upper space.
But let us always call it 'aeroplane' –
The magic letters of that word contain
The power to open the ethereal plain.

People of France, whatever have you done
With the airman, Ader, who had one,
Yes, just one precious word, and now has none?

Charles Baudelaire *The Owls*

Sheltered by black yews, owls congregate,
Perched in a broken row
Like foreign gods. Their red eyes glow.
They meditate.

Perched there until
That gloomy time of day
When shadows chase the sun away
And seize control, they stay quite still.

Seeing their attitude the wise
Will recognize
This truth: we must avoid all stress, all motion

We are obsessed with fleeting shadows and,
Being so, are always prey to the vague notion
That there is better ground than where we stand.

Paul Verlaine *Girl*

She has the body of a Boucher nude
Without the looks, no powder in her hair,
But all those wild blonde locks, and such an air
Of sex about her, as would turn a prude

Into a libertine. An easy catch,
She seems exclusive when I kiss her mane
Or feel her burning cunt ignite again
My entire nervous system, like a match.

She is a wall of fire about the gate
Of paradise, the mother of mankind,
The golden fleece we all set out to find,
I place her, prize her at no lower rate.

And then there is her body – who can sing
Its contours, but her poet and her priest,
Her master and her slave, her most and least,
Who'd gladly burn in Hell for one last fling?

Hers is the body that he loves and knows,
A medley of exotic harmonies,
Pink as a lily under purple skies,
As white as fresh milk, or the whitest rose.

The back, the loins, the belly and the thighs,
The rounded buttocks, and the upright breasts,
A feast, sole object of the frenzied quests
Of every sense, of hands, and mouth, and eyes.

That shifting pillow that bewitches me,
And those mad sheets – are they still on your bed
Under the drapes of deepest, sinful red?
Darling, let's waste no time! Let's go and see!

Paul Verlaine *Art of Poetry*

Music's the thing.
Lines of different lengths help there –
Vaguer, more soluble in air,
Never weighing, or placing.

Another piece of sound advice:
Choose words in a pedantic way –
And you're lost – poems should be grey,
Precisely *im*precise.

It's lovely eyes
Behind a veil, broad trembling midday light,
Or the blue blur of bright
Stars in tepid autumn skies!

And always the pursuit
Of Nuance. Colours? None.
Oh! Nuance, which alone
Links dream with dream, or horn with flute.

Also to be religiously eschewed
Are murderous Meaning, cruel Wit,
Crude Laughter; the blue Heavens weep at it –
All that garlicky peasant food.

Take eloquence and throttle it. And,
If you want something else to do,
Tone down your rhymes a little too:
Be vigilant, or they'll get out of hand.

The wrongs of rhyme – oh, who can list them? Who –
What deaf child, or mad savage – forged the thing –
A twopenny-ha'penny jewel, whose ring
Under the file is never true?

Music again, and always! Verse must be
The thing in flight, the thing
Felt fleeing from a soul that's taking wing
For new skies, and new loves. Your poetry

Should represent the pure
Good luck dispersed on the brisk morning breeze
Smelling of mint and thyme. Your aims are these.
The rest is literature.

A Note on Translation

A good image for translation, and I dare say it's not a new one,
is that of the transfer of water, by pitcher, from one, full tank,
to another one (the host language) that is empty and waiting.
Inevitably, some water will be lost. But the leakiness of the
pitcher depends on what is being translated. With Tolstoy, or
so Russian friends have told me, not a great deal of water need
be spilt, if the translator knows his or her job. Apparently,
with Dostoyevsky, spillage is a more serious problem. Well, with
poetry translation, it is endemic. The wisest thing a poetry translator can do is to accept that leakiness and spillage, as an inherent,
continual part of the process, and go with it. By doing that, one
becomes free, and being free, one is better able to serve the
original poet. As the Earl of Roscommon writes, in his *Essay
Upon Translated Verse*, one may 'grow unjust by being overnice/
As superstitious virtue turns to vice'. Dryden, the king of verse
translators, put the same point a slightly different way. In his
preface to an edition of his translations he says that the translator's duty is to make the work appear 'as charming as possibly
he can' while at the same time deviating as little as possible from
what D calls the 'character' and we would call the 'spirit' of the
original. That stipulation may even seem a trifle strict, until one
realizes that 'character' is a pretty loose concept. In what sense
is Dryden's *Aeneid* Virgil? A loose enough one, surely. The same
things happen, and there is a certain pervasive sonority, and
dignity of movement, but that's about it, and that's by no means
all that's going on in Dryden's version. Dryden's translation is, of
course, a great poem in its own right – a great English poem –
greater than the original, I suspect, because Dryden was probably
a greater poet than Virgil. And in it you have an excellent example
of how accepting the leakiness of the pitcher, and going with it,

even being prepared to turn it to positive advantage, can work wonders.

To take an example at random, or perhaps not quite at random, given its subject, looking at my rendering of Verlaine's Art Poétique ('The Art of Poetry'), I suppose I could say that I have, to more or less good effect, accepted the leakiness of my pitcher. I have got in every physical detail, every image, and that is, I think, particularly important with symbolist poetry. As a matter of fact, the concepts are all in there too. At the same time, I have managed to maintain formal discipline. The rhymes are all there, in the right places, not arbitrarily or opportunistically chosen. And there is an acceptable regularity of rhythm. On the other hand, when it comes to the music itself, spillage has been fairly serious, I fear. I don't want to run it down as a version, because I think it's quite neat, and neatness must count for something. But, for example, 'Never weighing or placing' doesn't come close to 'Sans rien en lui qui pèse, ou qui pose' which is marvellously musical – alliteration, assonance, the works. Again, the music of: 'Oh! La nuance seule fiance/Le rêve au rêve et la flûte au cor' is nowhere to be seen in 'Oh, nuance, which, alone/ Links dream with dream and horn with flute.' On the other hand, the wit and urbanity of the original are there, I think, and are as much a part of the 'character' as the music, even though the first line might suggest otherwise. Moreover, to get the thing to work as a poem at all, given the formal stipulations I made for myself, is something too, and perhaps even half the battle.

It's worth remembering that translation, and poetry translation in particular, is a very Blairite activity – it is, quintessentially, about choices, some of which are bound to be tough. The choices you make depend on two things: your own technical strengths, and the nature of the poetry you're working on. I've already suggested that the concrete aspect, the imagery, tends to be more important in French symbolist poetry, than the abstract aspect, the concepts. In this it differs markedly, to pluck a contrast out of the air, from French Baroque poetry, which is hugely conceptual, just like its English counterpart. That was my first choice made for me, very quickly and definitely, by the subject matter. The second was no less obvious. What am I good at, if anything? Answer: rhyme, and rhythm (or meter, if you prefer). This leads me on to my golden rule in verse translation. I call it 'the two thirds' rule. To express it in terms of my opening metaphor: spill a third or so of the water and no more, and you're doing pretty well. By keeping all the imagery – being more or less determined to jettison nothing, though here and there you may have to juggle, and by maintaining great formal discipline, I have obeyed my self-imposed rule. One should not forget that, anarchic though many of these poems may appear, and though they differ widely from one another in many ways, what they have in common is an extreme discipline of form. In fact, part of their great charm comes precisely from this prima facie contradiction between the weirdness of what is expressed, and the great elegance and formality with which it is expressed.

An example of choices, comes from my version of Verlaine's 'Fille' ('Girl') – the final verse.

> Mignonne, allons voir si ton lit
> A toujours sous le rideau rouge
> L'oreiller sorcier qui tant boue
> Et les draps fous. O vers ton lit!

My rendering:

> That shifting pillow that bewitches me,
> And those mad sheets – are they still on your bed
> Under the drapes of deepest, sinful red?
> Darling, let's waste no time! Let's go and see!

Here you can see very clearly the options that have been taken. To begin with, in my book, form before everything – de la forme avant toute chose, to paraphrase the opening line of 'Art Poétique'. In that regard, some nice, strong rhymes offer themselves at once, always remembering that, in English verse, as a rule, the stronger rhymes are, the more pleasurable they are. So, hanging there like ripe peaches on a tree, the seasoned rhymster spots at once those juicy words 'lit' and 'rouge'! These are begging to go in. But how to work them in, given that they are in the wrong place, as far as Verlaine's scheme goes, and I am determined to obey that scheme? After all, I've managed to do so thus far, so I don't have much option now, even if I wanted it. And that's where the choosing, to say nothing of the juggling, comes in. Thus, you will notice that line one gets split, in my version, between lines two and four – the bed in line two, the injunction in line four; line two, with the exception of toujours, is deferred till line three; line three gets shifted up to line one; and line four, like line one, is split – the sheets going to line two, the injunction kept in its right place, and also serving there for the injunction in line one. Thanks to this juggling, no concrete detail has been left out, and form, the other all-important ingredient, has been preserved. The only piece of naughtiness is that suspiciously conceptual 'sinful'. Perhaps it should go, but meter demands something, and the alternative would probably be some equally unwelcome, and purposeless, conjunctions, or some such. What we have here is a very good instance, I think, of the on-going, almost frantic, decision-making process that is part and parcel of verse translation, or at any rate rhymed and scanning verse translation.

And what of the remaining third, if I may persevere with the crass mathematical parlance? Well, I suppose that is where your own licence, as a poet of sorts in your own right – a poet for the occasion, at any rate – comes in. Because, if you're lucky, some of that third of spilt water can be made up for by felicities that creep in, either through your own skill, or simply of themselves, serendipitously, because the language you're translating into has its own quirks, and some of these are, of themselves, delightful. English is, after all, an unusually delicious language to be working in, and one is lucky there. It seems a bit of a hopeful hypothesis, but such felicities, some more or less accidental, others less so, may compensate in some measure for the loss of, for example, the musicality in 'Art Poétique'. That certainly seems to be what Roscommon and Dryden are both suggesting, when they advocate a measure of freedom. For poetic licence, read translator's licence.

Andrew Motion

Versions of three poems by
Hong Ying

The Final Episode

The man opposite opens his window carefully,
only to shut it with a thump, and clamp both hands
over his mouth stifling a dry grunt.

The window is two metres high. The sallow grass
          beneath
clatters several layers of frost, and on the dark red
          wall
a scorpion tries to climb through the glass. Tries and
          fails.

The man breathes out a mist, flattens his nose on a
          window-pane,
then prowls round his room. He kicks up dust clouds;
his white jacket blanches his face to a famished lime-
          colour.

There is a cudgel in his hand which points to this and
          that,
as if at any moment he might shatter the glass and
          jump
into the glaring daylit world through a jagged O
rimmed with his own blood. But he does nothing of
          the sort.

And anyway: you and I can't be bothered with him
          any more.
The frost is thickening on our windows too.

That's right – why would anyone be interested
in watching him now? In watching anyone. Or
           anything.
That scorpion, for instance, or whatever it is.

The Parliament of Frogs

Faced with a blather of different opinions,
he thinks of frogs –
but the oily green water which suddenly appears
looks like an execution ground,
and he's not inclined to listen any more.

He knows that if there were a fire, frogs that climbed
           out
onto dry land would be caught and hung up
above the flames; the smell of them cooking
would be too much for anyone who got close.

He also knows: these people, who already understand
what deliciousness is, speak a language so measured,
they could even get some order into a chaos like this.
Though there wouldn't be anything left in the end
of the frogs, those beautiful, brainless creatures.

He admires the logic of all this
as he puts the oily green water behind him,
and understands the meaning of execution.
A pleasure-pulse beats through him.
The best thing about it is:
now he can make everyone listen to him.

Remembrance

Ideas arrive here eight hours sooner
than on the West Coast. Which means I can already
           tell you:

madam is prowling on the terrace, gripping a bunch
of innocent flowers.

Yes, this is her all right, repeating her night-walks
during the day,
the bronze-bladed knife out of sight but definitely
hovering.

Michael Hofmann[1]

A translation of *The Leviathan*
by Joseph Roth

1.

In the small town of Progrody there lived a coral merchant who
was known far and wide for his honesty and the reliability and
quality of his wares. The farmers' wives came to him from far-
distant villages when they needed an ornament for some festive
occasion. There were other coral merchants who were closer at
hand, but they knew that from them they would only get cheap

---

1. One of the attractions and goals of translating, a virtue like fidelity that is its
own reward, is translating several works by the same author. Living is best, but
dead is OK too.

A case in point would be the great American-born translator, Ralph
Mannheim, whom I visited in Paris in the 1980s. He worked on the big Brecht
edition, and Céline and from the Serbo-Croat, and all sorts of things, but he was
also the translator – exclusively, or near-exclusively – of both Grass and Handke,
for perhaps thirty or forty years. In a sense, to do less, to help oneself, or, more
likely, help out here and there, is not quite serious. There are all sorts of ways of
viewing translation, most of them deeply and probably rightly unflattering –
performance, imposture, forgery, pandering – but most of them gain dignity, or a
scandalous impressiveness, when done serially.

The nearest I have come to this desirable state of affairs is with the Austrian
writer Joseph Roth (1894–1939), whom I read, then wrote about, and finally
progressed to translating in a short book called *The Legend of the Holy Drinker*.
'The Leviathan' will appear in a collection of Roth's shorter fiction called *Strawberries*, the sixth celebration of our one-sided collaboration. 'The Leviathan' is a
product of his late years in exile, partly serialized in 1934, a part of it published
in French, finally slated for publication in Holland in 1937 and again
(posthumously, for Roth) in 1940. It had been set, but not bound, when the
Germans marched into Holland – and finally appeared after the end of the War.

stuff and no-good tat.[2] And so, in their rickety little carts they travelled many versts to Progrody and the renowned coral merchant Nissen Piczenik.

They tended to come on market days, which were Mondays and Thursdays, for horses and pigs respectively. While their menfolk were busy sizing up the animals, the women would go off together in little groups, barefooted, their boots dangling over their shoulders, with their brightly coloured scarves that shone even on rainy days, to the house of Nissen Piczenik. The tough bare soles of their feet pattered happily along the hollow-planked wooden pavement, and down the broad cool passage of the old building where the merchant lived. The arching passageway led into a quiet yard where soft moss sprouted among the uneven cobblestones, and the occasional blade of grass raised its head in summer. Here Nissen Piczenik's flock of chickens came joyfully out to meet them, the cocks leading the way with their proud red combs as red as the reddest of the corals.

They would knock three times on the iron door with the iron knocker. At that Piczenik would open a little grille cut into the door, see who was outside, and draw the bolt and allow the farmers' wives to come in. In the case of beggars, travelling musicians, gypsies and men with dancing bears, he would merely pass a coin out through the grille. He had to be very careful because on each of the tables in his large kitchen and his parlour he had fine corals in large, small and middle-sized heaps, various races and breeds of corals all mixed up, or already sorted according to colour and type. He didn't have so many eyes in his

---

2. Beginnings are important. They establish the tone for what follows, and they tend to attract the most ink in the processes of revising and editing. I like the idea of doing something provocative, perhaps even jarring, near the beginning of a translation, because it will give me more latitude later on from the reader. If you don't start pulling stunts until you're halfway through, he will just say: 'What is this?' The – very mild – extravaganza here is 'no-good tat', a little breach of decorum, a lowering of level. Roth's words, 'Tand' and 'Flitter' are more literary – 'Tand' of course may have suggested 'tat' – but his story is actually full of incongruity of tone and feeling and understanding. I don't really believe I should have to account for myself over these small details; they are the translator's province; I did it because I liked it – it sang to me, as they say in French.

head that he could see what every beggar was up to, and Piczenik knew just what a temptress poverty could be. Of course, some prosperous farmers' wives sometimes stole things, too; for women are always tempted to help themselves illicitly and clandestinely to an item of jewellery they can comfortably afford to buy. But where his customers were concerned, the merchant would tend to turn a blind eye, and he included a few thefts in the prices he charged for his wares anyway.[3]

He employed no fewer than ten threaders, pretty girls with keen eyes and soft hands. The girls sat in two rows either side of a long table, and fished for the corals with their fine needles. They put together beautiful regular necklaces, with the smallest corals at either end, and the largest and most brilliant in the middle. As they worked, the girls sang. On the hot, blue, sunny days of summer, when the long table where the women sat threading was set up outside in the yard, you could hear their summery voices all over the little town, louder than the twittering skylarks and the chirruping of the grasshoppers in the gardens.

Most people, who only know corals from seeing them in shop windows and displays would be surprised to learn how many different varieties of them there are. For a start, they can be polished or not; they can be trimmed in a straight line or rounded off; there are thorny and stick-like corals that look like barbed wire; corals that gleam with a yellowish, almost a whitish red, like the rims of tea-rose petals; pinkish-yellow, pink, brick-red, beet-red, cinnabar red corals, and finally there are those corals that look like hard, round drops of blood. There are rounds and half-rounds; corals like little barrels and little cylinders; there are straight, crooked and even hunchbacked corals. They come as stars, spears, hooks and blossoms. For corals are the noblest plants in the oceanic underworld; they are like roses for the

3. Nothing to do with me, but an instance of Roth's amazing complexity of tone and level: in this fairy story – anything beyond the Russian frontier is straightaway remoter to Roth – his fairy story of a thalattatropic death-wish, he lets us know his protagonist is canny enough to cheat, but so nicely. You blink, and think he couldn't've!

capricious goddesses of the sea, as inexhaustible in their variety as the caprices of the goddesses.

As you see then[4], Nissen Piczenik didn't have a shop as such. He ran his business from home, which meant that he lived among the corals night and day, summer and winter, and as all the windows in his parlour and kitchen opened onto the courtyard, and were protected by thick iron bars, there was in his apartment a beautiful and mysterious twilight that was like the light under the sea, and it was as though corals were not merely traded here, but that this was where they actually grew. Furthermore, thanks to a strange and canny quirk of nature, the coral merchant Nissen Piczenik was a red-haired Jew with a copper-colored goatee that looked like a particular kind of reddish seaweed, which gave the man a striking resemblance to a sea-god. It was as though he made his corals himself, or maybe sowed and reaped them in some way. In fact, so strong was the association between his wares and his appearance that in the small town of Progrody he was known not by his name, which had gradually fallen into disuse, but by his calling. For instance, people would say: 'Here comes the coral merchant' – as though there were none but him in all the world.

And in fact, Nissen Piczenik did feel a kind of affinity or kinship with corals. He had never been to school, couldn't read or write, and was only able to mark his name crudely – but he lived with the wholly unscientific conviction that corals were not plants at all, but living creatures, a kind of tiny reddish sea-animal – and no professor of marine science could have convinced him otherwise. Yes, for Nissen Piczenik corals remained alive, even when they had been sawn, cut, polished, sorted and threaded. And perhaps he was right[5]. Because with his own eyes he had seen how on the breasts of sick or poorly women his reddish strings of corals would begin to fade, while on the breasts of healthy women they kept their lustre. In the course of his

4. A perennial problem, with the German impersonal 'man', altogether more resilient grammatically than 'one'. Given the array of tones and approaches, I have nothing against giving the narrator the power of direct address.

5. What a staggering, unashamedly mystical sentence!

long experience as a coral merchant, he had often observed how corals that – for all their redness – had grown pale from lying in cupboards, once they were put round the neck of a healthy and beautiful young peasant woman, would start to glow as if they drew nourishment from the woman's blood. Sometimes the merchant was offered corals to buy back, and he recognized the stones he had once threaded and cherished – and he could tell right away whether the woman who had worn them had been healthy or unhealthy.

He had a very particular theory of his own regarding corals. As already stated, he thought of them as sea-creatures, who as it were, out of prudence and modesty, only imitated plants and trees so as to avoid being attacked and eaten by sharks. It was every coral's dream to be plucked by a diver and brought to the surface, to be cut, polished and threaded, so as finally to be able to serve the purpose for which they had been created: namely to be an ornament on a beautiful peasant woman. Only there, on the fine and firm white throat of a woman, in close proximity to the living artery – sister of the feminine heart – did they revive, acquire lustre and beauty, and exercise their innate ability to charm men and awaken their ardour. Now the ancient god Jehovah had created everything, the earth and the beasts who walked upon it, the sea and all its creatures. But for the time being – namely until the coming of the Messiah – he had left the supervision of all the animals and plants of the sea, and in particular of corals, to the care of the Leviathan, who lay curled on the sea bed.

It might be supposed that the trader Nissen Piczenik had a reputation as something of an eccentric. Nothing could be further from the truth. Piczenik lived quietly and unobtrusively in the small town of Progrody, and his tales of corals and the Leviathan were treated with complete seriousness, as befitting the opinion of an expert, a man who must know his business, just as the haberdasher knew his German percale from his corduroy, and the tea merchant could tell the Russian tea from the famous firm of Popov from the English tea supplied by the equally famous firm of Liptons of London. All the inhabitants of Progrody and its surroundings were convinced that corals are living creatures, and that the great fish Leviathan was responsible for their well-being under the sea. There could be no question of that, seeing as Nissen Piczenik said so himself.

In Nissen Piczenik's house, the beautiful threaders often worked far into the night, sometimes even past midnight. Once they had gone home, the trader himself sat down with his stones, or rather his animals. First, he examined the strings the girls had threaded, then he counted the heaps of corals that were as yet unsorted and the heaps of those that had been sorted according to type and size, then he began sorting them himself, and with his strong and deft and reddish-haired fingers, he felt and smoothed and stroked each individual coral. There were some corals that were worm-eaten. They had holes in places where no holes were required. The sloppy Leviathan couldn't have been paying attention.[6] And reproachfully, Nissen Piczenik lit a candle, and held a piece of red wax over the flame until it melted, and then dipping a fine needle into the wax, he sealed the worm-holes in the stone, all the while shaking his head, as though not comprehending how such a powerful god as Jehovah could have left such an irresponsible fish as the Leviathan in charge of all the corals.[7]

Sometimes, out of pure pleasure in the stones, he would thread corals himself until the sky grew light and it was time for him to say his morning prayers. The work didn't tire him at all, he felt strong and alert. His wife was still under the blankets, asleep. He gave her a curt, indifferent look. He didn't love her or hate her, she was merely one of the many threaders who worked for him, though she was less attractive now than most of the others. Ten years he had been married to her, and she had borne him no children – when that alone was her function. He wanted a fertile woman, fertile as the sea on whose bed so many corals grew. His wife, though, was like a dried-up lake. Let her sleep alone, as

6. Another, unapologetic, sharpening of contrast: blunt criticism to temper arcane faith.

7. A reverent swindle – and all contained, or intimated in Roth's typically cadenced, balanced, but slyly provoking sentences. That balance, the ability to convey a complicated state of affairs both with economy and with beauty is what makes him as a writer. One would have expected someone making that sort of sound to be simplistic. He isn't.

many nights as she wanted. According to the law, he could divorce her. But by now he had become indifferent to wives and children. Corals were what he loved. And there was in his heart a vague longing which he couldn't quite explain: Nissen Piczenik, born and having lived all his life in the middle of a great land mass, longed for the sea.

Yes, he longed for the sea on whose bed the corals grew — or rather, as he was convinced – disported themselves. Far and wide there was no one to whom he could speak of his longing, he had to carry it pent up in himself, as the sea carries its corals. He had heard about ships and divers, sailors and sea captains. His corals arrived, still smelling of the sea, in neatly packed crates from Odessa, Hamburg and Trieste. The public scribe in the post office did his correspondence for him. He carefully examined the colourful stamps on the letters from his suppliers abroad before throwing away the envelopes. He had never left Progrody. The town didn't have a river, not so much as a pond, only swamps on all sides, where you could hear the water gurgle far below the green surface, without being able to see it. Nissen Piczenik imagined some secret communication between the buried water in the swamps and the mighty waters of the sea – and that deep down at the bottom of the swamp, there might be corals, too. He knew that if he ever said as much, he would be a laughing-stock all over town. And so he kept his silence, and didn't talk about his theories. Sometimes he dreamed that the Great Sea – he didn't know which one, he had never seen a map, and so where he was concerned, all the world's seas were just the Great Sea – would one day flood Russia, the part of it where he lived himself. That way, the sea which he had no hope of reaching, would come to him, the strange and mighty sea, with the immeasurable Leviathan on the bottom, and all its sweet and bitter and salty secrets.

The road from the small town of Progrody to the little railway station where trains called just three times a week led through the swamps. And even when Nissen Piczenik wasn't expecting any packages of coral, even on days when there weren't any trains, he would walk to the station, or rather to the swamps. He would stand often for an hour or more at the edge of the swamp and listen reverently to the croaking of the frogs, as if they could tell him of life at the bottom of the swamp, and sometimes he felt he had taken their meaning. In winter, when the swamp froze over, he even dared to take a few steps on it, and that gave him a peculiar delight. The mouldy swamp-smell seemed to convey something of the powerful briny aroma of the sea, and to his eager ears the miserable glugging of the buried waters was transformed into the roaring of enormous green-blue breakers. In the whole small town of Progrody there was no one who knew what was going on in the soul of the coral merchant. All the Jews took him for just another one like themselves. This man dealt in cloth, and that one in kerosene; one sold prayer shawls, another soaps and wax candles, and a third, kerchiefs for farmers' wives and pocket knives; one taught the children how to pray, another how to count, and a third sold kvas and beans and roasted maize kernels. And to all of them Nissen Piczernik seemed one of themselves – with the only difference that he happened to deal in coral. And yet – you will see – he was altogether different.

2.

His customers were both rich and poor, regular and occasional. Among his rich customers were two local farmers. One of them, Timon Semyonovitch, was a hop-grower, and every year when the buyers came down from Nuremberg and Zatec and Judenburg, he made a number of profitable deals. The other farmer was Nikita Ivanovitch. He had no fewer than eight daughters, whom he was marrying off one after the other, and all needed corals. The married daughters – to date there were four of them – a month or two after their weddings gave birth to children of their own – more daughters – and these, too, required corals, though they were only infants, to ward off the Evil Eye. The members of these two families were the most esteemed guests in Nissen Piczenik's house. For the daughters of these farmers, their sons-in-law and their grandchildren, the merchant kept a supply of good brandy in reserve, home-made brandy flavoured with ants, dried mushrooms, parsley and centaury. The ordinary customers had to be content with ordinary shop-bought vodka. For in that part of the world there was no purchasing anything without a drink. Buyer and seller drank to the transaction, that it might bring profit and blessing to both parties. There were also heaps of loose tobacco in the apartment of the coral merchant, lying by the window, wrapped in damp blotting paper to keep it fresh. For customers didn't come to Nissen Piczenik the way people go into a shop, merely to buy the goods, pay and leave. The majority of the customers had covered many versts, and to Nissen Piczenik they were more than customers, they were also his guests. They drank with him, smoked with him, and sometimes even ate with him. The merchant's wife prepared buckwheat kasha with onions, borsch with sour cream, she roasted apples and potatoes, and chestnuts in the autumn. And so the customers were not just customers, they were guests of Nissen Piczenik's house. Sometimes, while they were hunting for suitable corals, the farmers' wives would join in the singing of the threaders; then they all would sing together, and even Nissen Piczenik would hum to himself, and in the kitchen his wife would beat time with a wooden spoon. Then, when the farmers returned from the market or from the pub to pick up their wives and pay for their purchases, the coral merchant would be obliged to drink brandy or tea with them, and smoke a cigarette. And all the old customers would kiss the merchant on both cheeks like a brother.

Because once we have got a drink or two inside us, all good honest men are our brothers, and all lovely women our sisters – and there is no difference between farmer and merchant, Jew and Christian; and woe to anyone who says otherwise!

3.

With every year that passed, unbeknown to anyone in the small town of Progrody, Nissen Piczenik grew more dissatisfied with his uneventful life. Like every other Jew, the coral merchant went to synagogue twice a day, morning and evening, he celebrated holidays, fasted on fast days, he put on his prayer shawl and his phylacteries, and swayed back and forth from his waist, he talked to people, he had conversations about politics, about the war with Japan, about what was printed in the newspapers and pre-occupying the world. But deep in his heart, there was still the longing for the sea, home of the corals, and, not being able to read, he asked to have read out to him any items relating to the sea when the newspapers came to Progrody twice a week. Just as he did about corals, he had a very particular notion of the sea. He knew that strictly speaking the world had many seas, but the one true sea was the one you had to cross in order to reach America.

Now it happened that one day the son of the hessian seller Alexander Komrower, who three years previously had enlisted and joined the navy, returned home for a short leave. No sooner had the coral merchant got to hear of young Komrower's return than he appeared in his house and started asking the sailor about all the mysteries of ships, water and winds. Whereas the rest of Progrody was convinced that it had been sheer stupidity that had got young Komrower hauled off to the dangerous oceans, the coral merchant saw in the sailor a fortunate youth, who had been granted the favour and the distinction of being made, as it were, an intimate of the corals, yes, even a kind of relation. And so the forty-five-year-old Nissen Piczenik and the twenty-two-year-old Komrower were seen walking about arm in arm in the market place of the little town for hours on end. People asked themselves: What does he want with that Komrower? And the young fellow asked himself: What does he want with me?[8]

During the whole period of the young man's leave in Progrody, the coral merchant hardly left his side. Their exchanges, like the following, were bewildering to the younger man:

'Can you see down to the bottom of the sea with a telescope?'

'No,' replied the sailor, 'with a telescope you only look into the distance, not into the deep.'

8. Is there anything homoerotic here, in this now almost upsettingly worldly/ unworldly tale?! Or is that a brutal anachronistic reading? One wouldn't dare to rule it out.

'Can you,' Nissen Piczenik went on, 'as a sailor, go down to the bottom of the sea?'

'No,' said young Komrower, 'except if you drown, then you might well go down to the bottom.'

'What about the captain?'

'The captain can't either.'

'Have you ever seen a diver?'

'A few times,' said the sailor.

'Do sea creatures and sea plants sometimes climb up to the surface?'

'Only some fish like whales that aren't really fish at all.'

'Describe the sea to me!' said Nissen Piczenik.

'It's full of water—' said the sailor Komrower.

'And is it very wide and flat, like a great steppe with no houses on it?'

'It's as wide as that – and more!' said the young sailor. 'And it's just like you say: a wide plain with the odd house dotted about on it, only not a house but a ship.'

'Where did you see divers?'

'We in the navy,' said the young man, 'have got our own divers. But they don't dive for pearls or oysters or corals. It's for military purposes, for instance, in case a warship goes down, and then they can retrieve important instruments or weapons.'

'How many seas are there?'

'I wouldn't know,' replied the sailor. 'We were told at navy school, but I didn't pay any attention. The only ones I know are the Baltic, the Black Sea and the Great Ocean.'

'Which sea is the deepest?'

'Don't know.'

'Where are the most corals found?'

'Don't know that, either.'

'Hm, hm,' said the coral merchant, 'pity you don't know that.'[9]

At the edge of the small town, there where the little houses

9. Like the debate with the pearl seller later, this is basically a theological discussion. In the most glancing, subtle, lovely and unconventional way, 'The Leviathan' is about 'right living and right dying'.

of Progrody grew ever more wretched until they finally petered out altogether, and the wide hump-backed road to the station began, stood Podgorzev's bar, a house of ill-repute in which peasants, farm labourers, soldiers, stray girls and layabouts congregated. One day the coral merchant Piczenik was seen going in there with the sailor Komrower. They were served strong, dark-red mead and salted peas. 'Drink, my boy! Eat and drink, my boy!' said Nissen Piczenik to the sailor in fatherly fashion. And he ate and drank for all he was worth, for young as he was, he had already learned a thing or two in ports, and after the mead he was given some bad sour wine, and after the wine a 90-proof brandy. He was so quiet over the mead that the coral merchant feared he had heard all he was going to hear on the subject of the sea from the sailor, and that his knowledge was simply exhausted. After the wine, however, young Komrower got into conversation with the barkeeper, and when the 90-proof brandy came, he fell to singing at the top of his voice, one song after another, just like a real sailor. 'Do you hail from our beloved little town?' asked the barkeeper. 'Of course, I'm a child of your – my – our little town,' replied the sailor, as if he wasn't the son of the plump Jew Komrower, but a regular farmer's boy. A couple of tramps and ne'er-do-wells came over to join Nissen Piczenik and the sailor at their table, and when the boy saw he had an audience, he felt a keen sense of dignity, such dignity as he thought only ships' officers could possibly have. And he played up to them: 'Go on, fellows, ask all you like. I've got answers to all your questions. You see this dear old uncle here, you all know who he is, he's the best coral seller in the whole province, and I've told him a lot of things already!' Nissen Piczenik nodded. And since he felt uneasy in this unfamiliar company, he drank a glass of mead, and then another. Gradually all these dubious faces he'd previously only seen through the grille in his door became as human as his own. But as caution and suspicion were ingrained in his nature, he went out into the yard, and hid his purse in his cap, leaving only a few coins loose in his pocket. Satisfied with his idea, and soothed by the pressure of the money against his skull, he sat down at the table again.

And yet he had to admit to himself that he didn't really know what he was doing, sitting in the bar with the sailor and those criminal types. All his life he had kept himself to himself, and prior to the arrival of the sailor, his secret passion for corals and the ocean home of corals had not been made public in any way. And there was something else that alarmed Nissen Piczenik deeply. He suddenly saw his secret longing for waters and whatever lived in them and upon them as coming to the surface of his own life, like some rare and precious creature at home on the sea bed, shooting up to the surface for some unknown reason – and he never thought in images. The sudden fancy must have been prompted by the mead and the stimulating effect of the sailor's stories. The fact that such crazy notions could come to him upset and alarmed him even more than suddenly finding himself sitting at a bar room table among vice-ridden associates.

But all his alarm and upset remained submerged, well below the surface of his mind. All the while, he was listening with keen enjoyment to the incredible tales of the sailor Komrower. 'And what about your own ship?' his new friends were asking him. He thought about it for a while – his ship was named after a famous nineteenth-century admiral, but that name seemed as banal as his own, and Komrower was determined to impress them all mightily – and so he said: 'My cruiser is called the "Little Mother Catherine". Do you know who she was? Of course, you don't, so I'll tell you. Well then, Catherine was the richest and most beautiful woman in the whole of Russia, and so one day the Tsar married her in the Kremlin in Moscow, and then he took her away on a sleigh – it was forty below – drawn by six horses to Tsarskoye Selo. Behind them came their whole retinue on sleighs – and there were so many of them, the road was blocked for three days and three nights. Then, a week after the magnificent wedding, the wanton and aggressive King of Sweden arrived in Petersburg harbour with his ridiculous wooden barges, but with a lot of soldiers standing on them because the Swedes are very brave fighters on land – and this king had a plan to conquer the whole of Russia. So the Tsarina Catherine straightway got on a ship, namely the very cruiser I'm serving on, and with her own hands she bombed the silly barges of the King of Sweden and sank the lot of them. And she tossed the King a lifebelt and took him prisoner. She had his eyes put out, and ate them, and that made her even more clever than she was before. As for the blind King, he was packed off to Siberia.'

'Is that so?' said one of the layabouts, scratching his head. 'I can't hardly believe it.'

'You say that again,' retorted the sailor Komrower, 'and I'll be obliged to kill you for insulting the Imperial Russian Navy. I'd have you know I learned this whole story at our naval academy, and His Grace, our Captain Voroshenko told it to us in person.'

They drank some more mead and one or two more brandies, and then the coral merchant Nissen Piczenik paid for everyone. He had had a few drinks himself, though not as many as the others. But when he stepped out onto the street, arm in arm with the young sailor Komrower, it seemed to him as though the middle of the road was a river with waves rippling up and down it, the occasional oil lanterns were lighthouses, and he had to stick to the side of the road if he wasn't to fall into the water. The young fellow was swaying all over the place. Now, from his childhood days Nissen Piczenik had said his prayers every evening, the one that you say when it starts to get dark, the other one at nightfall. Today, for the first time, he had missed them both. The stars were twinkling reproachfully at him up in the sky, he didn't dare look at them. At home his wife would be waiting with his usual evening meal, radish with cucumbers and onions, a piece of bread and dripping, a glass of kvas and hot tea. He felt more shame on his own than in front of other people. He had the feeling, walking along arm in arm with the heavy, stumbling young man that he was continually running into himself, the coral merchant Nissen Piczenik was meeting the coral merchant Nissen Piczenik, and they were laughing at one another. However, he was able to avoid meeting anyone else. He brought young Komrower home, took him into the room where the old Komrowers were sitting, and said: 'Don't be angry with him, I went to the bar with him, he's had a bit to drink.'

'You, Nissen Piczenik, the coral merchant, have been drinking with him?' asked old Komrower.

'Yes, I have!' said Piczenik. 'Now good night!' And he went home. His beautiful threaders were still all sitting at the four long tables singing and fishing up corals with their delicate needles in their fine hands.

'Just give me some tea,' said Nissen Piczenik to his wife. 'I have work to do.'

And he drank his tea, and while his hot fingers scrabbled about in the large, still unsorted heaps of corals, and in their delicious rosy cool, his poor heart was wandering over the wide and roaring highways of the mighty ocean.[10]

And there was a mighty burning and roaring in his skull. Sensibly, though, he remembered to take off his cap, pull out his purse and put it back in his shirt once more.[11]

4.

The day drew nigh when the sailor Komrower was to report back to his cruiser in Odessa – and the coral merchant dreaded the prospect. In all Progrody, young Komrower is the only sailor, and God knows when he'll be given leave again.[12] Once he goes, that'll be the last you hear of the waters of the world, apart from the odd item in the newspapers.

The summer was well-advanced, a fine summer by the way, cloudless and dry, cooled by the steady breeze across the Volynian steppes. Another two weeks and it would be harvest time, and the peasants would no longer be coming in from their villages on market days to buy corals from Nissen Piczenik. These two weeks were the height of the coral season. In this fortnight the customers came in great bunches and clusters, the threaders could hardly

10. Practically a trope in Roth, the hot fevered fingers in the cool precious stones: the Shah does it in 'The String of Pearls'.

11. What price mysticism, God, the paranormal and extra-sensory now?! The prudent Piczenik has a head-ache from the weight on it of his purse!

12. Any tense in a storm. This casual flexibility is another hallmark of Roth. Is there any English writer like that?

keep up with the work, they stayed up all night sorting and threading. In the beautiful early evenings, when the declining sun sent its golden adieus through Piczenik's barred windows, and the heaps of coral of every type and hue, animated by its melancholy and bracing light, started to glow as though each little stone carried its own microscopic lantern in its delicate interior, the farmers would turn up boisterous and a little merry, to collect their wives, with their red and blue handkerchiefs filled with silver and copper coins, in heavy hobnailed boots that clattered on the cobbles in the yard outside.[13] The farmers greeted Nissen Piczenik with embraces and kisses, like a long-lost friend. They meant well by him, they were even fond of him, the lanky, taciturn, red-haired Jew with the honest, sometimes wistful china blue eyes, where decency lived and fair dealing, the savvy of the expert and the ignorance of the man who had never once left the small town of Progrody. It wasn't easy to get the better of the farmers. For although they recognized the coral merchant as one of the few honest tradesmen in the area, they wouldn't forget that he was a Jew. And they weren't averse to haggling themselves. First, they made themselves at home on the chairs, the settee, the two wide wooden double beds with plump bolsters on them. And some of them, their boots encrusted with silvery-grey mud,[14] even lay down on the beds, the sofa or the floor. They took pinches of loose tobacco from the pockets of their burlap trousers, or from the supplies on the windowsill, tore off the edges of old newspapers that were lying around in Piczenik's room, and rolled themselves cigarettes – cigarette papers were considered a luxury, even by the well-off among them. Soon, the coral merchant's apartment was filled with the dense blue smoke of cheap tobacco and rough paper, blue smoke gilded by the last of the sunlight,

13. A cocktail of Klimt and verismo.

14. In a story that's a symphony in red, I still can't help feeling a special regard for that silver-grey mud (and the golden-brown tea below): they're perhaps the most 'Rothian' tropes of them all, both terrene and transfigured. These alloyed silvers and golds come up again and again in his books. Miraculous, unfussy, unhallowed, and compatible in him with forebrain qualities like wit and alertness. Staggering.

gradually emptying itself out into the street in small clouds drifting through the squares of the barred open windows. In a couple of copper samovars on a table in the middle of the room – these too burnished by the setting sun – hot water was kept boiling, and no fewer than fifty cheap green double-bottomed glasses were passed from hand to hand, full of schnapps and steaming golden-brown tea. The prices of the coral necklaces had already been agreed on with the women in the course of several hours' bargaining in the morning. But now the husbands were unhappy with the price, and so the haggling began all over again. It was a hard struggle for the skinny Jew, all on his own against overwhelming numbers of tight-fisted and suspicious, strongly built and in their cups potentially violent men. The sweat ran down under the black silk cap he wore at home, down his freckled, thinly bearded cheeks into the red goatee, and the hairs of his beard grew matted together, so that in the evening, after the battle, he had to part them with a little fine-toothed steel comb. Finally, he won the day against his customers, in spite of his ignorance. For, in the whole wide world, there were only two things that he understood, which were corals and the farmers of the region – and he knew how to thread the former and outwit the latter.[15] The implacably obstinate ones would be given a so-called 'extra' – in other words, when they agreed to pay the price he had secretly been hoping for all along, he would give them a tiny coral chain made from stones of little value, to put round the necks or wrists of their children, where it was guaranteed to be effective against the Evil Eye or spiteful neighbours and wicked witches. And all the time he had to watch what the hands of his customers were up to, and to keep gauging the size of the various piles of coral. It really wasn't easy!

In this particular high summer, however, Nissen Piczenik's manner was distracted, almost apathetic. He seemed indifferent to his customers and to his business. His loyal wife, long accus-

15. A pleasing, almost Shakespearean pairing: is 'thread' one of the million ways of saying 'cheat' in English?

tomed to his peculiar silences, noticed the change in him and took him to task. He had sold a string of corals too cheaply here, he had failed to spot a little theft there, today he had given an old customer no 'extras', while yesterday he'd given a new and insignificant buyer quite a valuable necklace. There had never been any strife in the Piczenik household. But over the course of these days, the coral merchant lost his calm, and he felt himself how his indifference, his habitual indifference towards his wife suddenly turned into violent dislike. Yes, he who was incapable of drowning a single one of the many mice that were caught in his traps every night – the way everyone in Progrody did – but instead paid Saul the water-carrier to do it for him, on this day, he, the peaceable Nissen Piczenik threw a heavy string of corals in his wife's face as she was criticizing him as usual, slammed the door and walked out of the house to sit by the edge of the great swamp, the cousin many times removed of the great oceans.

Just two days before the sailor's departure there surfaced in the coral merchant the notion of accompanying young Komrower to Odessa. A notion like that arrives suddenly, lightning is slow by comparison, and it hits the very place from where it sprang, which is to say the human heart. If you like, it strikes its own birthplace. Such was Nissen Piczenik's notion. And from such a notion to the adopting of a plan is only a short distance.

On the morning of the departure of the young sailor Komrower, Nissen Piczenik said to his wife: 'I have to go away for a few days.'

His wife was still in bed. It was eight in the morning, the coral merchant had just returned from morning prayers in the synagogue.

She sat up. Without her wig on, her thin hair in disarray and yellow crusts of sleep in the corners of her eyes, she looked unfamiliar, even hostile to him. Her appearance, her alarm, her consternation all confirmed him in a decision which even to him had seemed rash.[16]

---

16. What quiet, psychological acuity here: an instant contrariness!

'I'm going to Odessa!' he said with unconcealed venom. 'I'll be back in a week, God willing!'

'Now? Now?' stammered his wife amongst the pillows. 'Does it have to be now, when all the farmers are coming?'

'Right now!' said the coral merchant. 'I have important business. Pack my things!'

And with a vicious and spiteful delight he had never previously felt, he watched as his wife got out of bed, saw her ugly toes, her fat legs below the long flea-spotted nightgown, and he heard her all-too familiar sigh, the inevitable morning song of this woman with whom nothing connected him beyond a distant memory of a few nocturnal tendernesses, and the usual fear of divorce.

But within Nissen Piczenik there was a jubilant voice, a strange and familiar voice inside him: Piczenik is off to the corals! He's off to the corals! Nissen Piczenik is going to the home of the corals! . . .

5.

So he boarded the train with the sailor Komrower and went to Odessa. It was a long and complicated journey, with a change at Kiev. It was the first time the coral merchant had been on a train, but he didn't feel about it the way most people do when they ride on a train for the first time. The locomotive, the signals, the bells, the telegraph masts, the tracks, the conductors and the landscape flying by outside, none of it interested him. He was preoccupied with water and the harbour he was headed for, and if he registered any of the characteristic details of railway travel, it was only in order to speculate on the still unfamiliar details of travel on board ship. 'Do you have bells, too?' he asked the sailor. 'Do they ring three times before the ship leaves? Does the ship have to turn round, or can it just swim backwards?'

Of course, as inevitably happens on journeys, they met other passengers who wanted to get into conversation, and so he had to discuss this and that with them. 'I'm a coral merchant,' said Nissen Piczenik truthfully, when he was asked what it was he did. But when the next question came: 'What brings you to Odessa?' he began to lie. 'I have some important business there.' 'How interesting,' said a fellow-passenger, who until that moment had said nothing, 'I, too, have important business in Odessa, and the merchandise I deal in is not unrelated to coral, although it is of course far finer and dearer!' 'Dearer it may be,' said Nissen Piczenik, 'but it can't possibly be finer!' 'You want to bet it isn't,' cried the man. 'I tell you it's impossible. There's no point in betting!' 'Well then,' crowed the man, 'I deal in pearls.' 'Pearls aren't at all finer,' said Piczenik. 'And besides they're unlucky.' 'They are if you lose them,' said the pearl trader. By now everyone was listening to this extraordinary dispute. Finally, the pearl merchant reached into his trousers and took out a bag full of gleaming, flawless pearls. He tipped a few into the palm of his hand, and showed them to the other travellers. 'To find a single pearl,' he said, 'hundreds of oyster shells have to be opened. The divers command very high wages. Among all the merchants of the world, we pearl traders are the most highly regarded. You could say we're a special breed. Take me, for example. I'm a merchant of the first guild, I live in Petersburg, I have a distinguished clientele, including two Grand Dukes whose names are a trade secret, I've travelled halfway round the world, every year I go to Paris, Brussels and Amsterdam. Ask anywhere for the pearl trader Gorodotzky, even little children will be able to direct you.'

'And I,' said Nissen Piczenik, 'have never left our small town of Progrody, and all my customers are farmers. But you will agree that a simple farmer's wife, decked out in a couple of chains of fine, flawless corals is not outdone by a Grand Duchess. Corals are worn by high and low alike, they raise the low, and grace the high. You can wear corals morning, noon and night, wear them to ceremonial balls, in summer and in winter, on the Sabbath and on weekdays, to work and in the home, in time, happy and sad. There are many different varieties of red, my dear fellow passengers, and it is written that our Jewish King Solomon had a very special kind for his royal robes, because the Phoenicians who revered him had made him a present of a special kind of worm that excretes red dye in its urine. You can't get this colour any more, the purple of the Tsars is not the same, because after Solomon's death the whole species of that worm became extinct. Nowadays it is only in the very reddest corals that the colour still exists. Now whoever heard of such a thing as red pearls?'

Never had the quiet coral merchant held such a long and impassioned address in front of a lot of complete strangers. He put his cap back and mopped his brow. He smiled round at his fellow passengers, and they all applauded him: 'He's right, he's right!' they all exclaimed at once.

And even the pearl merchant had to admit that, whatever the facts of the case, Nissen Piczenik had been an excellent advocate of corals.

They finally reached the glittering port city of Odessa, with its blue water and its host of bridal-white ships.[17] Here the armoured cruiser was waiting for the sailor Komrower, as a father's house awaits his son. Nissen Piczenik wanted very much to have a closer look at the ship. He went with the young fellow to the man on watch and said, 'I'm his uncle, can I see the ship?' His own temerity surprised him. Oh yes, this wasn't the old terrestrial Nissen Piczenik who was addressing an armed sailor, it wasn't Nissen Piczenik from landlocked Progrody, this was somebody else, a man transformed, a man whose insides were now proudly on the outside, an oceanic Nissen Piczenik. It seemed to him that he hadn't just got off the train, but that he had climbed out of the water, out of the depths of the Black Sea. He felt at home by the water, as he had never felt at home in Progrody, where he was born and had lived all his life. Wherever he looks, he sees nothing but ships and water, water and ships. There are the ships, the boars, the rugs, the yachts, the motor boats apple-blossom white, raven black, coral red, yes, coral red – and there is the water washing against their sides, no, not washing but lapping and stroking, in thousands of little wavelets, like tongues and hands at once. The Black Sea isn't black at all. In the distance,

17. Ships in Roth are quite regularly 'bridal-white'; but of course there is something to be consummated here, with the final appearance of the hitherto internal paramour: the sea.

it's bluer than the sky, close to, it's as green as grass. When you toss a piece of bread in the water, thousands and thousands of swift little fishes leap, skip, slip, slither, flit and flash to the spot. A cloudless blue sky arches over the harbour, pricked by the masts and chimneys of the ships. 'What's this? What's the name of that?' asks Nissen Piczenik incessantly. This is a mast, that's a bow, these are the life-belts, there is a difference between a boat and a barge, a sailing vessel and a steamship, a mast and a funnel, a battleship and a merchantman, deck and stern, bow and keel. Nissen Piczenik's poor undaunted brain is bombarded by hundreds of new terms. After a long wait – he is very lucky, says the first mate – he is given permission to accompany his nephew on board, and to inspect the cruiser. This ship's lieutenant appears in person to watch a Jewish merchant go on board a vessel of the Imperial Russian Fleet. His honour the lieutenant is pleased to smile. The long, black skirts of the lanky red-haired Jew flutter in the gentle breeze, his striped trousers show, worn and patched, tucked into scuffed boots. The Jew Nissen Piczenik even forgets the laws of his faith. He doffs his black cap in front of the brilliant white and gold glory of the officer, and his red curls fly in the wind. 'Your nephew's a fine lad,' says His Honour, the officer, and Nissen Piczenik can think of no suitable reply. He smiles, he doesn't laugh, he smiles silently. His mouth is open, revealing his big yellow horsey teeth and his pink gums, and the copper-coloured goatee drops down almost to his chest. He inspects the wheel, the cannons, he's allowed to peer down the ship's telescope – and by God, the far is brought near, what is a long way off is made to seem close at hand, in that glass. God gave man eyes, but what are ordinary eyes, compared to eyes looking through a telescope? God gave man eyes, but He also gave him understanding that he might invent the telescope and improve the power of his eyesight! And the sun shines down on the top deck, it shines on Nissen Piczenik's back, and still he doesn't grow hot, for there is a cooling breeze blowing over the sea, yes, it's as though the wind came out of the sea itself, a wind out of the very depths of the sea.

Finally, the hour of parting came. Nissen Piczenik embraced

young Komrower, he bowed to the lieutenant and then to the sailors and he left the battle cruiser.

He had intended to return to Progrody straight after saying goodbye to young Komrower. But he remained in Odessa. He watched the battleship sail off, the sailors waved back to him as he stood on the quay side, waving his red and blue striped handkerchief. And he watched a lot of other ships sailing away, and he waved to their passengers as well. He went to the harbour every day, and every day he saw something new. For instance, he learned what it means 'to lift anchor', 'furl the sails', 'unload a cargo, tighten a sheet', and so forth.

Every day he saw young men in sailor suits working on ships, climbing up the masts, he saw young men walking through the streets of Odessa, arm in arm, a line of sailors walking abreast, taking up the whole street – and he felt sad that he had no children of his own. Just then he wished he had sons and grandsons and – no question – he would have sent them all to sea. He'd have made sailors of them. And all the while his ugly and infertile wife was lying at home in Progrody. She was selling corals in his place. Did she know how? Did she have any appreciation of what corals meant?

In the port of Odessa, Nissen Piczenik rapidly forgot the obligations of an ordinary Jew from Progrody. He didn't go to the synagogue in the morning to say the prescribed prayers, nor yet in the evening. Instead, he prayed at home, hurriedly, without proper thought of God, he prayed in the manner of a gramophone, his tongue mechanically repeating the sounds that were engraved in his brain. Had the world ever seen such a Jew?

At home in Progrody, it was the coral season. Nissen Piczenik knew it, but then he wasn't the old continental Nissen Piczenik any more, he was the new, reborn, oceanic one.

There's plenty of time to go back to Progrody, he told himself! I'm not missing anything! Think of what I still have to do here!

And he stayed in Odessa for three weeks, and every day he spent happy hours with the sea and the ships and the little fishes.

It was the first time in his life that Nissen Piczenik had had a holiday.

6.

When he returned home to Progrody, he discovered that he was no less than one hundred and sixty rubles out of pocket, with all the expenses for his journey. But to his wife and to all those who asked him what he had been doing so long away from home, he replied that he had concluded some 'important business' in Odessa.

The harvest was just now getting under way, and so the farmers didn't come to town so frequently on market days. As happened every year at this time, it grew quiet in the house of the coral merchant. The threaders went home in the afternoon. And in the evening, when Nissen Piczenik returned from the synagogue, he was greeted not by the melodious voices of the beautiful girls, but only by his wife, his plate of radish and onion, and the copper samovar. However, guided by the memory of his days in Odessa – whose commercial insignificance he kept secret – the coral merchant Piczenik bowed to the habitual rules of his autumnal days. Already he was thinking of claiming some further piece of important business in a few months' time, and going to visit a different harbour town, for instance, Petersburg.

He had no financial problems. All the money he had earned in the course of many years of selling corals was deposited and earning steady interest with the money lender Pinkas Warschawsky, a respected usurer in the community, who, though pitiless in collecting any outstanding debts owing to him, was also punctual in paying interest. Nissen Piczenik had no material anxieties; he was childless, and so had no heirs to think of, so why not travel to another of the many harbours there were?

And the coral dealer had already begun to make plans for the spring when something strange happened in the small neighbouring town of Sutschky.

In this town, which was no bigger than the small town of Progrody, the home of Nissen Piczenik, a complete stranger one day opened a coral shop. The man's name was Jeno Lakatos, and, as was soon learned, he came from the distant land of Hungary. He spoke Russian, German, Ukrainian and Polish, and yes, if required, and if someone happened to ask for it, then Mr

Lakatos would equally have spoken in French, English or Chinese. He was a young man with slick, blue-black pomaded hair – and he was also the only man far and wide to wear a shiny stiff collar and tie, and to carry a walking stick with a gold knob. This young man had been in Sutschky for just a few weeks, had struck up a friendship with the butcher Nikita Kolchin, and had pestered him for so long that he agreed to set up a coral business jointly with this Lakatos. There was a brilliant red sign outside with the name: Nikita Kolchin & Co.

In its window this shop displayed perfect shining red corals, lighter in weight than the stones of Nissen Piczenik, but also cheaper. A whole large coral necklace cost one ruble fifty, and there were smaller chains for eighty, fifty and twenty kopecks. The prices were prominently displayed in the window. Finally, to prevent anyone still walking past the shop, there was a gramophone inside belting out merry tunes all day long. It could be heard all over town, and in the outlying villages, too. There was no large market in Sutschky as there was in Progrody. Nevertheless and in spite of the fact that it was harvest time – the farmers flocked to the shop of Mr Lakatos to hear the music and buy the cheap corals.

One day, after Mr Lakatos had been running his business successfully for a few weeks, a prosperous farmer came to Nissen Piczenik and said: 'Nissen Semyonovitch, I can't believe the way you've been cheating me and everybody else these past twenty years. But now there's a man in Sutschky who's selling the most beautiful coral chains for fifty kopecks apiece. My wife wanted to go over there right away, but I thought I'd see what you had to say about it first, Nissen Semyonovitch.'

'That Lakatos,' said Nissen Piczenik, 'is a thief and a cheat. There's no other way to explain his prices. But I'll go over there if you give me a lift in your cart.'

'Very well,' said the farmer, 'see for yourself.'

And so the coral merchant went to Sutschky. He stood in front of the shop window for a while, listening to the music blaring from inside the shop, then finally he stepped inside, and addressed Mr Lakatos.

'I'm a coral seller myself,' said Nissen Piczenik. 'My wares come from Hamburg, Odessa, Trieste and Amsterdam, and I can't understand how you are able to sell such fine corals so cheaply.'

'You're from the old school,' replied Lakatos, 'and if you'll pardon the expression, you're a bit passé.'

So saying, he emerged from behind the counter – and Nissen Piczenik saw that he had a slight limp. His left leg was obviously shorter, because the heel of his left boot was twice as high as the one on his right. Powerful and intoxicating scents emanated from him – and one wondered what part of his frail body could possibly be home to all these scents. His hair was blackish blue as night. And while his dark eyes appeared gentle enough, they glowed so powerfully that a strange redness appeared to flare up in the midst of all their blackness. Under his curled black moustaches, Lakatos had a set of dazzling white and smiling mouse teeth.

'Well?' said the coral merchant Nissen Piczenik.

'Well,' said Lakatos, 'we're not mad. We don't go diving to the bottom of the sea. We simply manufacture artificial corals. I work for the company of Lowncastle Brothers, in New York. I've just had two very good years in Budapest. It doesn't bother the farmers. It didn't bother them in Hungary, it'll never bother them in Russia. Fine red flawless corals are what they're after. And I've got them. Cheap, competitively priced, pretty and wearable. What more do they want? Real corals don't come any better!' 'What are your corals made of?' asked Nissen Piczenik. 'Celluloid, my dear fellow, celluloid!' cried a delighted Lakatos. 'It's no good arguing with science! Anyway, rubber trees grow in Africa, and it's rubber that you make celluloid out of. What's unnatural about that? Are rubber trees any less part of nature than corals? How is a rubber tree in Africa any worse than a coral tree on the sea bed? – Well, so what do you say? – Do you want to do a deal with me? – Just say the word! – A year from now, all your customers will have gone over to me, and you can take all your fine real corals back to the seabed they came from. So, will you come in with me or not?[18]

'Give me two days to think it over,' said Nissen Piczenik, and he went home.

18. A deadly blend of theology and business!

7.

And that was how the Devil first came to tempt the coral merchant Nissen Piczenik. The Devil was Jeno Lakatos from Budapest[19], who introduced artificial coral to Russia, celluloid coral that burns with a bluish flame, the same colour as the ring of purgatorial fire that burns around Hell.

When Nissen Piczenik got home, he kissed his wife indifferently on both cheeks, he greeted his threaders, and he started looking at his beloved corals with confused eyes, eyes confused by the Devil, his living corals that didn't look nearly as flawless as the fake celluloid corals that his rival Jeno Lakatos had shown him. And so the Devil inspired the honest coral merchant Nissen Piczenik with the idea of mixing fake corals with real.

One day he went to the public clerk in the post office and dictated a letter to Jeno Lakatos in Sutschky, and a few days later he received no less than twenty pud of fake coral. Dazzled and led astray by the Devil, Nissen Piczenik mixed the fake and the real corals, and thereby he betrayed both himself and the real corals.

The harvest was in progress out in the countryside, and hardly any farmers were coming to buy corals. But from the few who did occasionally turn up, Nissen Piczenik now earned more than he had before, when he had had many customers, thanks to the fake corals. He mixed genuine and fake – which was even worse than selling only fake. Because that is what happens to people when they are led astray by the Devil – they come to outdo him in devilishness. And so Nissen Piczenik outdid Jeno Lakatos from Budapest. And all that Nissen Piczenik earned he took conscientiously to Pinkas Warschawsky. And so corrupted had the coral merchant been by the Devil that he took real pleasure in the thought of his money being fruitful and multiplying.

Then one day the usurer Pinkas Warschawsky suddenly died, and at that Nissen Piczenik panicked, and he went right away to

19. The sort of heroic, old-fashioned, unhesitating identification for which I think people might like to read Joseph Roth in these relativizing, multi-perspectival, mealy-mouthed times!

the usurer's heirs, and he demanded his money back with interest. It was paid out on the spot, and the sum came to no less than five thousand four hundred and fifty rubles and sixty kopecks. With the money he paid Lakatos for his fake corals, and he ordered another twenty pud.

One day the rich hop farmer came to Nissen Piczenik and asked for a chain of corals for one of his grandchildren, to ward off the Evil Eye.

The coral merchant threaded a chain made up entirely of fake corals, and he said: 'These are the most beautiful corals I have.'

The farmer paid him the price for real corals, and returned to the village.

A week after the fake corals had been placed round her neck, his granddaughter came down with diphtheria, and died horribly of suffocation. And in the village of Solovetzk where the rich farmer lived (and also in the surrounding villages), the news spread that the corals of Nissen Piczenik from Progrody brought bad luck and illness – and not only to those who had bought from him. For diphtheria began to rage in the surrounding villages, it took away many children, and the rumour spread that Nissen Piczenik's corals brought sickness and death.

And so that winter no more customers came to Nissen Piczcenik. It was a hard winter.[20] Every day brought with it an iron frost, hardly any snow fell, and even the ravens seemed to freeze as they crouched on the bare boughs of the chestnut trees. It grew very still in Nissen Piczenik's house. He dismissed his threaders one by one. On market days he sometimes ran into one of his old customers, but they never greeted him.

Yes, the farmers who in the summer had embraced him, now behaved as if they no longer knew the coral merchant.

The temperature fell to forty degrees below. The water froze in the water carrier's cans. A thick sheet of ice covered Nissen Piczenik's windows, so that he could no longer see what was going on in the street. Great heavy icicles hung from the crossbars of the iron grilles, and blinded the windows still further. Nissen Piczenik had no customers, but he blamed the severe winter for

20. Equally categorical are his seasons: Winter.

it, rather than the fake corals. And yet Mr Lakatos' shop in Sutschky was continually bursting at the seams. The farmers bought his perfect cheap celluloid corals in preference to Nissen Piczenik's real ones.

The streets of the small town of Progrody were icy and treacherous. All the inhabitants teetered along with iron-tipped canes. Even so, some of them fell and broke their legs or their necks.

One evening, Nissen Piczenik's wife took a fall. She lay there unconscious for a long time before kind neighbours took pity on her and took her home.

She began to vomit violently. The army doctor of Progrody said she had a concussion.

She was taken to the hospital, and the doctor there confirmed the diagnosis of his army colleague.

The coral merchant visited his wife every day in the hospital. He sat down at her bedside, listened for half an hour to her meaningless babble, looked at her fevered eyes, her thinning hair, remembered the few tender times he had given her, sniffed the acrid camphor and iodine, and went back home, stood in front of the stove and prepared borsch and kasha for himself, cut bread and grated radish and brewed tea and lit the fire, all for himself. Then he tipped all the corals from his many bags onto one of his four tables, and started to sort them. Mr Lakatos' celluloid corals he stored separately in the chest. The genuine corals had long since ceased to be like living creatures to Nissen Piczenik. Ever since Lakatos had turned up in the area, and since he, the coral merchant Nissen Piczenik had begun mixing up the flimsy celluloid stuff with the heavy real stones, the corals in his house were dead. Corals nowadays were made from celluloid! A dead substance to make corals that looked like live ones, and even more beautiful and perfect than the real live ones! Compared to that, what was the concussion of his wife?

Eight days later she died, it must have been of the effects of the concussion. But Nissen Piczenik told himself that she had not died only from her concussion, but also because her life had not been linked to that of any other human being in this world. No one had wanted her to remain alive, and so she had died.

Now the coral merchant Nissen Piczenik was a widower. He

mourned his wife in the customary fashion. He bought her a relatively durable gravestone and had some pious phrases chiseled into it. He spoke the kaddish for her morning and night. But he did not miss her at all. He could make his own meals and his own tea. With his corals, he didn't feel lonely. All that saddened him was the fact that he had betrayed them to their false sisters, the celluloid corals, and himself to the dealer Lakatos.

He longed for spring, but when it came Nissen Piczenik realized that his longing had been pointless. In former years before Easter, when the icicles started melting a little at noon, the customers had come in their creaking wagons or on their jingling sleighs. They needed corals for Easter. But now spring had come, the sun was growing warm, with every day the icicles on the roofs grew shorter and the melting piles of snow by the side of the road grew smaller – and no customers came to Nissen Piczenik. In his oaken coffer, in his wheeled trunk which stood iron-hooped and massive next to the stove, the finest corals lay in piles, bunches and chains. But no customers came. It grew ever warmer, the snow vanished, balmy rains fell. Violets sprang up in the woods, and frogs croaked in the swamps: no customers came.[21]

At about this time, a certain striking transformation in the person of Nissen Piczenik was first observed in Progrody. Yes, for the first time the people of the town began to suspect that the coral seller was an eccentric, even a peculiar fellow – and some lost their former respect for him, and others laughed openly at him. Many of the good people of Progrody no longer said: There goes the coral merchant – instead, they said: There goes Nissen Piczenik, he used to be a great coral merchant.

He had only himself to blame. He failed to behave in the way that the law and the dignity of widowerhood prescribed. If his strange friendship with the sailor Komrower was forgiven him, and their visit to Podgorzev's notorious bar, then his own further visits to that establishment could not be taken so lightly. For almost every day since the death of his wife, Nissen Piczenik visited Podgorzev's bar. He acquired a taste for mead, and when

21. Spring.

in time it got to be too sweet for him, he started mixing it with vodka. Sometimes one of the girls would sit beside him. And he, who all his life had known no other woman than his now dead wife, who had taken no pleasure in anything but stroking, sorting and threading his true loves, the corals, suddenly in Podgorzev's dive he succumbed to the cheap white flesh of women, to the pulsing of his own blood which mocked the dignity of a respectable existence, and to the wonderful narcotizing heat that radiated from the girls' bodies. So he drank and he stroked the girls who sat next to him or occasionally even on his lap. He felt pleasure, the same pleasure he felt when playing with his corals. And with his tough, red-haired fingers he groped – less expertly, with laughable clumsiness, in fact – for the nipples of the girls, which were as rosy red as some corals. And, as they say, he let himself go more and more, practically by the day. He felt it himself. His face grew thin, his bony back grew crooked and he no longer brushed his coat or his boots, or combed his beard. He recited his prayers mechanically every morning and evening. He felt it himself. He was no longer the coral merchant, he was Nissen Piczenik, formerly a great coral merchant.[22]

He sensed that within a year, or maybe only six months, he would be the laughing stock of the town – but what did he care? Progrody wasn't his home, his home was the ocean.

And so one day he made the fateful decision of his life.

But before that he went back to Sutschky one day – and there in the shop of Jeno Lakatos from Budapest he saw all his old customers, and they were listening to the blaring music on the phonograph, and buying celluloid corals at fifty kopecks a chain.

22. Can we still be in the same story?! Is this moment of Zolaesque decline, the end of morality, sobriety and liturgy, 'girls' bodies' and coral nipples, part of that depthless fable set in some Eastern never-never-land, with some cipher character, stuck in rigid impossibility like the coral seller in the middle of the land? Roth makes it happen. The most drastic metamorphoses are encompassed in his books. Other writers give you stories that lengthen or broaden; Roth is almost unique in the way his stories almost only deepen. He sets himself, like tests or challenges, the most neutral or folkloric or shallowly satiric premises – and pushes them into a third dimension. They plummet.

'So what did I tell you last year?' Lakatos called out to Nissen Piczenik. 'You want another ten pud, twenty, thirty?'

Nissen Piczenik said: 'I don't want any more fake corals. I only want to deal in real ones.'

8.

And he went home, back to Progrody, and he discreetly looked up travel agent Benjamin Broczyner, who sold boat tickets to people who wanted to emigrate. These were for the most part deserters from the army or else the very poorest Jews, who had to go to Canada and America, and who provided Broczyner with his livelihood. He represented a Hamburg shipping company in Progrody.

'I want to go to Canada!' said the coral seller Nissen Piczenik. 'And as soon as possible.'

'The next sailing is on the *Phoenix* which leaves Hamburg in two weeks. We can have your papers all ready by then,' said Broczyner.

'Good. Good,' replied Piczenik. 'And I don't want anyone to know about it.'

And he went home and packed all his corals, his real ones, in his wheeled suitcase.

As for the celluloid corals, he placed them on the copper tray of the samovar, and he set fire to them and watched them burning with a blue flame and a terrible stench. It took a long time, there were more than fifteen pud of fake corals. Indeed, all that was left of the celluloid was a gigantic heap of gray-black scrolled ashes, and a cloud of blue-grey smoke twisting round the oil lamp in the middle of the room.

That was Nissen Piczenik's farewell to his home.

On 21 April, he boarded the steamship *Phoenix* in Hamburg, as a steerage passenger.

The ship had been four days at sea when disaster struck: perhaps some still remember it.

More than two hundred passengers went down with the *Phoenix*. They were drowned, of course.

But as far as Nissen Piczenik was concerned, who went down at the same time, one cannot simply say that he was drowned along with the others. It is truer to say that he went home to the corals, to the bottom of the ocean where the huge Leviathan lies coiled.

And if we're to believe the report of a man who escaped death – as they say – by a miracle, then it appears that long before the lifeboat was filled, Nissen Piczenik leapt overboard to join his corals, his real corals.[23]

I, for my part, willingly believe it, because I knew Nissen Piczenik, and I am ready to swear that he belonged to the corals, and that his only true home was the bottom of the ocean.

May he rest in peace beside the Leviathan until the coming of the Messiah.

23. The last stand in this story of the voice of scepticism.

Alan Sillitoe

Notes on Joseph Conrad

In 1948 I was, for a few days, a wireless operator on a Royal Air Force pinnace, which was acting as radio link and dogsbody for a flotilla of naval vessels laying out a bombing range off the north-west coast of Malaya. Unlike near the mangrove swamps further south, there was no smell except that of the pure sea.

Even at dead of night the air was overpoweringly warm and, on anchor watch, the boat at rest in the bay of a jungle covered island, I would periodically sling the lead to make sure there was no drift onto abrasive rocks nearby. I was tempted, as each counted minute passed, to lay down on the deck and fall criminally to sleep, so in order to resist I slung the lead more often than necessary, such irregular splashings not pleasing to those trying to sleep below.

My period of work on the pinnace – short as it was, for I was no sailor – led me to consider exchanging the wireless qualifications gained in the air force for those of a Marconi officer in the merchant marine, as soon as I was demobilized. Those high-funnelled rusting steamers seen in Penang harbour from our camp under the palm trees on the mainland had an aura of romance, and I could easily see myself occupying the wireless cabin on one of them, calling around the East Indies and along the China coast. Throughout my childhood I had swallowed wholesale the romance of Empire and now, with the Dutch being pushed from Batavia, and the beginning of the Malayan Emergency, that Empire was crumbling around me.

Fate decided that my dream of working on ships would not become reality. In Malaya, maps and charts had been my mainstay in forever fixing the position as to where I was and, in my work of shortwave direction finding, telling others by morse where *they* were. Such continual preoccupations with the earth's surface held the clue to present and future wanderings, which fact seemed even more pertinent when I later read that classic of psychology and geography so poignantly matched in *The End of the Tether*. There was much about the Far East just after the Second World War that still gave off an atmosphere of Conrad's fiction, and reading his work not only brought places vividly to mind but moved me because I too was becoming a novelist.

The earliest known photograph of Conrad shows him holding a toy whip, and behind the child's expression of angelic mystery is a more subtle tone of pitiable disturbance. He seems already to have reached the end of his tether, a facial conflict suggesting that one half of himself will drive the other half from the village of Terechova, both to escape the torment in which he was born, and in an attempt to cure the anguish which impels him.

An ineradicable lust to move is formed before birth. People are congenitally influenced, but the tragic occurrences of Conrad's young life forced him to travel as far as possible from where he was born. This urge took him to places and into an occupation diametrically opposed to what he would become, as if he would devote his life to resisting such a fate. In the most extreme physical situations, as seaman and officer of sailing ships, he struggled all the more fiercely the closer he came to the destiny of turning into a writer.

According to Robert Graves it is necessary for a poet to die in his youth and be born again, if only symbolically, so as to then enter the positive phase of his vocation. Conrad attempted suicide in Marseilles early in 1878, and shortly afterwards obtained work on an English ship. After such a symbolic death and subsequent rebirth he was unable to deny the elemental force that had always been in him.

Conrad was born near Berdichev in 1857, and baptized in the Roman Catholic church in Zhitomir. No guidebook to Russia that I have seen recalls his association with the area, perhaps because he was ideological poison to both the Tsarist and Soviet regimes. Travelling by car through the Ukraine in the summer of 1967, I was prevented from driving into Berdichev by a militia-man, and made to go back to the bypass.

Carrying an old Austrian survey map, I had also noticed a

place called Verkhovnya, thirty miles east of Conrad's birthplace. Anyone familiar with the life of Balzac will know that he not only spent the end of 1848 and the whole of 1849 there but was married at Berdichev to the 'noble and virtuous' Countess Eveline Hanska, after sixteen years of pursuit – because she was a married woman with five children and he had to wait for the husband to die.

Conrad came of course to know Balzac's work, and must have been aware of his familiarity with the district seven years before his own birth. Later in life he indicated that Balzac and Stendhal were the authors he most admired. Though the guidebooks don't mention Conrad, the fact of Balzac's marriage was recorded by Chekhov when Chebutykin quotes that famous line from a newspaper in *The Three Sisters*, in order to deny that nothing ever happened in provincial Russia: 'Balzac was married in Berdichev.'

Heredity and circumstance mix, and it is often difficult to tell one influence from another, because the geography of the birthplace has cemented them together. Such fusion sets going the divine urge present in the heart of a child who is destined to become a novelist.

Conrad in his youth was to put seemingly insuperable obstacles in his own path. Continual attempts to break out of a cul de sac, and the experience of being many times at the end of his tether, led him to choose the most distant and congenial blind alley of the English language.

A message which the ending of youth hammers home is that life will not go on for ever, and that a vital choice must be made, which means correctly divining the course which Fate has chosen – in other words by recognizing and then accepting the subconscious drive with neither quibble nor reservation.

Novelists shape lives, give form to chaos, and hope their characters will stay in the human imagination for ever. Conrad's people have this profound and haunting quality because they were created by a man who was himself a victim of Fate. He chose between living and writing, as Fate willed him to do, the price demanded for the privilege of becoming an artist. That the life which Fate forced him into accepting would have to be paid for was indicated by those signs of turmoil lurking behind the infant's features. The author is doomed from birth, and it is no surprise that the gallery of people produced out of Conrad's agonized mind are similarly doomed in their different ways. Every novel is born out of a broken heart.

After the tribulations of early life, and having accepted that there is nothing to do but write, the artist is empty of any explicable personality, and passes the rest of his existence trying to find out who he is, creating one person after another in the hope that one of them will be himself. It is part of the unspoken treaty that such a discovery can never be made, though the search goes on for as long as he continues to write.

Conrad had so many conflicting personalities within him trying to get out, each with the potential for tragedy, that he went towards an occupation, and then a culture, which provided the framework enabling him to live within it. The greater the effort the more successful he would be. A radical change of language provided the most rigid framework of all.

Following the compass of the heart Conrad relinquished the carapace of a ship's captain to take on the protective anonymity of an English country gentleman, so that he would be able to write his novels and stories. Of all his works *The End of the Tether* most sums up his inner struggle to stay on course. It is his most pessimistic novel, but such East European pessimism enriched the English novel to the extent that from being the master of a ship he became a master of that also, having all his life fought the good fight to become the master of his soul.

In *The End of the Tether* Captain Whalley, who is going blind, keeps the fact secret because he needs the salary to provide for his daughter, and because he has to recoup the money put into a partnership with the vessel's owner. He must also, according to his social code, maintain his honour until he can voluntarily give up his command. In the event he is forced to succumb to the corruption which all his life he has scorned. By concealing his blindness he is responsible for wrecking the *Sofala*, in that reef-infested region between Pangu and Batu Beru, reefs as lengthily and frighteningly described by Conrad as if he had to go through them himself every day – and which recalled for me those reefs I'd had to be wary of on the pinnace in the Straits of Malacca.

Conrad was fluent in at least five languages, but he chose English to write in, giving rise to the adage that one of the greatest English writers was a Pole. Perhaps he saw the taking on of another language as the final corruption, though one without which he could neither live nor write. Nor could the conventional trappings of an Englishman altogether calm the spiritually violent sea within. The reef-infested region would not allow him to rest easy, all the time fearful that his moral eyesight would be inadvertently deflected by a magnetic lodestone near the compass of the heart.

His life was spent on a ship which never reached port, having set out from one under the guidance of a chart which allowed for no return. He carried the burden of artist and foreigner, and wrote about people who did not know themselves in an attempt to harness that powerful force which would allow him to know himself and at the same time keep his confidence as an artist. He had all the qualifications for doing this, and those which he did not inherit he forged with the labour of a blacksmith who knows that at any moment his strength might fail.

Andrew Pidoux

The Dead Sheep

The sheep that drift through the space
between my garden and yours
are not the sheep you bought
five years ago when you were cold.

They leave their threads on wire fences,
unravel themselves slowly,
withered heads like the ends of matches.
They frighten the children. I can't say I'm happy.

At night I read a while in the ring
of a lamp or listen to voices on the radio.
You can hear sheep drinking from the river,
their lips drawn up like skirts.

Inquisitive Children

A bird opens its throat on the roof of a prefab.
A donkey wobbles on its collapsible frame.
Inquisitive children crawl towards animals,
their faces fragile with concentration.
Mothers and daughters watch them politely.
What became of last year's babies? Now
hoisted onto feeble legs, they're led about
in shadows of skirts, with envious looks.
Meanwhile, the little ones pursue their interests –
animals, each other, rainbows, anything
that can be extracted from the fleshy earth
and sucked on. Their knees and palms are black
with crawling, their faces are full of tantrums
waiting to happen, their fingers lollipops.

Nell Leyshon

Cows

Mary could see the fire from where she stood on the hill. It was beyond the farm, in the four acre. She watched the smoke rise straight up into the still autumn air. Tomorrow they would light the other fire, the heap of wooden beams and old fence posts in the village hall field.

She had helped her mother make the guy's face, had pushed her sharp needle in and out of the ripped white sheet, then pulled the threads tightly till they contorted the fabric into a tourniquet round his neck. She had not taken too much care with the face. It would be ash tomorrow.

She walked down the hill and along the lane to the farm. Her bag brushed against the rose hips which weighed down the branches. The old man's beard bled feathery scraps onto the road.

Her mother's car was in the farmyard, the boot wide open, full of plastic carrier bags. A tin of corned beef had rolled out and lay in a puddle. Mary picked it up and took two of the carrier bags out of the car and carried them in. Her mother was in the kitchen. A pile of empty carrier bags lay in the corner; a pile of cardboard packets of food sat on the table.

'How was school?'

Mary shrugged out of her bag and coat. 'Same.'

She left the room and went upstairs. She could see the fire from her bedroom window. She could see the shapes of her father and Shane, pitchforking. The smoke rose and blended into the grey of the sky.

She pulled off her uniform and sat on the edge of the bed in her bra and pants. She looked over at the fire again. Shane stood away from it and she thought she could make out his face looking towards her window. She stood up and walked over to it, stood there looking out in her bra and pants.

Her mother had emptied all the bags. The fridge door was hanging open and the food inside stood in coloured bands and squares. Blocks of red cans, yellow oblongs of cheese. Stacks of green-filled plastic bags in the bottom drawer. Jean handed her two red cans.

'Take these to the men.'

As Mary got closer to the fire, she could see the black shapes sticking up out of it. Yellow flames rose up from the red core. Shane turned to look at her and where he stood in front of the heat, he shimmered and moved. Ash rose up in the smoke, danced into the air. She stepped closer again and looked at the branches on the fire, saw they weren't branches, but legs raised up to heaven.

She passed Shane one can, passed the other to her father. She heard the two clicks and then the hisses.

She watched Shane tip his head back and drink, watched his neck move with the liquid passing down.

'Have you got many more to do?' she asked.

Shane looked at her father. Her father took off his cap, rubbed his tightly curled hair, put it back on and adjusted it.

'Last lot,' he said. He crumpled his can and threw it into the fire.

Mary watched the flames for a while. The fire adjusted itself as it consumed and the cow on top fell down further, the legs moving as if it was still alive. They heard the crackle of the burning fat.

'Yep,' her father said. 'That's the end of that.'

They ate later, pizzas which draped across their cardboard bases as her mother carried them from the microwave to the table.

Mary's father stood up as soon as he had finished. 'C'mon, Jean.' Her mother stood up, still chewing. He looked at Shane. 'You comin'?'

'I'll be down later,' Shane said.

Her father nodded and they left.

The door closed. Shane looked at Mary. He stood up and undid his blue overalls, peeled them off his shoulders and chest and legs. He stepped out of them and his wellington boots at the same time, leaving the boots upright and the overalls ready to climb back into. He moved his head towards the door. Mary stood up and walked in front of him, out of the kitchen and up the stairs. He followed her into her room and closed the door.

Shane picked up the panda and the blue bear from the slim bed and put them on the floor. He lay down and Mary lay next to him, both of them on their sides so as not to fall off. She breathed in and smelled the fire on him. Smelled roast beef on him.

While he was on her, she looked out of her window across the fields. She watched the smoke rising. He moaned and she looked at him to see if he was all right. There were particles of ash and burned cow caught in his hair.

'I better go,' he said.

She nodded.

'Your mum and dad'll be checking the time.' He sat up. 'Don't want them coming back to look for me.'

He bent forward and kissed her, flicking his tongue in her mouth. She could taste pizza. 'You're all right, you are,' he said.

She watched him pull his jeans up and buckle his belt. He kissed her again. 'I'll see you.'

Mary lay on the bed and listened to him go. She heard the door close and the sound of his moped starting and driving off, echoing through the yard and the empty barns and milking parlour. When she could no longer hear the whine of the engine, she got up and pulled her clothes back on. She went down the stairs and walked into the kitchen. The cardboard discs that the pizzas had stood on were still on the table, stained red from the tomato topping, and deep knife cuts in them. She opened a cupboard and took out a packet from a brightly coloured stack and put it in the microwave. She watched it circle round then took it out when it stopped. The bag had inflated and when she opened the top of it, steam escaped. She started dipping in, picking out one popcorn at a time, careful not to burn her tongue on the hot sauce.

She wandered into the next door room and stood in the dark. She looked round at the photographs on the wall, faded, yellowing, the frames thin and black. Two of them had cracks in the glass across the corners. Her grandfather, white coat on, holding a rope with a massive bull on the end of it. She looked at the rosette on the halter, the curled hair over the powerful head and shoulders. There'd been no bulls since she'd been born, just the man in the van with the thin vials of sperm.

Her grandfather was in the nursing home now, his dribble being wiped up by people in their white coats.

The cloud was clearing outside and it would be a cold night. Mary could smell winter. She walked across the home field and then across the four acre towards the fire. It was still burning.

She put more corn in her mouth, then picked up a stick and leaned forward and poked the edge of the fire with it. The stick slipped into the ash like water and particles moved up into the sky.

She could see something by her foot, a small stick, and she went to throw it on. Her fingers felt the ridged texture. She held it up and saw the pointed end, the gradation of colour. She threw the horn onto the fire and rubbed her hand on her leg.

Tomorrow they would burn her guy. She would watch him be sacrificed to the flame. See it scald her father's old shirt with the frayed collar. Watch the old sheet she had slept on become charred.

She looked back at the fire.

At school a while ago, last year maybe, she had had to work from a book which kept falling open at the same page. Two photographs. One a piled up fire, the flames just getting going, people around it, all dressed in white sheets like the one she had ripped up. One woman in white stood on a platform at the end, and prayed. One foot was stepping out to launch herself onto the pyre. And the other photograph: a thin white cow lying on the road, flies at its weepy eyes, its wet nose resting in the dust, people walking round it, one child looking back at it.

She took the last of the popcorn from the bag and ate it, licked her fingers and threw the bag on the fire. She waited till it smouldered, then burst into flames, and she turned and walked back to the house.

John Kinsella

Nature

The steam shovel gives lip, the long white coat
a passport straight into the Studio,
so much of Ireland in New York. Pathos
and dissymetry break like day over

Glenrowan: distracted and incarnate,
the apocalyptic portrait makes for
a fab trophy! Twenty-seven witness
a-cappella-wild-colonial-boy drive

his customline head-on into the road-
block – but that's the Nature of rural life.
Ah, such is the telecine process, and
half tone, fine screen, black fed, and flat white claims

of neat casting, skull theft and paperweights
at the institute of anatomy.

Louis de Bernières

Rabbit

Joan walks with the Major, and with Leafy, wife of the redoubt-
able Colonel Pericles Barkwell. It is an evening late in March,
but the day has seemed more like one from the end of June. They
have gone out warmly dressed, because it is only March, after
all, and now they are huffing and sweltering as they circle the
bounds of the fields behind Joan's home. Joan doesn't like to
sweat so much because she doesn't want people to know that she
has been struck by the menopause, and it is beside the point that
this particular sweat is caused by a very English refusal to concede
that any March day might be other than cold and blustery.

The Major is clad in green wellingtons, corduroys, a grey
woolly jumper, and a khaki-coloured quilted body-warmer that
enhances his military mien. In his pocket is a supersonic whistle
for the dog, which he never uses because he has trained the dog
to respond to parade-ground orders. 'Dogs will retire. Ab-o-u-t
turn!' he roars, and the black labrador obediently comes to heel.
The supersonic whistle is a present from his son in the city, who
believes in high-tech solutions to problems which no one had
previously recognized as problematical.

Leafy Barkwell is dressed in wellies, and a tweed skirt that
has seen smarter days. Its wool has been teased by bramble and
thorn for a decade, and some people have taken to commenting
unkindly that now it looks like a sisal doormat. It is the only
scruffy garment she has, because indoors she is elegant, and
indoors is where she most likes to be. Today, however, she has
succumbed to the warmth of the day, and has come out at the
same time as the primroses, with which she shares some of her
delicate beauty even though she is no longer young.

In the Scots pines in the clump at the end of the field, noisy
squadrons of rooks croak and squabble. It is nesting time, and

the birds are raiding all the surrounding trees in order to snap off the ends of twigs. These twigs they bring back to the pines, where other birds try to snatch them away. There are quarrels and tugs of war, and the booty almost inevitably gets dropped to the ground, whereupon the birds fly off back to the willows and oaks in order to break off more twigs with elaborate exertion that involves much acrobatical risk. The fallen twigs they stupidly do not bother to collect, so that under the rookery the ground begins to look as though a small hurricane has just passed by. In the old days when the peasants had been poor, when, in fact, there actually had been peasants, they used to come and collect the fallen twigs, and bind them into faggots. Now there is only one peasant left, malodorous old Jack Thorn, with his stubble like file-card and his teeth like tombstones, and he is soon to come to a sorry passing away in the wake of a social revolution. Jack Thorn is probably the only person left who can remember what it was like to collect rook faggots and eat rook pie.

Leafy begins to compose verses in her head that one day she might send to *The Lady*, or *Country Life* magazine. She writes mainly about the beauties of nature, which normally she experiences from the other side of her drawing-room window. Her poetry is very like the stuff that used to be anthologized in the 1920s by people like J.C. Squire, and she represents an England that urban intellectuals and university lecturers monotonously assert to be dead, merely because they wish that it were so. Millions of country-people are quite unaware that this version of pastoral England is supposed to have gone, and so they continue to live in it with perfect calm and acceptance. Leafy writes poetry that rhymes inexactly, and struggles to scan, about blackbirds singing on fence-posts, and about clouds, and about beating hearts in unison. Many of her poems are tinged with the respectable reassurance of her Anglican faith. She is as unaware of being quaint as she is of the poetry of T.S. Eliot or Lorca, so let us love her for that.

On the village green the man with the ridiculous dog called Archie is throwing golfballs in the hope of training it to retrieve them. On the other side of the copse the crack of Polly Wantage's twelve bore announces that she is once more persecuting squirrels.

Up the hill Miss Agatha Feakes sounds the horn of her vintage Swift as she careers past the convent with a goat on the back seat. On the common the rector, armed with a plastic sack and a yellow plastic beach spade, is patrolling the bridleways and collecting horse-shit for his roses. In the graveyard of St Peter's church, Mrs Mac converses with the ghost of her husband. In her house on the green Mrs Griffiths opens a gin bottle and pours herself a tiny tipple that she dilutes with Ribena. In the middle of the field, a small posse of Friesian cows stands motionless beneath the huge oak that has been there since the English revolution. In the wood the bluebells are up, but have not yet blossomed, and the snowdrops and winter aconites have flowered awhile and gone.

Joan exclaims, 'Ooh look, what's Wellington up to?'

The other two follow the line of her pointing finger, and see Wellington the black labrador bounding up and down in one spot, his ears flopping forward. He appears to be nudging something. He goes down on his forepaws, his backside in the air, and barks senselessly.

'He must have found something,' says Leafy.

With one accord they change course, and fifty yards later they see that Wellington has indeed found something. Joan makes Wellington sit, and slips on the lead. Side by side they look down, without a word.

'Poor little bugger,' says the Major at last.

'It's so awful,' says Leafy, her voice trembling with shock and sorrow.

'It makes you sick,' says Joan.

'To think this was introduced on purpose . . . by man,' says the Major. 'It's vile, it's dammed vile. What a bloody thing to do. Whoever invented this ought to be strung up and flogged.'

At their feet, in the last extremity of its suffering, is a myxomatosis rabbit. Its flanks have caved in from thirst and starvation, its lustreless coat is loose, hanging in folds. Deaf and blind, it cowers in the long grass, dimly aware that something is happening, but too weak to move. It is attempting to eat the grass, but its mouth is too swollen. It chews on nothing, or perhaps on the ulcers of its own tongue. It chews mechanically and thoughtlessly, as if, by this token eating, it can assuage some of the hollow agony of its unassuageable hunger.

The little creature is so abject, so miserable, so pitiful, that it is heartbreaking just to stand and look. The worst thing, the most horrifying, is that its eyelids are stuck together, and what were its eyes behind them have inflated to the size of table-tennis balls. The effect of this swelling is entirely grotesque, the horrifying globes transforming the rabbit into something that seems other than a rabbit. It has become a monster imagined by the cartoonist of a horror comic.

'I can't bear it,' says Leafy Barkwell.

'The poor little mite,' says Joan.

The rabbit does not try to get away. It remains still and quiet, trying to eat, hoping that if it remains still for long enough, everything might begin to get better. It is so harrowed by misery that it has lost all sense of self-preservation. For days now it has stayed out in the same place in the grass, unable to find its burrow, freezing and shivering by night in the March frosts, drenched by the March rain, buffeted by the March gales, enduring the slow cruciation of this casually-inflicted death, its own insignificant, tiny, world-destroying calvary. It stays perfectly quiet, and never loses hope, but in reality it is a most unfortunate miracle that it has not yet been found by a fox.

The Major is an old soldier, and he knows his duty. He takes no pleasure in saying, 'I am going to have to kill it.'

Leafy puts her hands to her face and exclaims, 'Oh please, not with me here.'

'Wait till we've gone,' pleads Joan.

The Major is relieved not to have to do it immediately. He says, 'I'll come back with the airgun.'

Back at the house the Major takes the airgun out of the cupboard. It is a Webley Mk 111, very heavy, with a tapered barrel. It is a powerful .22 and is ideal for hunting small game over open sights. At one time it represented the best in British engineering, except that some idiot designed the rails so badly that they lifted off when you tried to mount telescopic sights. Years ago the Major had bought it as a present for his little son, feeling that it was his duty to teach him the manly arts, thinking that perhaps he might grow up to be a soldier, or that one day, if there was yet another war, it would be useful for the sons of England to know how to handle themselves in a firefight. The Major had taught his boy how to do rapid fire, how to allow for movement, how to follow through, but now he works in the City, pale and sleepless, conjuring money out of thin air, his mouth spewing out American business jargon, driving around in a Porsche instead of a proper car, displaying a kind of energy and merriment that seem entirely artificial and out of character with the teenager that he used to know. The Major strokes the walnut stock of the Webley and thinks of the fantasies he used to entertain on his son's behalf, before the world turned into something that he hadn't realized he had been fighting for. He handles the walnut stock of the Webley and remembers the .303 Lee Enfield that stayed with him undamaged from the start of the war to its end. He wonders what happened to it.

He takes the airgun out into the field behind the house, and is sorry to find that the piteous, oblivious little creature is still there. He realizes that he really will have to do his duty. He bends down and strokes the rabbit down the length of its nose. It barely reacts. It occurs to the Major that the animal is so nearly dead that he might just as well leave it to die at its own pace, let it make its own quietus. He remembers Glub Pasha telling him years ago that his Arab troops believed that animals should be given time to think about life whilst they die, which is why they used to cut their throats with three strokes of a knife. 'Whatever happened to Glub Pasha?' he asks himself.

The Major strokes the rabbit's nose again, and says, 'Little fellow, I want to say how sorry I am for what's . . . for what's been done to you. Poor little bugger. I'm so sorry.' He strokes the animal's flank and feels the hard starkness of the ribs.

He straightens up and cocks the underlever of the Webley. He takes a lead pellet from the tin in his pocket, opens the tap of the gun, and drops the pellet in. He checks it has gone home properly, and closes the tap. Against his will, but in accordance with his duty, he places the barrel of the gun between and just forward of the rabbit's ears. He steels himself, squeezes the trigger, and feels the gun leap in his hands.

At his feet the rabbit has flung itself onto its side, and from its mouth there is spurting a small cascade of inconceivably brilliant scarlet blood. Its back legs kick feebly, and, most heartrendingly of all, so great is the pain of its starvation compared to the pain of its deathwound, that it continues trying to eat, its jaws moving ceaselessly.

It kicks again, and then the Major makes a mistake. He knows that really it is dead already, that it died instantly, but he wants it to stop kicking and chewing. He reloads the gun and places the gunbarrel against the side of the rabbit's head, right against the hideous globe of its left eyesocket. He pulls the trigger and then leaps back in horror, because a thick shower of bright white pus has exploded out of its head and spattered his trousers, his jacket, his hands, the barrel of his gun. It had never occurred to him that the swelling had been anything other than a swelling. He walks backwards a few paces, sees that the animal is completely dead, wishes it, perhaps ridiculously, a safe homegoing to wherever it has gone, and walks swiftly home, too upset for thought.

Joan has waited in the kitchen, and she sees him come in, his face white with distress. She puts her hand to his face, and he says in tones of quiet disbelief, 'Its head was full of pus, and it exploded.'

She looks at him as he takes a paper towel and wipes down the gun. 'Go and change,' she says, 'I'll put your clothes in the machine.'

The Major sits at his desk in his study, his hands on his knees, looking out of the window at the laurels. A squirrel spirals up the oak tree, and a green woodpecker inspects its crevices for bugs. His clean clothes feel stiff and unyielding. His wife comes in with a cup of tea. It is her own blend, half Tetley teabag, and half Earl Grey. She puts it down carefully on his blotter and asks, 'Are you all right, darling?'

He says, 'It was very upsetting.' He pauses, and then asks her, 'Did I ever tell you about the German soldier?'

'Which one, darling?'

'When we were sent out to collect the papers from the dead.'

'No, you didn't tell me.'

He continues to look straight out of the window. 'We'd been

fighting for three days,' he said. 'We were all exhausted. No sleep. It was bloody hot. It had been hot for weeks. It was appalling . . . very tough. Bloody Hell, actually. Then the Germans withdrew, and my platoon was detailed to collect the papers from the dead. For the Red Cross. Send them back through Switzerland.'

He pauses in order to collect himself. 'I found this body. In a foxhole. He was damned bloody fat, this German. I remember thinking he was too fat to fight, that the Germans must have been damned desperate to go round recruiting anyone as fat as that.

'He had a nice belt, a black leather one, and it so happened that mine was buggered. Broken at the buckle. I was holding my trousers up with a string. Not very soldierly.

'I tried to undo the German's belt, but it was too tight, so I put my foot on his stomach to get some purchase. That was when I found out that he wasn't fat, he was swollen.'

The Major continues to look out at the laurels. 'I vomited. I've seen lots of corpses. They don't seem like people, not even the corpses of your friends. But that was the first one that actually exploded.

'Afterwards we looked through all the papers. They were all love letters and pictures of girls. Piles and piles of them. We sat and looked at them and said nothing. He was called Manfred Schneider, the one with the belt. Up until that day I loved killing Germans. It was all I wanted to do. Nothing I'd rather. I had a passion for it. But after that I stopped hating Germans. After that I killed only for duty.'

Joan places her hand on his shoulder. He looks up at her and she can see that his eyes are glistening with choked-back tears. She strokes his thin grey hair, and kisses him lightly on the top of the head. Discreetly she turns and leaves the room. With his hands on his knees, his cup of tea cooling on the blotter, and his eyes brimming with a lifetime's unshedable tears, he looks out over the laurels, and remembers. He will never tell anyone, not even Joan, about the mercy-killing that is sometimes all one can do for a friend.

Elspeth Barker

Missing

'*C'est un beau chien,*' said the Frenchman. Mary and he stared at the black lurcher curvetting and galloping in and out and round about the vast cylindrical straw bales, zigzagging almost horizontal to the stubble.

'She's a bitch,' said Mary. 'Actually,' she added, so as not to seem rude, although she felt like being rude. Why was he here at all, when he was her daughter's friend? And why wasn't Ellen here?

'*Chienne alors,*' shrugged the Frenchman, '*même chose.*'

Rage mounted in Mary.

'It's not at all the same thing; perhaps it is in France. Here we look differently at dogs.'

Woodpigeons cooed and mourned in the heavy August trees, tarnished already with the ebbing days of summer. An exhaust backfired, scattering the pigeons out against the clouded sky. Ellen's car jolted up the drive, roaring and revving. Two huge grizzled dogs glowered from the windows. Thank God for that, thought Mary. Now perhaps he'll go. In the sharp shadow cast by the bales he looked like Louis Jourdan playing Dracula. Or the man on the old Gitanes packet. Or was it Gauloises? She was too old for all this. Now Ellen stood beside him in her dreadful paramilitary trousers, and they were beaming at her. Extraordinary behaviour. The low sun dazzled her eyes.

'We've something to tell you, Mother,' said Ellen. The Frenchman nodded vigorously.

'You say,' he urged.

'No you.' Ellen pushed him forward.

Mary's heart lurched. Surely they weren't planning to marry. Not *Ellen*. He cleared his throat.

'I have found the grave,' he pronounced, each word slow and careful. 'I have found at last the grave of your husband.'

Ellen's mother Mary had learned a few things in her time, as she sometimes told her unfriendly daughter. One of these was to live with grief, or rather to live without it, beyond it. She had been alone a long time now, existing, Ellen thought, not only beyond grief, but also beyond love. Mary's husband had died invisibly in the Normandy landings, missing, presumed dead, a couple of months before Ellen was born. These days Mary didn't think about him much. Sometimes, but not often. And she had never thought much about Ellen. She was old and dusty and almost immaterial, shrinking her way out of life. She tried to live in abeyance from mortality. She preferred the evanescent, brooding endlessly on wind and weather, hunched over her wireless. If she considered life or death she became weighed down, oppressed; there had been too much of both and she could not succumb to either. The passing moment exacted all the strength she had left. 'I'm tired of living and I'm tired of dying,' she sang to herself. That wasn't right and she couldn't remember any of the other lines and she didn't care. Words came uninvited and tangled in her brain and set themselves to music. They would hang about for weeks, until they were replaced by something else, a phrase or two or poetry, an advertising slogan, some old-time ribaldry.

Even on this strange evening, when Ellen and the Frenchman had gone, and dusk and owls had invaded her garden, her skull was buzzing with a sprightly jingle:

> It's a fine tanking day
> And as balmy as May
> And the crew to the tank parks have hurried . . .

She persuaded herself there was nothing she could do about it, and it was better than thinking, when there was time to pass before any hope of sleep. So, humming briskly, she moved her frail body about her house; her bones clicked and creaked like knitting needles. The air was cold now, so cold that she sipped it, rather than breathed it; draughts skittered through the window frames and lifted the edges of threadbare rugs. As darkness gathered through those unlit, unpeopled rooms, she could almost believe that she had attained the ghostly state of her aspiration. There but not there. Intimations of the past lay all about her and in her solitude she might choose to remember, to forget, or to rearrange. Only very rarely, as now, was she caught unawares, overwhelmed by a great, retching pang of agonized grief, which left her shaken and gasping, clutching at the walls for support, slithering to the floor.

She sat there very still and stared at the runnels on her fingertips where dust and skin cells merged; ashes to ashes. An old familiar image lingered in her head, a heave of sea the colour of muddy milk, waves racing and breaking under a dingy sky, frameless, boundless, implacable. And with it a sense of absolute terror. Slowly it receded. She breathed more steadily and concentrated on her becalming method, a memory of a house from her childhood, the home of her cousins. It was damp and half derelict, and when they had got round to making it habitable, after many years of habitation, a slab of rotten plaster had crumbled from the wall, revealing a staring, ecstatic eye, a web of golden hair. Soon a colonnade of saints and heavenly bodies gazed out in troubled piety from the dining-room walls.

'All the way round too,' grumbled Uncle Randal. 'What on earth are we to do?' The planned rewiring would cause grievous injuries. The mighty, smoking fire would discolour and desiccate. Worse was to come. In the upstairs corridors and largest bedroom an ancient hunting scene emerged, all swishing tails and stabbing fangs and spears. A boar at bay snarled and a crown rolled beneath the stamp of hooves, just where the socket for Aunt Ruth's electric fire should be.

'Wheesht,' said Randal. 'Aye, wheesht's the word,' agreed the workmen. Within days the figures were again immured, sealed in by thick layers of plaster and distemper. As a nervous small child, Mary had found the thought of those saints and horsemen, vigilant but invisible, wonderfully comforting. Now she imagined herself joining them, becoming part of that house, fading slowly into the plaster, into self-effacement, there and not there. Thus fortified she accomplished without effort the three hot-water bottle evening ritual and retired to bed.

But this night was different. Peter has been found. Or, more likely, bits of Peter. She thought again of that muddy sea, breaking forever on its forlorn strand. She had gone to that great curve of beach once, years ago, with her friend Josephine, trying to imagine what Peter had seen, last seen before he fell. Josephine had said it would be good for her, a laying of a ghost. Mary didn't find it good at all. Josephine had brought a picnic to enjoy at this maritime charnelhouse. Mary walked down to the sea; the tide was far out and the sands shone under a pallid, fitful sun.

She was remembering the first time she met Peter. He was dressed in cricket whites, waiting to bat. He leaned slightly forward on his bat and she saw a crusader leaning on his sheathed sword. A perfect, gentle knight in a world then crowded with possibility, a future in which the past would renew itself, complementing and deepening the present; no opportunity would ever be cancelled, no prospect rendered void. One would grow a little older, but not to any irretrievable degree. There had been a day in Oxford when they had wandered together through water-meadows thronged with cowparsley and birdsong. Mary was intensely happy. So many years later, how well she recalled that day. It was warm and uncertain; spring sunlight glanced through rain-soaked leaves and the air was blurred and pungent with blossom and earth and damp, charged with an erotic excitement and poignancy which Mary had noticed then and since in ancient university cities. An exhalation compounded of hundreds of yearning springtimes, aspiration thwarted, unfocused desire, urgent joy and mild, pastoral melancholy. She felt a quiver of fear.

'You want to watch this place,' she said. 'It's an ambush, isn't it? Toils of enchantment. Toil and moil, warp and weft. Funny that; could you say it warps you?' She eyed Peter sidelong, hoping to provoke him. But he wasn't listening; or rather he was listening to the bells, clamorous as always, and the cuckoo calling over the high walls. Springstruck, he moved, tranced as a pilgrim through the scent of wallflowers and then of bluebells as they turned into woodland along the river. A path, freshly hacked through undergrowth, led them to a clearing, and in the centre of the clearing a scowling priapic statue squatted, one arm extended as if grudgingly to shake hands. As they drew closer they saw that in fact the arm was pointing them back towards the river. Beyond stretched an overgrown garden, starred pink with campion and bramble. The sun shone strongly now and insects hummed and buzzed through the tall flowering grasses, nettles and elder. The house at the top of the garden was smothered in creeper; vine and clematis clambered to the roof edge, felt their way under the tiles, still dark from the early rain, and curved luxuriantly down again. They had wrenched the balconies from the wall and suspended them in airy cages of leaf and tendril. Above the porch an odd rectangle of brickwork remained bare, shadowed randomly by the faintest of markings, like ancient drawings or a forgotten script.

'Look,' said Peter, 'just watch this.' The markings were gaining in definition; they resolved into imposing Roman capitals, they grouped, they formed a word: PARADISE, they proclaimed. Mary sat down abruptly in the sodden grass. She was frightened and hot and something had bitten her on the eyelid. Her heart thudded. Peter was smiling down at her.

'It's all right,' he said, 'don't look like that. It's meant to be a surprise. And I didn't know if it would really happen.'

'What on earth do you mean? How did you know? Have you been here before? What is it *doing*?'

Peter pulled her up and hugged her. 'It's lichens.'

Lichens. Mary had never heard this word pronounced. *Lichens*. She was overwhelmed with love for him.

'This place used to be a pub or an inn or something and it had metal letters on the wall. You get these lichens left underneath them and they develop just for a few minutes when it's hot after it's been raining. Then they fade away again. Wait and see.'

Mary could not bear to watch the fading.

'Let's go, quick, and then it'll always be there.'

It was too late; the space was blank again and an ancient, angry face glared down from an upstairs window. Squashed and distorted against the pane, its bulging cheeks resembled the gargoyle features in the clearing.

So it had been.

She became aware now of the chill of the sands; she was shivering. She glanced back at the picnicking Josephine and could only make out a huddled form, intent on its Tupperware boxes. The shore and the dunes and the further cliff line were blanked out by a low hanging thick white fog. Looming here and there near the waterline, the tractors which dragged speedboats down to the sea might have been the rusty skeletons of tanks, and occasional distant figures were visible only in parts, a head, a glimpse of torso, a flailing arm. The tide crept swiftly inshore, the colour of her imagining, muddy milk. Fear gathered, thudding, in her head and heart.

So on that cold August night, Mary lay awake; she thought of Peter and his grave and all the half life lived since he had gone, the surprising resolution of middle age into old age and her relief then that soon it would all be over. And her guilt now at so many years wasted, that others could have cherished. But if Peter had not been taken from her, how different it would have been. She might have loved Ellen, instead of finding her a dismal encumbrance. Ellen might have grown up to be pretty and loving and marriageable instead of going around in army surplus clothes and breeding weird curly-coated dogs with webbed feet.

'As mentioned in Shakespeare. *Water-rugs*,' she claimed.

Everything that had mattered was so long ago; she thought her feelings had all leached away and she had nothing left. Nothing but that intermittent pain of missing Peter, of missing being loved, of the abiding loss of her share of the world.

All that summer a comet had hung in the sky above Mary's garden. Ellen claimed that it was also suspended above the shanty town ensemble of wire-netting pens and corrugated iron huts which comprised her kennels, but Mary had certainly not seen it there. She enjoyed the comet's strangeness, its air of preoccupation, as if it were brooding upon its imminent departure into unreachable black voids for another four thousand years. She felt personally privileged by its coming and she treasured its unmatchable evanescence; it made her bold and dismissive and untruthful.

'What then is life?' she asked it. She was seized by an irrational fear that it would disappear while she and Ellen were in France at Peter's grave. The night before they left she stood out on her dewy lawn, hands clasped tight; staring up at it she recited silently a rhyme half forgotten from childhood:

> Star light, star bright
> First star I see tonight
> I wish I may, I wish I might
> Have the wish I wish this night.

But she didn't know what to wish. The comet dreamed on, impervious. Somewhere across the river a goose was laughing.

They drove to Portsmouth in Ellen's rackety, dog-smelling car. Tufts of fur eddied down shafts of sunlight and strewed themselves delicately over the padded shoulders of Mary's severe grey coat and skirt, still very serviceable after fifty years of wardrobe and mothballs. On the boat, out on deck and hanging on to the rail, she shut her eyes and tried to will herself to push through time and emerge on the far side, a forties sweetheart, a forces sweetheart, Peter's sweetheart. But her legs were too wobbly and her hands too gnarled. The bright breeze made her cheekbones ache; her eyes watered.

Ellen had rented a house near Caen. It was unnecessarily large, and gloomy; on the walls were tattered, blackened copies of ancient funeral notices and Ellen announced proudly that it was here that Charlotte Corday had stayed in the weeks before she murdered Marat.

'It's dead cheap because of that,' she said.

But it had a large and beautiful garden where apples hung red and gold from trees swagged with mistletoe. At night shooting stars plunged from the heavens, but Mary looked in vain for the comet.

On a brilliant blue day of Indian summer, Ellen took Mary to the graveyard. Slow and silent, they walked together up the long, green slope between the crowding multitude of white stones. Mary leaned heavily on Ellen's arm; she had no thoughts at all, no feelings, only a thudding heart and a great weariness. But as they turned down the avenue of Peter's grave her step quickened. She let go of Ellen's arm; she pushed her hair back and smoothed it, she shook out her skirt and moved forward, head high, serene and eager, a ghostly bride advancing to her lover.

In late afternoon they returned to the house. Ellen's friend François brought tea out to the garden. Mary took her cup and smiled at him, surprising him.

'Thank you, Peter darling,' she said, surprising him more. She studied her tea, its swaying disc of surface. It was reminding her of something, but she could not focus on it; she saw a pinpoint of sunlight reflected and she heard the roaring of the sea. She slipped sideways from her chair to the grass and lay there, staring unseeing up at François, her hands still clasping the delicate cup.

They cremated her in Caen and Ellen took the ashes, a rosebush and a trowel back to the war graves. She laid the ashes in Peter's oblong of turf and above she planted the rose. She walked away down the green slope to the gateway. Poppies trembled there in the long grass and she thought how strange it was that they should be the flowers of remembrance and of forgetfulness. She believed then, and not for the first time, that she had inherited her mother's cold, passionless nature, for she felt nothing but a powerful longing to be done with all this, and never to return. Several days later she found beneath a carpet in Mary's house a dusty brown paper bag. In it was a photograph of her parents as she had never seen them, he in his uniform, she in a flowered dress, but laughing and young and ardent, gazing at each other.

'Before my time,' Ellen thought. Out in the twilight sky, the comet was tilting away into renewed aeons of solitude. She was overwhelmed by desolation, a longing to arrest the moment, to declare that love is as strong as death; but this she could not do. Anyhow, it was time to feed her dogs.

Helen Dunmore

At the Hare and Hounds

'Stop here.'

You don't want to go into the pub car park. The verge of the lane is wide and the car rocks up onto it, steadies, then nudges deep into the hedge on the left-hand side. Jerome switches off the engine. Birdsong pushes into the car, and there's a succulent country slap of leaves as you try and fail to open the car-door.

'Climb over my seat.'

You're both outside now. It's very quiet. Not a popular Sunday pub with crowds sitting outside and a play area for children to spill their grab-bags of crisps. It has an air of emptiness, even though there are two men in the little dark room, warming beer-glasses with their hands. They look up at you, then back into the middle distance where they are happier. A lot of trouble has been taken to keep light out of this room. Deep windows, nicotined walls, and lumpy, dark furniture. But the room smells of beer and fags and you want to sit down and be at home here.

But you can't. You prowl. How old are those men? How long have they been coming here? One of them is at least sixty. In 1967 he would have been . . .

Twenty-six. Old enough to be part of it. There might be a flash of it somewhere, lodged in his brain, if you could cut it out.

'These seats all right?' asks Jerome. He lays a hand lightly over the clotted, varnished wood. What was Jerome doing in 1967? He was inside his mother, far away. You were inside too, over here. You were a ball of acid in her stomach. You always let her know that you were there.

She was sick with you right up to the nine months.

So, you've been here before, and if you'd been able to look through the walls of your mother's flesh and clothes you might remember this room. She was here too, sweating and sick, her face pale, her pretty blonde hair plastered to her skull. All the witnesses agreed that she looked not right. She looked as if something was up.

She came in here alone and ordered herself a drink at the bar. It was rare for women to do that then. The barman noticed how pale she was. She asked for a Babycham but when it came and she'd paid, she didn't drink it.

I've changed my mind. I'll have a gin-and-lime.

She would have watched the lime-juice fall through the gin and spread out like a sail. She drank it quickly, then she asked for another, which she took to the table just behind the door.

It's the one you are sitting at now, watching the broad sweetness of Jerome's back as he bends forward to see what kind of crisps they've got. You hear the rustle of the crisp bags and the sharp *tang* of the till. Jerome stuffs his change into his pocket in the way you love, and turns with his Guinness and your tomato juice. You want your head to be clear. You certainly don't want to make yourself start imagining things.

She sat here for twenty minutes, crossing and uncrossing her legs. She was wearing a short, sleeveless, red cotton dress. Her legs were bare and on her feet she had white thong sandals. Beside her on the seat there was a white handbag. She kept looking at the door and it was obvious that she was waiting for someone. Once she half got up as if she was going to order another drink, then she changed her mind and sat down again.

You were there too. You were there under the ruck of that red cotton, warm with the warmth of her body. You were the swelling that couldn't be seen because of the way she was sitting. You were the reason that her breasts were heavier than before.

She smoked three cigarettes while she was waiting. She tapped off the ash with a sharp, bright tap into the brass ashtray. She always smoked Consulates because she thought they didn't make her breath smell.

Jerome slides into the seat beside you. One of the men snaps his fingers at a Staffordshire bull terrier which must have been under the table all the time, silent and invisible. It gives you a look as it goes out after its master. The second man nods at the dog, and then creaks over to the bar and says he'll have the other half. He's drinking pints.

'They don't do sandwiches,' says Jerome.

He knows why you're here. He's been with you all the way.

She was the youngest. There was Connie, then Jennifer, then little Jean. Pretty, blonde little Jean with her white-bubble hair, six years younger than Jennifer, eight years younger than Connie, who was already married with a six-month-old baby by the time Jean sat here in her red dress.

Your Aunty Jean. But don't say anything because you'll upset your Nana.

If she's my aunty, why don't we go and see her?

She lives a long way away from here.

But she wasn't far away then. She was all around you. Her heat, her bumping heart, the cigarettes she smoked and the bright tarnish of gin going down her throat. You knew how frightened she was because the adrenalin of it poured through you and made you bump bump bump against the walls of your cell.

Men looked at her smooth bare legs and her white sandals. She had her white bag on the other side of her, between her body and the wall. When she crossed her legs, her red dress rucked above her knee, over her thigh. She looked at the fag which was down to its burning end, and then carefully stubbed it out.

Jerome's arm is lying on the table beside yours, parallel. He is wearing a white T-shirt and his arm is smooth and dark beside yours. He was far away while all this was happening, but now he's close. Every bit of your body remembers every bit of his. If he went away now, what would you do? If he came into this bar on a sunlit evening, blinking, with another girl, how would you rise to meet him?

Jean would have known the sound of the engine. She'd been in that car enough times. That's where you were made, in the front of an MG. She would have known the way the wheels spat and then went quiet.

MGs are ridiculous cars. In your opinion, there's no style in them at all. Jean thought the same. The kind of man he was had no business with a play car. He belonged with something black and snub and violent.

Probably he came in with a grin on him like the metal smile of a car radiator. He had the other girl with him. She was called Nicolette. Of course that wouldn't have been her real name. But why bother to trace it, why bother to find out what she was really called? It could have been her or it could have been anyone.

Lovely, bubble-curled Jean grew up and had to iron her hair to get that straight sheet of yellow. She delved into her white handbag the way women do, rooting for keys or tissues. But she took out something that didn't belong to her. It was his, and he kept it safe in his top handkerchief drawer. Again it was the wrong kind of gun. It was little and playful-looking and it easily went into a white handbag. If he'd had a proper gun, like he should have, none of this would have happened.

But even playful guns are heavy things. For some reason she had wrapped it in newspaper and the paper crackled as she took it out, still inside her bag. She was half-standing and very pale now. He still didn't see her because she was sitting behind the door. She had the gun right out now but down at her side and as she was left-handed that meant it was still between her body and the wall. Nobody saw it. The barman glanced across and thought he would not serve her again. Probably been drinking before she came in. Barmen have all these thoughts about people very quickly, inside a second.

She stepped forward. She said his name. He turned and they faced one another. His face screwed up and he said, not to her but to Nicolette, 'Well, look who's here.'

His voice was flat, as if nothing she could do or say would surprise him.

Jean said nothing. She brought up her left hand and poked the play gun in his stomach. Then she moved it away until it was higher, against his chest. He still didn't click what she was doing. His eyes went wide as if she was touching him up. They were so close that her belly must have touched him. Inside, you were holding on. Nobody looked at Nicolette. Your mother and your father stood locking eyes until she shot him.

It was pure bad luck that gave her aim. She knew nothing about guns and had never fired one.

You were in on it. You were complicit. When the gun went

off, the shock of it thudded through your body, making you slosh from side to side in your sac of water. Your heart roared along with your mother's.

'I was there', you say to Jerome, understanding it for the first time. His arm touches yours, but he says nothing. The smell of Guinness is grainy on his breath. Suddenly you wonder what your father drank. If Jean hadn't emerged from her seat behind the door, he would have gone up to the bar and rapped on it and ordered drinks for himself and for Nicolette. Maybe, on their way in, he'd asked her what she'd have. The barman would have served him quickly, because he was that kind of man. And Jean would have been far away, a dream of a red dress, warm thighs, a white handbag.

Although she didn't know how to fire the gun, and had never fired one before, she did it. The shock threw her backwards and she dropped the gun. Nobody picked it up. There were more people in the pub on that day: plenty of witnesses. Jean fell back without a mark on her, but people thought at first that she was the one who had been shot. It took minutes for the pub to make sense of what had happened.

The landlord called the ambulance, and the police. He used a sturdy black bakelite telephone which doesn't exist any more. He dialled by carrying his fingers around the dial and then letting go, in a way that also doesn't exist any more. Jean staggered, then went back to sit in her seat behind the door. She had dropped the white handbag and did not try to pick it up. She sat there blankly until someone lit a cigarette for her and put it in her mouth. Meanwhile he was slipping to the floor, slowly, his feet scraping where people tried to hold him up. Nicolette was in a terrible state. Look what she had got caught up in, and she hardly knew him at all. She knew Jean, but didn't recognize her straight away, maybe because she was so pale.

Someone shut the pub door and said nobody must leave. Someone else was doing first aid to the pulsating reddish mess in the middle of your father. Your father's legs jerked as he lay on the floor. He was conscious, glaring. There was an animal smell of blood. Jean kept on sitting there as if she was waiting for something, but she never looked at what she'd done. She didn't seem to know where she was or what was going on. This was the general verdict afterwards. When the police arrived she spoke for the first time. She said, 'I'm pregnant,' as they got her up from her seat. They weren't being rough with her, but perhaps she was remembering something she'd been told: that they don't hang pregnant women.

They didn't hang anyone in 1967. It had all been abolished. 'So this is it,' says Jerome quietly, looking around. 'This is the place.'

It had seemed strange that it was on a map, on an ordinary road which dwindled to a lane. And that the pub was still open, still serving pints and smelling of smoke and beer. You are sitting where Jean sat. Here, now. You've sat here before.

Together you were driven off to the police station. Jean's body wrapped around yours as warmly as ever, and her heart pumped its red tide inside her red dress. She still said nothing. She seemed not to know where she was, or understand what she had done.

When you left her at last, you were handed to Connie, wrapped in a cobweb blanket which Jean had knitted herself. Nobody in the family had known that Jean could knit. You were a small, dark-haired baby, not at all like your mother. Who else you might resemble, nobody liked to say. You were Connie's then. You would grow up almost like a twin sister to baby Louise, who was eleven months older than you. When you were little you would both hear the grown-ups say Aunty Jean's name. She lived a long way away and never came to visit. Connie would have you both on her knee and ride you up and down, bumpety bumpety bump, the way the farmer rides, the way the gentleman rides, the way the lady rides. There was no distinction made between you and Louise.

You are here because you had the right to be here. You had the right to find out who your mother was. Even though hanging was abolished, she hanged herself with a cut-up sheet. That was after eight years of prison. Lucky that you didn't know, that nobody knew, that you were now Connie's and Louise was your sister. Not your twin sister, you often had to explain that, but nearly as close as twins. You always shared a bedroom.

She sat here, then she stood up with the gun in her left hand.

Maybe that man there, the only one remaining, knows what she did. Maybe he saw it. It was only thirty-four years ago. It is not history.

You were there too. Maybe she felt you swing inside her as she stood up and her weight shifted. Maybe that's what gave her the strength to pull the trigger.

Outside the pub, on the other side of the car park, there's a river. It's not the kind of river where anyone would want to plant tables and bright umbrellas. It's a farm river, swollen and stinking of chemicals. Perhaps it was different, when Jean came here.

Jerome is exactly the same age as you. His mother was pregnant then, too, but in Guyana, not here. It makes you feel that you can breathe more easily, when you know that Jerome was far away from it all, growing up under a different sky, until one day he came to meet you.

Stephen Romer

St Stephen

For Hugo Williams

'We couldn't talk about love the other night, but I
assume you are doomed, also?'

I got your card: Stephen bowed,
asking for the coup de grâce-
a point-blank boulder coming from behind.

And come it does, she's wed.

For ten years in the wings
she bore my comings and goings
my disappearance in the crowd.

Gently, gently, she lets me down.

Now I'm cast in Gothic
I hope I can be gracious,
dignified, courteous, kind.

I hope I can carry my head
with a rock
encrusting it like a crown.

Beverley Bie

A Kind of Madness

(Peter Brook aux Bouffes du Nord)

All night the wind batters our house
With a rubble of words.
Curtains grow bellies and flatten.
The mirrors reassemble their pieces.

'Doctor, do you believe in God?'
The man who remembered everything
Wanted to leave his brain to science.
They had been friends for years.

'No,' replied Alexander Romanovitch Luria.
'I believe my life is a brief passage
Through eternity. And you, my friend,
Do you believe in God?'

'But what is before and after eternity?'
'Nothing.'
'How can there be *nothing* if I can picture it?
          Nothing
Is a smoke signal; it has a bitter taste.'

The Russian scientist kept a valise
So he could make a quick get away.
He didn't believe in averages;
He believed in the individual case history.

The man who remembered everything
Remembered too much. When the spectators
Filed out of the old vaudeville theatre
He was left in the dark

On a catwalk constructed of words,
All of them unforgettable.
The man who remembered everything
Believed in God. What else was there?

Background Music

At three I flung open the tall window
I never open except on hot summer nights
To entice a cool riff of breeze through.
A car radio played Arab music
So I leaned out to listen, dreaming Casbah, harem,
Belly-dancer's jangling bracelets,
Rosewood worry beads carved like raindrops
Dripping through nicotine fingers.

Then a voice rumbled up the stairs to me.
'When the storm comes
I'll have to get up and close it,'
And I replied without turning around,
'There's no sign of any storm,'
But I couldn't see where the music was coming from
Because the voice on the pillow insisted
The paper'd said there'd be a thunderstorm.

Now this hush of rain. Fat drops
Flatten themselves on the maple leaves, on the green
Striped cushions, steady streams
Overflowing the world's sound system,
Trickling, plinking, trip-trapping atoms
Of worry beads. It's all I hear
When I close my eyes, a time signature,
Percussive and soothing as background music.

Janice Galloway

Ich Kann nich fassen

[from a novel in progress]

Too hot to leave in June, too unstable in July, Schumann told them after dinner at the Linden. He also told them, stood on a chair to do it, that he had decided to be not one but two men now, a Poet and a Hero, each with different names. Even father laughed. In August she was full of measles and Berlin was full of cholera – the heat's fault, everything was the heat's fault. Still blotchy on her birthday, she walked with Schumann to Conne-witz, leaving her father to his planning. Schumann was writing a novel, an opera, a play. He was always writing something. He read her single lines, fragments, licked the words on his lips like salt. *I have a tender heart*, he said: *sometimes* (he whispered this part, a shocking trust) *sometimes even music disgusts me* and Clara, freshly twelve, believed it. She believed every word the lodger said. Father, on the other hand, believed nothing: all those hints of despair, those melodramatic wishes for bullets through the head, the hypochondria – who could take that stuff seriously? It was just Schumann, how he behaved. Keeping a clear eye on the future, forcing one's plans upon it – that was serious. After months of delay, what was serious won through. No external crises would stop them, no domestic complications either. Clem-entine had been pregnant before, she'd manage. Schumann saw them off as far as Bitterfeld, watched the great wheels of their coach churning mud, taking them elsewhere. She recalls his face, or thinks she does, growing smaller, whiter; the interior of the coach a black frame round his shrinking form. After that she thought of him hardly at all. If he got drunk for three days solid, wrote letters to himself, passed out, played Bach till he was dizzy,

wept and laughed alone in his terrifying new rooms she knew
nothing of it. Not then. A Poet and a Hero. *Ach Gott. Gott.*

*

Gone six months, what did she do?

Weimar	Erfurt	Gotha
Eisenach	Arnstadt	Cassel
Frankfurt	Darmstadt	Maintz
Paris	Metz	Saarbruck
Frankfurt	Hanau	Fulda

She learned faces, times of day, the different smell of another
country's streets, the mean dispositions of foreign hotels.

She travelled with her father. She played the piano.

What did *he* do? Ha!

He moved rooms twice, played, wrote, rejoiced, despaired and
masturbated till his wrist cramped. He read. He read a great deal.
He read about cholera and jaundice, typhus and flu. He studied
Beethoven and cures for chronic skin complaints. He read Goethe,
Bach, Herder and enough Shakespeare to cause indigestion. He
scanned texts on nervous debility. He devoured Hoffman and
Heine, Schubert and Chopin, essays on syphilis, sight-problems
and gout. He read letters from his mother full of blame made to
sound like love, bad love-letters full of exquisite, racking pain.
He felt guilt, fear, shame and loneliness. He worried. He didn't
sleep enough. He read the works of Jean-Paul to while his sleepless hours – Lord! Sabienkäs back from the dead, looking into
his own grave! Branches tapping the windows! – and slept even
less. He was raddled with sensibility. He drank too much; hated
himself; drank more; lit cigars; got high as a kite; sang till the
small hours and woke among sheets spattered with burn-holes,
butt-ends, trails of wine. He resolved to CHANGE. To CHANGE.
To drink less, smoke less, spend less, leave his cock alone. And
so he did. Till next time, when it started all over again, again,
again. Many times he wished for a soul-mate, a dear friend, a
brother in thought and spirit: someone as unlike his real brothers
as possible. Some men were married and settled by his age, they
were famous. Mendelssohn, the darling of London; Chopin with

two concertos under his belt. Mozart didn't bear thinking about. Some were in the army. Dear God! Just thinking it brought him out in a rash. He dreamed he told them his eyesight was poor and they drafted him anyway, woke sweating, sick, white. He read in his journals. It was just as he thought. He'd become nervous. A year ago, he'd felt fit to trust his luck. He had given up his Lawbooks, landed the teacher of his choice, set his heart on Music at last. He had his portrait painted. He had chanced upon Variations by a young Polish composer in an out-of-town music shop and couldn't believe his ears; he had gorged on Jean-Paul, the only writer who mapped precisely the territory of the sensitive mind, who *understood*; he had played for the charity student at Wieck's, a mezzo with a dark voice who had followed him back to his rooms, had come inside without waiting to be asked, had slid her finger in his mouth to stop him suggesting she sing. Christel, beautiful Christel, a mouth round a thumb. He had Jean-Paul, he had Chopin, a woman. Something unsuspected – a *woman*. For the first time, he was a man, he thought. And he was not alone. He was – what? The more he thought about it, the more the same answer came back. He was – two. Like Vult and Walt, Abelard and Héloïse, Hamlet. Everything meaningful sprang from duality, after all; why not himself? Some days his head raced; he felt invincible, stuffed with *being*: other days he felt melancholy, even withdrawn – a splitting that had become more marked these past two years. For the first time it struck him this was not an inconsistency. It was a ripening, a coming into his own. He was, patently, *two people*. In the same moment he knew this, he knew the first one's name. *Florestan*. It needed no explanation. Florestan without doubt. The other side named itself later, tumbling from the pages of a dropped book. A Saint's Day Almanac too near the edge of the table, brushed to the floor by the skirts of an angel, fell open at *Eusebius*. Eusebius, martyred for his nobility of thought, his name day two after Clara's on the calendar. Robert picked up the book trembling: on his fevered days, everything was a sign, and this might as well have come with thunderbolts, choruses, shafts of light. Florestan and Eusebius, he had it now! Both beyond question, and both himself. It certainly explained things. It explained a good deal. Those days when he felt his head was at war with itself, shifting his mood from laughing to crying irrespective of his own wishes – well, they were only to be expected. Perhaps they vied with each other. Perhaps they switched in rapid rotation. Whichever, he knew these twin components were necessary as each other to his seeing, his hearing, his whole existence. Which is to say his *normal state of being*, not madness, as he once feared, before he saw them clearly. Which is to say, he was simply *how he was*. How he *both* was. Ha! And some day these two might fuse more congenially; marry up, as it were, as he did with Clara when they played Schubert four-handed, the two of them side by side on the piano stool. RARO, he would call it – ClaRA RObert; their fusion into the one perfect piece to name his own, perfected self. Florestan, Eusebius, RARO – together, they explained everything. All his striving and present being, his promised future. Lord how clearly he could see things – *everything* – sometimes! He could stand at his window, open the shutters wide and see all the way to Alsace if he tried. All the way to America, the moon, the stars. At peace with himself, his first piece newly published, his sheets stiff with sex, his lungs full of clean German air and his head full of champagne bubbles, Herr Schumann felt stout as Napoleon. How long had it lasted? Two weeks? Three? Then his cock started bleeding, the novel, the opera, the poems, the *études* he'd been writing dried up, and he turned twenty-one. He put Narcissus water on his foreskin and stopped answering the door. He wept. Twenty-one! Draft age! A marker on a road that led only forward, the path behind melting into nothing at all. On bad days, he suspected his youth was finished, his chances were gone, his conscription to some lunatic skirmish on the Prussian border a foregone conclusion: on bad nights, he knew it for sure. Twenty-one. He drank himself senseless, burned candles, developed stomach cramps and a cough. When his mother wrote that Julius, the brother who looked most like father, was coughing too, more-over coughing *blood*, Robert recalled the portrait he'd had painted when the world was at his feet, and took to his bed, terrified. People were falling like skittles in Berlin – cholera, typhus, lord knew what else. Cramps and dysentery came first, then stools like rice-water flaked with bits of intestine. He knew because Wieck told him. Wieck told him other things too, horrible hurtful things about his playing that threatened to drive him mad, but those were the kinds of things Wieck said. To his sons he said worse, and they were children. The Old Man had to be endured. He had to be endured because there was no arguing with him. Because he was the best teacher in Saxony. Most of all just because. Because he was *there*. No matter how confusing the rest of life became, you knew something solid if you knew Wieck. He was a rock, a crag, and Robert was grateful for it. When the rock packed its bags for Paris, then, the shock was palpable. Clara, too. Dear God what was he to trust now? *In six years I will make you a virtuoso to equal Moscheles*, he had said: had he meant it at all? Or had his eyes been on his daughter, meant that prize for her, a girl of twelve, all along? He felt shamed and pitiable suddenly, unable to speak. He had found new lodgings – a young male student could hardly live alone with his pregnant teacher's wife, after all; people would *talk* – helped choose the music they should take. He didn't complain with anything but his eyes and only the girl noticed. *I will miss you, Herr Schumann*, she said as they left. *I will buy you something pretty.* He watched them go, the Chopin pieces he had discovered along with them, went back to his new digs alone. A long walk, time to think. He would reinvent, he thought, leaves blowing up at his face like slaps. He would change his whole direction. Spiteful, he chose a new role-model. Belleville, Clara's nearest rival, moreover a rival with breasts. He bought a new hat, a coat with longer frocking, a finger-stretcher. Four hours a day he practised with his wrists high, his fourth finger weighted to make it strong. For a time it worked. Then it didn't. He didn't stop to think. He added more weights. By the time Clara's accolades were arriving by post, his digit was curling in on itself, numb as a vegetable. The more he read her reviews, the worse it got. Holding the pen as best he could, he wrote to his coughing brother, his mother, his sisters-in-law, pouring out his fears. What if it never got better, if he could no longer play? What were they to say? Mother sent money and Rosalie, sweet Rosalie, Rosalie who married his sniffy brother Carl, came all the way from Schneeberg with a cake. Dr Reuter and Dr Carus and lord knew who came too, but still his finger sickened. It drew towards the centre of his palm, like a spent penis. What, he thought, suddenly horrified, what if it's punishment? A warning? That evening, when Christel arrived with flowers and beer, he wouldn't even open the door. Safer to keep himself and his extremities out of her way, he thought. Till he healed. Till he healed. He had wasted time. He would waste no more. Eusebius would think only lofty thoughts: Florestan would be resolute. There would be no more brooding or late, lost nights. No more wrist-flexing under the sheets. No more dwelling on the debts, the awful letters from mother with the catalogues of disease, blame and fear, no more empty bottles outside the door or fretting about his bastard fingers. The cure for despondency was discipline. Wieck told him that too: Wieck's advice was hard but almost always sound. Always solid. And since his hand stopped him speaking at the keys, he'd write. Not a novel, not an opera, not reviews of concerts, but *music itself*. He'd done it before – all pianists did. Now he'd do it again, but in earnest. And something completely new. Mere months later, when the blossom was back on the cherry trees and the nights no longer began at four o'clock, when Alwin arrived, running – *Herr Schumann, they're coming! They're home* – he was ready. He straightened his neck-tie, adjusted his cuffs. Past the Thomas Church, through the town square, along Grimaisse Lane – he couldn't walk quick enough. His sideburns were longer, his new coat was brushed, and he had music under his arm. His *Opus 2*, his *Papillons*, pinned to perfection under a cover of cherubs, ivy, trailing vines. The hole in his boots was an irrelevance, his hand could be kept out of sight. He had something real to show for himself – for both himselves. He couldn't wait.

*

The new sister, four months old, was big as a cannonball. Clemens didn't know her and Gustav refused her hand. Cousin Pfund and Alwin, Emilie Reichold and mother, Schumann with his head tilted to one side waiting to hear what she had to say. Let Clara tell it, her father said. Don't forget she came too. Let Clara tell the story exactly as she recalls.

Weimar	Erfurt	Gotha
Eisenach	Arnstadt	Cassel
Frankfurt	Darmstadt	Maintz
Paris	Metz	Saarbruck
Frankfurt	Hanau	Fulda

Cold, unsprung coaches and no sleep, the acrid stink of piss-hardened whips and ancient horses, dragging another mile, another mile. Arriving late in the evenings with the towns shut and nothing to see, nothing to eat, almost never a welcome or a porter to carry bags; new rooms with old sheets and the noise of papa snoring in the bed beside hers till morning filled up the window, if there was a window, to see what lay ahead: breakfasts of bread and afternoons of hiring and haggling, demanding and blustering, of contracts, bookings, accounts. She had studied, sung, composed. She had stood by while papa made himself known to music-society presidents, administrators, critics, tuners, dealers, bodice-fitters, clerks, censors, town-officials who took three days to process a request then asked for another signature, another fee. And every day, after her three-mile exercise, she had made trips to hotel ante-rooms, the backrooms of dealers' warehouses, schoolrooms, parlours in rich people's houses to beg an instrument to play till the time came to view the brute they'd provided for the concert. Sometimes she wished she played the violin, the flute, something portable, most times she didn't. Pianists played pianos: this was how it was with her kind. Out-of-tune dustboxes to bought-in Pleyels, they took what was afforded, they played. Pianists gave concerts, that was the correct word, they *gave*, and she had given a great many; in halls little more than barns with not enough light to see by, others in palaces, with Royal Families in matching sets waiting round a piano so patterned with inlays and painted landscapes it seemed an affront to touch it at all. She had played for Goethe with all his hair after eighty-one years, who fetched her cushions and sweets; for Spohr who held her hands and told her they were *treasures from God*; for Mendelssohn and Hiller and Chopin who looked like princes till she saw them bear-fighting, giggling like girls in a salon ante-room; for Paganini, who remembered her and was kind and terrifying and showed her his three new missing teeth; for officials and generals and countless teacup-rattling Philistines, supporters and sniffers, for boors, bores and the merely curious. She had been given jewellery, medals, accolades, keepsakes, locks of hair from lovesick older girls; gold clasps, emerald combs and money. Most of the jewellery was money now too. But this was nothing to say. It wasn't a *story*. It had no polish, no continuity, nothing lofty to its name. What had she done? She had travelled with her father, she had played the piano. She could do nothing but say so – and they laughed. Father too. Relief lightened the air in the room like orange zest.

The things you say, her father smiled. He shook his head in a manner indicative of incredulity. *Ce n'est pas dire!*

And he told it himself, as he knew he would all along.

In Weimar, they were snobs. Gotha housed only ignoramuses and farmers. Eisenach and Frankfurt were miserable beyond belief. And Paris? Paris stunk. One tiny jug of water for washing in the morning and no more all day! Clementine's brother, however, couldn't be faulted, had even drawn an official portrait – Clara with no waist at all and her neck bare – that earned a few thaler *thank the Lord*. A new dress for *each appearance* and everything white, flat-soled shoes, only fresh flowers or seed-pearls for her hair which should *always* be up etc – the list Eduard had drawn up beggared belief. For himself, three pairs of yellow kid gloves, as many white stocks and half a dozen shirts *in one week alone!* Add Laundry bills, hairdressing, wraps, and shawls and one wondered why people put their daughters to touring at all. Salons were uncongenial; reeking of smoke, stale cologne, and Frenchmen. Programmes that didn't start till after ten at night then lumped everything together like stew – Spaniards lying full-length on the table with flowers between their teeth, chicken-faced sopranos with their dresses cut so low their nipples showed, cigar-scented divorcées with jaws like boxers – he'd seen it all. And the crush! Four hundred crammed into Kalkbrenner's tiny front rooms to hear Chopin play for fifteen minutes! And that hellish piano! What was it like, *Clärchen?* Eh? Kalkbrenner's instrument? A bag of bones, that's what, a disgrace. Listen, in Weimar, Goethe said our Clara had the strength of six boys.

Six boys. And how she needed it in Paris! Stiff actions, stiffer pedals – and all the same. You don't play these French brutes, you fight them! You fight to win! But we did what we could, eh *Clärchen*? We showed stout Saxon courage. And the true connoisseurs recognized our efforts. Spohr was kindness itself, Pixis and Mendelssohn. And Paganini, who recognizes talent when he hears it, did what he could. Kalkbrenner, on the other hand, was a raging snob. *In Paris we love Beethoven,* he said. *Programme her without it and you will reap little here.* Ha! Do you know what I said? *She plays Beethoven as she plays Schubert – at home and not for the mass until I say so, sir.* Until I say so.

He sighed. For the first time since he'd begun, he leaned back in his chair. Of course it was a regret not to have spoken to Chopin. The avant-garde should stick together. He slackened his collar. Then the young man is naturally reticent.

From where Clara watched, he looked thin, tired. The way he had looked for the past while. She recalled his insistence she wear the same dresses, sometimes not washed, for successive towns, his incredulity that things should have to be different for Paris. She recalled Eduard, who didn't look like Clementine at all, who didn't balk at her father's French or let him know the full rates for their expenses. Most of all, she recalled her father in the hateful salons, rooms full of stuffed leopards and embroideries, their walls so loaded with paintings and peacock feathers they might fall down, rooms that rustled with deafening whispers – his accent, the passé colour of his coat, Chopin thought him stupid and Kalkbrenner thought him a boor – while she forced herself to think in German, to block it, to not hear at all. Not knowing or caring, he led her to a piano, his velvet-covered arm under hers solid as oak. Past all eyes, sweating in his overtight shoes, his arm under hers solid as truth. *Artists are your own,* he whispered; *be in awe of none. As for the rest? Remember that none of these high-born sorts, no matter how much they think of themselves, not one of them can do what we can do.* And she played. She recalls she played. She played very well. And she recalled the poet Heine and his companion, a man with no name, knowing nothing of the applause of Weimar and Cassel, talking out loud as though she was insensible, as though she had not a word of French to her name: *Poor child! It seems as though she could tell us all a long story woven out of joy and pain, yet what does she know? Music.* Her face felt hot recalling it even now. They had endured it all for four concerts in small rooms, the fearful sense of being a tolerably amusing entertainment. When word of cholera made him pack their bags, she was almost glad. Through Metz and Saarbruck, swathed in flannel, a heaviness grew in her stomach, her head. In Frankfurt, another name for hell, she woke with night-sweats and her bones ached: no more than a passing chill but her father prayed and his face was grey. Shortly after, she bled. There was no hiding it. Her father said nothing but he stripped her bed and demanded fresh sheets, let her patch herself with rags as best she could. This was something that happened, she knew, it was not an illness. Sharing the room for much longer, however, was unbearable. As soon as she could dress herself, a cheap overnight coach and four had rattled them home. None of this was lofty either, but it was what stuck, what made the deepest ridges in her memory. Applause and performance she took for granted, merely something one did or did not do, yet they were what counted. They were triumph, success, the Real Story. She must learn to refocus her priorities, *then* she'd have something to say. Lessons. It was all lessons. To learn them better, she begged tiredness and left the company in the sitting-room, put on her oldest pinafore and looked for something to do in the kitchen. There was always something to do in the kitchens and Lise gave her salts and vinegars, soda and lemon juice, a recipe for metal paste. That made, worked. Her hair scraped back, a necklace worth 30 Reichsthaler in gold round her neck, she set herself to polishing knives. Next time, she thought, scouring, when papa said, *Tell Dr Carus how Paganini played, Clärchen; what Goethe said; what that rather stuck-up fellow Heine looks like; what refined manners Mendelssohn, the son of a Jewish banker, can display:* she would say something dazzling. The reflection of her face appeared in the blades as she worked, her lips parted as though ready to speak. She was Clara Wieck. These hands had been kissed by adult men. The great, the good, and the very rich indeed had looked her in the eye and she had looked straight back. One day, she thought, buffing till she broke sweat, she'd say something dazzling. *Ce n'est pas dire*. She'd say something to surprise them all.

In the room overhead, Schumann stayed on. He told Wieck about his struggles with Dorn, his medical advice, his plans for a newspaper and the pressing need for musical activism. When Wieck went to bed, Schumann stayed still. No one moved him on. He was a trusted friend of the family, as good as the Old Man's son. Music was playing somewhere on the other side of the street and the candles were down. With no one expecting him, nothing immediate pressing on his mind, Robert lit a cigar. Being a virtuoso was a thankless, hellish life, it seemed. For what joy it brought, Little Clara was welcome to it. He blew smoke into the darkness, watched it drift. He'd write, perhaps, take up cello. The tip of his cigar a beacon. He'd compose.

Geoff Dyer

The Despair of Art Deco

The only time I have ever seen a dead body was in South Beach, Miami, in the heart of the Art Deco district. It is possible that seeing a dead body there has had an undue influence on my view of Art Deco; but it is also possible that Art Deco has had an undue influence on my view of the dead body. The two are related, I think.

We flew to Miami from boring Nassau and got a bus to South Beach. It was a Sunday, the sidewalks were crammed with visitors, but finding a hotel was not difficult because it was a Sunday and visitors who had come for the weekend had already checked out of their hotels. We checked in at the Beachcomber, a nice-looking place on Collins in the heart of the Art Deco area. That is a pretty meaningless remark, I know. Art Deco, after all, means nice-looking, or, more exactly, not-as-nice-as-it-looks. Our room at the Beachcomber, for example, did not look quite as nice as the façade of the Beachcomber but it still looked pretty nice. An Art Deco lampshade bathed the Art Deco sheets in an amber Art Deco glow. When we drew back the curtains the Art Deco spell was broken. The window was cracked, grimy, and the surge of dusty sunlight revealed a damp patch spreading across the carpet from the bathroom wall almost to the centre of the room. Then a mouse raced across the marshy carpet and squeezed, with difficulty, under the skirting board of the cramped and mouldy bathroom. Dazed stood on a chair and said with – I promise – no trace of emotion, 'Eek! A mouse!'

'I'll deal with it,' I said.

'You mean you'll try to get a discount on the room?'

'Exactly.'

I went out to the pony-tailed fellow at reception and asked if we could change rooms because there was a mouse in our room, in the room we were in at the moment, and we would prefer a room without a mouse or, if no other room was available—

'Welcome to the tropics,' he said. He didn't shrug. There was no need. His *voice* shrugged. As it happens, we had just *come* from the tropics where we had not seen a single mouse and so I said, 'This is not the tropics.' Although the mouse was not a problem for me, I went on, my girlfriend was 'freaked out' – I used that exact phrase – by it.

'Whatever,' he said, handing me a key to a room on the first floor. 'Take a look at that one.'

It was nice, I said when I went back down, but it was not made up. Next he offered to upgrade us to a larger room, room 15, if I remember rightly. That was nice, too, but somebody had been smoking in there, I explained, and it smelt smoky.

'Try 13,' he said, handing me another key. I was beginning to wonder if any rooms were occupied. As it happens, 13 *was* – by a woman, French, I think, sitting on the toilet. This really baffled him. According to his computer, room 13 was definitely empty, but he suggested I try 6. Six was empty, mouse-less, smoke-less, made-up, unoccupied, actually nicer than where we were. An upgrade was as good as a discount. Fine, I said. In the meantime he had sent someone (who? As far as I could tell he was the only person around) up to 13 and there was no one there.

'You must have gone to the wrong room,' he said.

'Then how could I have opened the door?' I shot back.

'Some keys work for more than one room.'

'Ah.' We moved to 6 where we got stoned on this mad skunk. Then we went out, for a walk, to buy smoothies, to experience the Art Deco experience for ourselves. Although we had just booked in to an Art Deco hotel we kept stopping off at other Art Deco hotels to see if we would have been better off in another Art Deco hotel. We compared prices and quality ('the price–quality axis, as it were,' I said). There were several other hotels we could have stayed in but, overall, we had quite a good deal.

'We could have got a better deal,' I summarized. 'But we don't have the worst possible deal. Obviously, we could have paid more and stayed at a better place.'

'Or paid less and stayed at a worse place.'

'But we haven't found a place that was more expensive *and* worse.'

'And is that really what we're looking for?'

'In a sense yes. For peace of mind.'

'But there's always the chance that in looking for a place that is more expensive and worse we might find a place that is better and cheaper.'

'Thereby destroying any chance of ever achieving peace of mind.'

'Perhaps we shouldn't look at any more hotels, then.'

Except that's what you come to South Beach for: to see hotels. The hotels – the Art Deco hotels – are the attraction. Effectively, the Art Deco experience is the hotel experience. Staying in hotels is a side-effect of wanting to see them. In a place with so many hotels, it is the residents who are the tourists, who are not at home. So we continued to look at hotels but we refrained from enquiring about vacancies and rates. Except at the Mermaid Guest House which was a little more expensive than the Beachcomber but infinitely lovelier. Much of the Art Deco architecture in South Beach is actually a derivative or variant of Art Deco known as Tropical Deco; the Mermaid takes this tendency a little further, away from Deco towards Tropical. We both wished we were staying there – having come from the mouse-less tropics, it would have lent a continuity to our trip – but since we had already booked into the Beachcomber there was, Dazed said, 'no use crying over spilled milk'.

'It's funny isn't it, people say that, but of course that's exactly what makes you want to cry. The fact that it's spilled. Why would you cry over *un*spilled milk?'

'You don't like milk though do you, darling?'

'I like it in smoothies,' I said.

After the Mermaid we didn't ask about vacancies and rates at any other hotels. We didn't enquire at the Victor on Ocean Front Drive because this vast, gleaming white building was unoccupied: utterly vacant, a site of abandoned meaning, in fact, unless the provision of accommodation is considered a side-effect of the Art Deco effect in which case it was a site of purified meaning. With windows boarded-up and painted over it looked, Dazed said, 'like Rachel Whiteread's Art Deco sequel to "House".'

'What? Like "Hotel"?'

We were still really blasted from the skunk we had smoked earlier. A little further on, still on Ocean Front, a guy with drive-by shades asked Dazed where she'd got her hair braided. Dazed told him Cat Island. He was asking, really, on behalf of his girlfriend who was blonde and Russian. He was black and Cuban. They were a very modern couple but they were the product also of a long-standing political alliance. They asked us to take their picture in front of the house – mansion, actually – we were standing in front of.

'You know what house this is?' the Cuban said.

'No.'

'Versace's house,' he said. 'This is where he was gunned down.'

Dazed handed their camera back and they walked off. I studied the bloodless sidewalk. Dazed said, 'This is where he was gunned down.'

'Yes,' I said. 'This is where he was gunned down.'

'Do you remember what you were doing on the night he was gunned down?'

'People are always getting gunned down,' I said. 'No. What were you doing?'

'When?'

'On the night he was gunned down.'

'Who?'

'Specifically, Versace, but anyone really. Anyone who was gunned down.'

'Malcom X was gunned down wasn't he, darling?'

'Yes, although he wasn't nearly so well-known as a fashion designer.'

'But those glasses he wore have become very fashionable. You see lots of people wearing them. You have a pair don't you, darling?'

'Yes. And you know the really weird thing?'

'What?'

'They are made by Versace.'

'That is *so* creepy.'

While we were having this conversation quite a few people were photographed on the spot where Versace was gunned down. I was one of them: Dazed took a picture of me with the disposable camera we had bought in Nassau. Until we had done this we found it difficult to tear ourselves away from the spot, the spot where people were having their pictures taken, the spot where Versace had been gunned down.

It was time, Dazed suggested, to refresh ourselves with a smoothie. We sucked our smoothies – mine had a protein supplement – sitting on a wall by the beach. I made notes for an essay on Art Deco I knew I would never get round to writing.

It is not accurate, I wrote, *to say that a shabbiness lurks behind the façade of Art Deco: Art Deco is the façade. Art Deco is the most visible of architectural styles, arranged entirely for the eye – it's in colour! – rather than to be* inhabited. *Art Deco buildings are inhabited, of course, but whereas, from the outside, they look extraordinary, inside, the experience is fairly ordinary. But this is why the Art Deco style is so alluring.*

The block of flats where I have lived in Brixton, London, since the early '80s is, essentially, a utilitarian, age of austerity version of Art Deco, without the trappings of Art Deco – without the things that make it Art Deco. These could be added with next to no effort and at minimal expense and the building could be transformed into an Art Deco block, whereupon this area of flats would become as pleasing to the eye as South Beach. The flats themselves would remain the same – but how lovely it would be to feel that we lived in the Art Deco area of Brixton rather than in a shabby block of flats. We could even call it South Beach, Brixton.

Twilight was falling. The sand dulled. We began walking back to our hotel. Pale in the afternoon sunlight, neon – purple, glowing, green – was coming into its own. The sky grew ink-dark.

Back at the Beachcomber it turned out that we were not the only ones to have changed rooms. The mouse had come too. It was in the wastepaper basket, eating dinner. We preferred to think that it was the same mouse because that was preferable, I said, to admitting that the hotel was actually 'a vermin-infested rat-hole'.

'You can't call it a rat-hole,' said Dazed.

'Why not?'

'Because a mouse is not a rat.'

'But a mouse is a vermin isn't it?'

'I don't know what a vermin is.'

'Mice and rats are vermin.'

'Are you a vermin, darling?'

'And since rats and mice are vermin a mouse is, in a sense, a species of rat.'

'Am *I* a vermin, darling?'

'So, logically, it is absolutely accurate to call a place infested with mice a rat-hole.'

'It is a rat-hole isn't it, darling?'

That night I woke up several times, hearing rustling and scurrying. In the morning there were mouse droppings on the spare bed and the mouse had chewed through Dazed's make-up bag.

'Look,' she said, holding up a copy of our slightly nibbled guide to the Bahamas. 'It chewed off more than it could bite.'

'D'you think it might eat my computer?' I said.

'D'you think it might eat us?'

Before going out we stashed our belongings away on high shelves in the wardrobe, out of harm's way, so it would be harder for the mouse to eat them.

'The mouse is terrorizing us, isn't it?' said Dazed as we locked our room with a key that, in all probability, opened other rooms as well.

'It really is.'

'It's gnawing away at our self-esteem.'

By the time we had breakfast it was already hot as anything. The sky was a sharp blue. I had a seven-dollar haircut from a Cuban barber who sang while he worked, paying almost no attention to the job – cutting my hair – in hand. At a spacious bookstore on Lincoln Dazed bought a copy of *Miami* by Joan Didion.

'Good *choice*,' I said.

'Was it, darling?'

The sun ricocheted off the walls and sidewalk. Even though neither of us is interested in cars there were lots of interesting cars to look at. Without any warning Dazed asked what I would do if she threw herself in front of one of these cars. I said I didn't know, but my general policy is not to get involved. We went into record stores and clothes stores and picked up flyers for trance parties that had taken place the day before we arrived. Every clothes store played trance but we didn't find any clothes we wanted or any parties we could go to. We just walked around really, looking at hotels and flyers, buying smoothies, living the Art Deco life, getting stoned on this mad skunk. Then a hustler with wayward hair and unkempt eyes accosted us.

'D'you speak English?' he wanted to know.

'To a very high standard,' I said.

'Could you do me a favour?'

'Almost certainly not.' For a moment he looked totally crest-fallen. Then he went on his way without even saying, 'Fuck you.' In its way it was one of the most satisfying exchanges of my life. He could have been the risen Christ for all we cared.

What else? We watched some beach volleyball and then Dazed borrowed a guy's blades – her feet are quite big – and bladed for a while. She didn't even ask. He *offered*. I sat talking to him, just stuff to say while he swigged semi-skimmed milk from a carton and we both watched Dazed gliding and turning on his blades. After blading she wanted to go back to the hotel because it was so hot and the heat was getting to her. I walked with her, back to the Beachcomber, and then strolled on regardless.

In the course of my stroll I became convinced that The Gap, on Collins, was designed to look like an Art Deco whale, some kind of fish anyway. One window served for an eye, three more for teeth. It even had fins and gills. I stared at it for a while, unsure if this was just the skunk talking. Speaking of talking, I wished Dazed had been there so we could have had one of our so-called 'conversations' about the whale, about whether it was a whale or not.

Further on, one side of the street was cordoned off with black and yellow film: POLICE LINE DO NOT CROSS. A crowd, of which I was a part, gathered. Something had happened. You could tell something had happened by the way we were all standing round asking what happened. There was an ambulance, several police cars. A photographer was taking photographs, standing over . . . the body! I say body but I could see only the feet of the body, the grubby white socks. The rest of the body was hidden from view by bushes.

'What happened?' I said to the guy next to me. He had a tattoo of a washing machine on his arm.

'Suicide.'

'Oh my.'

'A seventy-two-year-old woman. She jumped.'

'Shit. Hey, I like the tattoo, by the way.'

'Thanks.'

'Is it any particular kind of washing machine?'

'Oh it's like, just a general model, I guess.'

'What floor did she jump from?'

'Fourteenth.'

'So, roughly speaking, that would be between the thirteenth and the fifteenth, right?' I said. I began counting from the ground floor up but soon lost track. The situation was made more complex by the way that, in America, the first floor is actually the ground floor and the second is the first and so on. The fourteenth was two-thirds of the way up.

'Happens all the time,' the guy with the tattoo of a washing machine on his arm said.

'Does it?'

'It's the heat.'

'What?'

'Drives people nuts.'

'What does?'

'The heat.'

'Yes,' I said. 'I can imagine,' but I was also thinking that Rome is just as hot as Miami and people don't throw themselves off fourteenth-floor balconies there.

'Drives people nuts,' he repeated.

'Perhaps Art Deco generates a kind of despair,' I said. 'Is that possible?'

'Anything's possible,' he said. Across the road the photographer was taking photographs of the body. In fact the whole scene looked like one of those staged photographs of the dead by Nick Waplington. I had never seen a dead body before and now I was seeing one. Or seeing a pair of socks anyway. I was not sure that counted. To really see a dead body perhaps you have to see the mashed head, the bloody face, but all I could see were the grubby white socks of the dead woman whose body would soon be zipped up in a body bag.

Back at the hotel Dazed was asleep on the bed and had not been eaten by the mouse which, I had to concede, was actually 'the mice', several of whom scurried away when I entered the room. I took a shower in the shoddy bathroom and then told Dazed about the dead woman. She was very sympathetic, reassuring me that, although I had only seen her socks, it still counted: I could say that I had seen a dead body.

That evening we ate in the same restaurant we had eaten in the night before. In the morning I took Dazed to the spot, the spot where the woman had jumped. Something about South Beach urges you to do this, to visit the spots where people have been gunned down or thrown themselves off balconies.

'It's a place,' Dazed said, 'with a remarkable capacity to generate sites of instant pilgrimage.' I could see now that the old lady had been extremely considerate, jumping into a recess, set back slightly from the sidewalk, so that she would not land on anyone. There was no stain or anything, no dent. Dazed took a picture of me but I was a little nervous standing there in case someone else came down on top of me.

'Hurry up,' I said.

'Why?'

'This is a part of the world where people fall through the air at speed,' I said. After Dazed had taken the picture we crossed the road and I saw that the balconies on one side of the building were all empty except for chairs on which no one sat. Dazed said that the building was flying at half-mast and I understood what she meant.

We looked at more hotels, enjoyed some more smoothies. Later in the day I saw an old woman hobbling along through the swarming, tanned bodies of the fit and young, the stoned trancers and tattooed bladers, the gay men all pumped up with protein supplements and power boosts, the pierced, slim, salad-eating women for whom Art Deco was an incentive to display and not a source of shoddy despair that could drive you to suicide. I admired the old woman's tenacity, the way she kept going, kept putting one arthritic foot in front of another. She smiled at me and I realized that it was the same woman I had seen yesterday, lying on the sidewalk. I was glad that she had made such a speedy recovery. I knew it was her because of her socks which were grubby, white, unbloodied.

Helen Ivory

Why I Don't Use Bubbles

It is enough to consider
the falling and rising of the moon
and the coming and going of the tide,
without considering
the sea changes present within myself.

Take last week for instance.
I was relaxing in a milk and juniper bubble bath
when a vision appeared before me.
It took shape as a bubble that rose
to the surface of the bath,
and wafted across the room.

Although the warmth of the water surrounded me,
I felt myself to be inside the bubble,
pushing at the coolness of its walls.
I could not change direction
and found myself careering towards the towel rail.

The bubble burst on impact,
and I got out of the bath to see where I had gone.
I scoured the floor, behind the sink,
even lifted the loo seat to see if I'd fallen down there.
I search for me every day now,
and sometimes, when it is very quiet,
I can feel the crackle of bubbles
nestling inside my skull.

Peter Robinson

Equivocal Isle

'Die Liebe hat einen Triumph und der Tod hat einen . . .'

— Ingeborg Bachmann

From out the shallows, our small craft,
its motor idling under cliffs'
wave-cut sandstone hieroglyphics,
expertly is left to drift.

By way of a narrow, rocky strait
with pine tree roots like varicose veins
and natural bonsai on each ledge
(our hull fitted tightly through it)
we enter almost open sea.

Up ahead, as fresh wind lifts,
an island on the skyline,
an island bearded with pine tree tufts
echoes the dark in its design.

A few outlying rocks stand guard,
and the salt-white lighthouse at its point
conjures an offing, ambivalent
urges to approach or veer shoreward
in brightness on the water.

Seagulls take snacks from outstretched hands;
they hang above the stern and cry.

Love triumphs over nobody
and, for that matter, neither does death —

its cypress isle, stark temple, calm sea,
punt, pale-shrouded soul: its kitsch.

Death triumphs over nobody.

Off in the lanes, ships roll and pitch.
The craft's outboard accelerates
on stiffening swell where seagulls scrike,
that equivocal island's silhouette
diminishing in our wake.

Lawrence Sail

A Flourish

What if it were not at all
as painters once thought, the resurrection –
no marble lids flipped up, no smart
unsurprised bodies somehow jerked
back to the vertical ?

Suppose it instead an abandonment, almost
casual, in springtime, all the cars
left on the sunlit roads, their doors
wide as open wingcases, engines
quietly ghosting.

Their owners having simply drifted over
to the cowslip kingdom of undropped keys,
into meadows where they kneel at flowers,
or beechwoods where they stroll across thresholds
of light and cover.

Here the orchid rises from the cross,
spilling droplets of blood from its stem,
and beneath the trees unlettered bluebells
wash onwards for ever, leaving the eye
at an utter loss.

Everything merges here – A and O
are as one, from Ophelia's early purples
to Ariel happily listening for owls;
and the little fritillary's chequered shade
is pure art nouveau.

And God? Would hardly, perhaps, believe
how simple his own life had become

on the far side of the trumpets, having
only to budget for continuance and devise
new sports and variations on love.

Matt Simpson

A Great-Grandmother

The awful daring of a moment's surrender.

Sarah Jane labours a squeaky mangle, squeezing
              sheets, till flannel
yields its greyness and, like crushed slush, suddenly
              burns white.

Above her, a clothes-rack tilts and sags, pulleys yearn
              with the weight
of children's things. She wobbles the wheel as if to
              croak out tunes.

'Where did you get that hat? Where *did* you get that
              hat?' Sarah Jane
doesn't know today will bring home agony. Not yet.
              Has no thought

what part she plays in history, how out there in the
              big wide world
they're finding things to change us all – X-rays,
              wireless telegraphy,

the cinematograph. Today is dolly-tub and Reckitt's
              Blue, slap-slap
of shirt on washboard; her routine. She's thinking of
              my great-aunts –

Florrie, Sally, Bella, Rubina – and slows the creaking
              rollers up
to listen out for them. They have been told! They
              have been told!

Where are George and Jimmy? Watching men play
          pitch-and-toss
against a wall or gazing down the headlong brew at
          the great

business of the river, its clutter of masts? Today (not
          yet, not yet)
is history spilling blood on cobblestones. Rubina
          Emily's.

I'm imagining things I know are tight in fact. The
          truth is these girls,
despite mother's orders, pushed out Rubina in her
          pram –

Florrie 8, Sally 4, and Bella 3 – with Rubina Emily
          just 14 months –
her pram clattering fatally out of control down
          Everton Brow. This,

with other things, explains the tight-lipped family I
          grew up in,
a great-grandmother, Sarah Jane, hands red-raw with
          suds, distraught

at her front door, a moustachio'd policeman asking
          names, and three
great-aunts shaking like skeletons in a cupboard
          underneath the stairs.

Alison Booth

The Clouds

I

Through the window I see the pale blue early morning sky, fringed by the long grey-green leaves of the eucalyptus tree. The eucalyptus leaves droop, like those of a willow tree. There is no breeze yet. The trunk of the tree is only a few feet away from my window, too close to the building, my husband would have said.

That tree would not have survived so close to our house.

The stalks of the leaves are glowing, reddish-brown in the early morning sunlight; the leaves glisten; small gum-nuts have formed from the last of the blossoms.

I owe it to my daughter that I can see this tree. She insisted on it. She made a scene the day we arrived here, months ago now, when it looked as if I would have a room with no outlook. Once, such a scene would have embarrassed me. Not any more. I am indifferent to fuss and bother. I do admire my daughter for her energy. She felt bad that I was coming here. She felt that the least she could do was to offer me a tree and a wide expanse of sky, as recompense. I could see the blind suffering love behind her gesture. She was prepared to begin battles, she was willing to wage wars, so that I should have this view. The matron was no match. She put up a feeble opposition, but she was soon vanquished by the force of my daughter's character, and her quick way with words. My daughter is not above using the magic of her position; now all the world knows that she is a barrister. The end justifies the means, she always says. That is not what I taught her.

But on this occasion I am grateful.

All autumn I have watched what I can see of the eucalyptus tree from my bed. I am hermetically sealed in here. All I can see of the outside world is the sky defined by the window-frame and the eucalyptus tree, the measure of my days here. There is such variety in the colours that I see. Each morning I watch the colours of the sky as the sun rises, each morning, after they have woken me, and sponged me in their too brutal fashion, too early, too energetic, too hearty. The sky glows fresh each daybreak, a new beginning, but not for me. Each day I wonder if this will be the last time I see the early morning sky, and each evening I hope it will be the last time that I see the sun setting.

The minutes pass. The sky is now a brilliant blue. I dive into its extraordinary depths, through the spaces between the dark leaves, I lose myself in the intensity of the sky, the sea, the ocean. I hear the distant sound of the surf on the shoreline, a continual murmur. But it is really only the hum of the late morning traffic on the motorway, a quarter of a mile away.

Now there are new sounds: the chattering of voices in the corridor outside my room, the squeaking of sneakers, the clack of high heels, the sounds of the late morning tidal wave of visitors; for me only one visitor, I hope only one.

At last, here is the footfall of the one I have been waiting for, my visitor for this morning, my ration. My beloved granddaughter Katie. Her step is staccato; she is light on her feet, and quick. She always wears the little leather boots that she bought with her birthday money. These leather boots, her first pair, bring her more joy than she will ever get from all her future purchases of shoes. I wish her a long lifetime of fine shoes, a lifetime of Italian leather and gentleness. She comes tip-tap down the corridor to see me. She bounds into the room, she leans over the bed to kiss me, her soft curly brown hair brushing my lips as she kisses my cheeks, first one cheek, then the other, mwa-mwa, a gentle butterfly touch.

II

Grandma's lying on the bed, looking frail and small, and very faraway, although she's looking up at me with her sky-blue eyes. She's got no spare flesh left on her face now. It's stripped down to the bare bones of her skull. She has the most beautiful bone structure. I'll draw her face, next drawing class. The sharp angles, the high cheekbones, the fine straight nose, the strong arch of bone above her eye sockets. From her jawbone loose folds of skin hang around her neck. She's tried to conceal these with a pale lavender chiffon scarf. Or maybe that's for protection from the cold, which she feels everywhere, even on the hottest day.

I bend down to kiss her, a kiss for each cheek. I smell the faint odour of the drugs they give her, overlaid by the cologne on the lace hanky she's clutching in her hand. She's not supposed to have any jewellery here, but she's wearing, next to her wedding ring, her enormous golden sapphire ring. She bought this for herself on her eightieth birthday. That surprised us all, especially my grandfather. That was nearly three years ago now, just before my fifteenth birthday.

My grandmother's white hair is still soft and fluffy, the remains of the perm I did for her just before she went into hospital. Her hair grows really slowly.

'You look nice,' I say to her.

'I look awful,' she says. Her voice is wistful though. It contains an appeal. I regret my comment. But now she smiles at me.

'I've brought you some flowers.' I show her my cone of newspaper containing a bunch of crimson roses. I know these are her favourite. 'I picked them from our garden this morning.'

I take the empty vase on her bedside table to the basin outside and fill it with water, and then I return to arrange the roses.

'Very artistic,' my grandmother says when I have finished. Her voice is weak this morning. 'They remind me of Eddie.'

Eddie was my grandfather, who died six months ago. My grandmother has lately abandoned the practice of referring to members of our family by the name I would use. Instead, she uses their first names. It's as if she's recognized that I'm grown up now.

'Though of course Eddie never picked flowers,' she continues. 'In fact, I don't think he liked the garden much. And he hated trees.'

I wonder if I should change the subject. I don't want my grandmother to get depressed. I sit down on the hard vinyl chair next to the bed. It's the vulgar sort that squeaks when you sit on it and squeaks if you move.

'I was in charge of the roses,' my grandmother says. 'Eddie just sprayed them for aphids at the appointed time.'

'That's what Dad does.'

'For sixty years.'

'Dad's not been doing it for quite so long.'

'Eddie didn't really like roses. He said they were like over-ripe fruit. Slightly repellent.'

'That's what I like about them. Over-lush.'

'Flamboyant,' she adds.

'Rococo.' I move in my chair, and the vinyl squeaks. We both laugh.

'How is college?' she asks.

I tell her in great detail what I've been doing at art school. I try to make my monologue lively, but she doesn't seem to be taking it all in. I continue anyway until I've brought her right up to the present with my doings, and then we sit in silence. It must be awful for her being stuck in this bed all the time at the mercy of her visitors and the hospital staff. When she shuts her eyes, I examine her face again. In another few decades my mother will be like that too. And after her, it will be me. I don't want to end up in a hospital bed, waiting to die, with no future and no hope. I want to die unexpectedly, like my grandfather Eddie. At an advanced age, with no warning. Until then, I want to live life to the full.

'Don't you work all the time, like your mother,' my grandmother says suddenly, as if reading my mind. She opens her eyes again, and looks at me intently, as if willing me to have a good time.

'I'll try to,' I say. 'I'm very ambitious on that score.'

We don't talk any more. I just sit here with her, and we watch the leaves on the tree outside the window. The leaves are moving slightly in the breeze; the sky beyond is such a bright cloudless blue. I'll open the sun roof on the drive to college.

Soon it's time for me to go. I hear the trolleys advancing up the corridor, and the hearty chatter of the women who serve lunch. It's Grandma's turn now. She doesn't like to be watched while she is eating, and anyway I have a lecture to go to. I kiss her again.

'I love you lots,' I say. I always say this, in case I never see her again. She squeezes my arm, but she doesn't say anything. The older generation of my family can't articulate their feelings, but I don't let that bother me. It's not their practice to express their love in words, but that doesn't mean it's not there. My grandmother smiles up at me. She looks even more tired than usual now.

I escape from the room, and down the corridor. I run down the stairs, two at a time, and out to the car park. My father's lent me his car for the day. I open the sun roof. I want to feel my freedom, and the wind in my hair.

III

My granddaughter has gone now, skipping lightly off. She told me where she was going, but I cannot remember what she said. She always puts on a bright face, a brave front, concealing her vulnerability with a wide smile. Although I cannot remember what she spoke about today, her lively voice is still with me, her gentle murmuring about her doings, her plans. Her future, which I shall never see. I hope she has a wonderful time in store for her, my beautiful young granddaughter.

The hospital staff come and go; I try to ignore them.

I look out of my window at the sky. It is throbbing with an intense blue light, throbbing like my pain. The sky is alive. Bits of it are moving, even though there are no clouds. But I know that it is only an illusion; my eyes are playing tricks on me again. I hold my hand up against the sky, the way I used to do when I was a child. I idly lift my hand up to the sunlight so I can watch the edges of my fingers glow pinkly against the bright background, and see the skeleton of my hand, the bones dark against the light. My hands have changed shape: the bones are twisted, distorted, so ugly.

It is a lifetime since I was a child.

The pain has receded now. I think I have eaten my lunch, but

I cannot remember what it was. The nurse must have given me an injection.

Or perhaps it was my granddaughter.

Time is distorted too; the minutes are either stationary, or vanish in great lumps. I feel now as if I am floating on a great soft white cloud, like one of those I see sometimes through my window. But the cloud is not like the ones you see from aeroplanes, insubstantial illusions of water vapour that would not offer any means of support. The cloud I am floating on is like an eiderdown quilt covered in white material; it is like the one my parents used to have. So soft. It is the eiderdown in which my mother wrapped me, all those years ago, when I was a small child ill with pneumonia.

I hear my mother speaking on the telephone downstairs, her clear voice carrying up the stairs and through my delirium: 'Isabel has pneumonia,' she is saying to some unknown caller.

I am terrified. I am too young to die. I climb out of my bed, but I cannot move far, my limbs are leaden and will not respond to what my brain is commanding. So I lie down on the floor in the middle of the room. That is where my mother finds me later, minutes, aeons later.

'What are you doing?' she hisses as she bends over me.

'People die of pneumonia,' I say, curling up into a foetal position.

'You're not going to do that,' she decrees.

She scoops me up in her arms and carries me into her bedroom. She lies me on the bed while she spreads out the great soft white eiderdown quilt that is kept neatly folded up at the foot of my parents' bed. She rolls me up in the quilt. Then she carries me, wrapped in the soft white cocoon, back to my bedroom, and stays with me until I fall asleep. She remains with me afterwards as well. I am aware, as I drift into and out of consciousness, of her presence there next to my bed, her cool hand on mine, a damp sponge on my forehead, her warm loving presence around me.

In this dreaming state, half awake, half conscious, all time is becoming an illusion. The minutes and the hours go by as if a great soft white cloud is being divided into thick slices; but the slicing is to no avail, for the cloud keeps on re-forming as a whole, no matter how it is cut. Nothing can stop the forces of cohesion, or maybe of regeneration. I lie floating, drifting out of myself. I am suspended above myself, dissociated, detached, and free.

IV

My mother is asleep. I look down at her, in her hospital bed. Her lower jaw has fallen slightly open. She is not wearing her teeth, and her lips have sunk in. It is hard to look dignified without any teeth. She is propped up on three pillows, but she has slipped off to one side. The nurses have not been watching her properly. She does not look comfortable. The flesh has fallen off her face in these last few months; her face looks like a skull. The loss of flesh has, strangely, been accompanied by a loss of skin. The thin brown skin that used to be so white is now tightly stretched across the fine bones of her face. Only her jowls are furrowed and slack.

She will be gone soon; I hope she goes soon. I cannot bear her pain.

The nursing sister says that my mother will not last much longer.

'It's only a matter of time', the sister says.

'How much time?' I ask.

'Hours, days, weeks.' She adds that she cannot commit, but she does not think it will be months. I know this, of course. I spoke to the doctor on the telephone yesterday.

I cannot bear to see my mother lying here in this cot, a travesty of the human being she once was.

What will my life be like without the security of my mother's presence? She has always loved me, even at my most unbearable. She forms a barrier that stands between me and my own death.

My mother did not want to grow old like this. She wanted an end with dignity. She wanted my father to push her off a cliff, she used to say, when she got too old to manage. She would have wanted my father to follow her off too, lemming-fashion. But she stopped saying this when she began to get frail, just before she started to use her stick.

I sometimes thought she might have left my father about then, if she had had the strength, because he had not pushed her off a cliff, because he would never push her off a cliff.

My father told me once that my mother was the only woman he had ever been in love with. And yet he was never one to show her his love by a grand extravagant gesture, the sort of gesture she would have appreciated. Like buying her a golden sapphire ring on her eightieth birthday. Or bringing her a bunch of crimson red roses, like the ones that Katie picked for her this morning.

But some time ago my father bought my mother a rose bush. I witnessed the way in which she forced his hand then. It was the day after the doctors had made their prognosis, and about a month before she moved in here. I had driven them both to the local nursery, which does the Devonshire teas they both loved. The tea-room is at the back of a large conservatory, housing perfect plants quite unsuited to our climate. The plants competed for our attention – great splashes of improbable pink, red and purple flowers, against well-fed glossy dark leaves. My mother and I shuffled between the pots; I held her arm, and she also used her stick. Even with that support, it was obviously painful for her to walk; our progress was uneven. My father followed close behind, ready to catch my mother if she fell. She stopped suddenly in front of a new variety of rose.

'I should like you to buy me that rose.' She leant on her stick, and swivelled around to fix my father with her bright blue eyes. It was as though she was challenging him to refuse, challenging him to make explicit the futility of planting a rose when she had so little time to live.

It was, to my knowledge, the first time she had ever asked him directly for anything, apart from her request to be pushed off a cliff.

My father did not say anything. He bent down to pick up the rose bush. He had some difficulty straightening up again afterwards. He had become very stiff. He paid for the rose, and took it out to the car before rejoining us for tea.

I was pleased by my mother's affirmation of life, her defiance in the face of her prognosis. My father planted the rose bush that afternoon, in my mother's circular rose garden. It was an effort for him to dig, but he would not let me do it. He looked as if he had been weeping when he returned to the house.

I think he buried my mother with that rose.

My father died not long afterwards, suddenly, in his sleep. My mother found him in the morning lying on his back in bed, his hands crossed on his chest; he had had a massive heart attack. We were all taken by surprise. It had always been assumed that my mother would die first; she was so much more frail. I was devastated by my father's death. My mother grieved for him too, but she made no secret of the fact she was pleased he had died first, and painlessly. He would not have to witness her deterioration, nor experience any deterioration himself.

I sit down now beside my mother, on the uncomfortable hospital chair. I admire Katie's flower arrangement on the bedside table. Several petals have fallen off. These are late autumn roses; how quickly they shrivel. I look at my mother's face, which was once so beautiful. She is stirring in her sleep; now she has woken up. She looks confused.

'Eddie?' she says.

'Not Eddie,' I say. 'Heather.'

She looks at me blankly.

'Your daughter,' I explain.

'I know that,' she says. She recognizes me now. She does not like to make a mistake, nor is she pleased to see that I have been watching her. She has always wanted to be the one doing the watching. I lean over the bed to kiss her, always on her right cheek. Her skin is dry and paper-thin. She recovers her nearly perfect manners.

'How are you, darling?' she says.

She asks for her teeth, and a comb. She waves away the mirror that I offer her. I run the comb through her thin hair, over her pale pink vulnerable scalp. I try to settle her more symmetrically on the pillows without hurting her. She feels so small and frail. Then I take her hand in mine. I cannot stop a tear oozing out from between my eyelids, which I am now holding tightly shut. I do not know if I wish her dead or alive.

She squeezes my hand. I wish I could love her exactly as my daughter Katie does, for herself, an old woman. But there is a ghost between myself and my mother, the ghost of the strong woman that she used to be.

I want to ask her what it feels like to be where she is, but I am too afraid of what her answer might be. So I ask her nothing, and I give her nothing in return.

I should like to tell her that I love her. I find it impossible to say the words. I kiss her instead, and soon after take my leave.

I am running late. I should have cancelled these late afternoon appointments.

V

My daughter has gone now. Today I am pleased to see her gone. It is not that I do not love her, but I cannot bear to witness her grief. She should be strong the way she usually is. I cannot shoulder any more the burden of her sadness.

Eddie was lucky to avoid this. His timing was always impeccable.

I have had a good life. But I have spent so many years waiting and watching for the end: I have spent nearly forty years hunting for the signs of my decay. I have sought out mirrors, searched my face for new lines, new pouches; I have made too many inventories of areas of sagging flesh.

The end will be welcome. I have spent too long waiting for the end.

I look out the window at my piece of sky. There are clouds now, banked up towards the west. These are no ordinary clouds. The bottom layer is stretched horizontally, stretching as I watch, stretching to breaking point, striations of cloud, breaking under the weight of a super-structure of cumulo-nimbus clouds that rear up like huge horses. A battle-scene in the sky. As I watch – I do not know how long I have been watching and waiting – the sun sinks further, and outlines the top of the cloud-horses with a glowing rim of gold. Now the whole sky is glowing with saffron light. The clouds change colour from grey to deep purple, a deepening purple, and now to a dark indigo-black.

The day is over.

I can remember the name of the cumulo-nimbus clouds. But I cannot remember the nurse's name, or what she fed me at tea-time.

The pain is returning. I hope the nurse comes soon with the morphine injection. But perhaps she will not come until tomorrow. Today, tomorrow, some time, never. I cannot remember when she comes. I am so tired, always so tired.

She is here. She is the angel of mercy, carrying a needle not a sword. As she pushes down on the hypodermic syringe, she makes some jest, as to a small child. I do not bother to reply. I have been polite for too many years. My mind has not gone, although all else is failing.

The nurse has left my room now. The lady of the lamp, the angel of mercy, the mercy of the angel. The mercy of death, if only.

If only.

I am floating now, the mercy drug is lifting me, softening the edges of my pain. I am supported on a yielding white cloud. My mother's soft white eiderdown quilt cocoons me, is lifting me gently.

I am floating.

I am suspended, I suspend.

Esther Morgan

Hints for Outback Motoring

The guidebook lists Essentials For the Trip:
detailed maps
tool set
repair kit
fan belt
fuel can (full)
funnel
jump leads
spark plugs
pump
radiator hose
two spare tyres
fire extinguisher
tow rope
black tape
pressure gauge
axe and spade
water.

In the event of a breakdown which isn't due
to a snapped fan belt
burnt out spark plug
split radiator hose
flat tyre (or two)
or electrical fire
stay with your vehicle.
Someone will find you.

To pass the time in a remote area
try to remember everything
your father ever told you

about the internal combustion engine.
Once you think you know
what the distributor is for
start sipping the water.

When it gets dark
there will be more stars
than you've ever seen before.
Try to remember
the names of constellations
you once knew by heart.
Recite yourself to sleep
on a groundsheet of detailed maps.
Someone will find you.

Next morning
you need to decide
once and for all
your Desert Island Discs.
Sing them silently
whilst sipping water
even more slowly
than the day before.

By noon you'll be playing loony tunes
with spanners from your tool kit
on the hot bonnet
of your stayed-with vehicle.
Use the radiator hose
to improvise a didgeridoo.
Sun arise.
Someone will find you.

Make large paper planes
out of the detailed maps.
Black insulation tape torn into strips
can be used to remove unwanted hair.
The Bible. The Complete Works of Shakespeare.
Take a sniff of fuel from the fuel can (full).

Soon the flying doctors will be looping the loop
skywriting your name.
If you could only remember
the name of the author
of your favourite book.
At this point you might
want to take an axe
to the mirage of a tree
then gauge your pressure.

By mid-afternoon
the only luxuries in the world
are shade and water
and nothing looks useful
except the tow rope and spade.
Practise tying slip knots, then start digging
whilst taking the odd nip
of petrol to keep going.

Night again.
Wander into the desert
clutching a detailed map.
When you think you've reached
The Middle of Nowhere
sprinkle the last drops of water
over your head
while trying to remember
your name.

Pour petrol letters
into the sand.
Watch HELP burn
and then die down.
Wrap the black tape around your eyes
then lift your face
to the smoke-veiled stars.
Stay where you are.
Someone will find you.

The Lost Word

She's lost a word
and searches for it everywhere –
behind the sofa, at the back
of dusty cupboards and drawers.
She picks through the buzzing rubbish sacks.

Under the carpet she finds lots of others
she'd forgotten she'd swept there
but not the one she's looking for.
The trouble is it's small – only two letters –
though no less valuable for that.

She stands racking her brains
for the last time she used it
but all that comes to mind
are failed attempts
when her mouth was full

of someone else's tongue.

Isobel Dixon

Meet My Father

Meet my father, who refuses food –
pecks at it like a bird or not at all –
the beard disguising his thin cheeks.
This, for a man whose appetite was legend,
hoovering up the scraps his daughters couldn't eat.

The dustbin man, we joked.
And here he is, trailing his fork
through food we've laboured to make soft,
delicious, sweet. Too salty, or too tough,
it tastes of nothing, makes him choke,
he keeps insisting, stubbornly.
In truth, the logic's clear. His very life
is bitter and the spice it lacks is hope.
He wants to stop. Why do we keep on
spooning dust and ashes down his throat?

William Scammell

Litany

Peace to the flinty old farmers.
Peace to their flat tweed caps,
their battered pickups, their 1930s
trousers and turnups, their waiting dogs,
humble as a patchwork rug.
Peace to the golem of their noses
pitted against all the devils above and below,
the ambivalent nods, the odds and sods
of jobs that are born needing doing again.
Peace to the ammoniac stench of piss
that moats the barn in winter,
the infinite spaces of the rainbarrel,
cobblestones hunched down for the long haul.
Peace to the long hours in his head,
the naked light bulb in the yard.

Goa

Since there is no elephant
or Mercedes to be had
the family is abroad
on a Vespa, all five of them
rippling through the early dark,
mother and baby gliding along
sidesaddle on the back.

The banyan tree drops down aerial
roots, enlarges itself in creepers,
making a temple of its own limbs,
a hanging garden, a torrent of suggestions;
plumps up space the way a dancer does,
the way a sitar plucks notes out of its belly
and hugs them, not sure where sorrow ends
and the rest of the world begins.

A trumpet sounds at the hotel gates
and there stands Ganesh himself
taller than you'd ever imagined,
parked up on his legs, fronting
the cameras, eyes lost and whalish
in that great head, dumb as the flames
they broke him with, which blacken
the pillars of my chest.

In the paddy fields they put and take
all day, bent over the eye of the needle
that stitches them to earth, warm hungry mud,
the long field path, straight as a rod.

294

Inflorescence of a Matisse
languorous on cerulean blue:
the bay as a hedonist masterpiece.

The palms have nothing to say to this.
Why should they? Beauty is all ours.
They lean upwards, as the law insists,
watching the ocean mop its muddy floors.

The lads go on hammering long poles
into sand, weaving their shady roofs
out of such handy materials
as the spiky, biodegradable leaves

of the spirit, recommended by gurus
everywhere, lest we think we are gods,
renting the sahib his sunbed and pillows
or selling him soapstone bits and bobs.

These are the one-off cafés, built each year
in a couple of days by quick and practised hands
to service the restless boulevardier
walking his cut-out shadow across the sand.

They riffle off notes with the head of Gandhi
bent over the spindle of his wheel,
all wire-rim specs, and self-sufficiency,
the ghost of that non-violent smile.

The fingers are drumming, drumming
under those exquisite raags,
the heel of the hand for thunder
rained down by unforgiving gods.

Gold for the gypsy women, gold and silk
riotous against oily black
hair and skin, done up as slaves
to mock the slavery of wives.

Andy Brown

Another Poem of Gifts, after Borges

For Molly May

'*Por el amor, que nos deja ver a los otros
Como los ve la divinidad.*'

'For love, which lets us see others
As the godhead sees them.'

I want to give thanks for the garden
    already in bloom this March
    as I sit here with you, curled
    like an aleph in your papoose;
for the balsam of your chatter,
    echoic & fluid,
    like an elver in the wash;
for the flexion of your tongue
    throwing muscular vowels
    into the fuzz of sun & dew,
    like the musical chimes of a gamelan;
for the brouhaha of the blackbird
    as it picks at a red berry,
    or last winter's lingering
    hips & haws;
for the synod of starlings
    gathered in the oak;
for the peony's growth
    we can almost hear
    surging through the soil;
for my dibber pushing through the clod,

to sow the seed that promises blue
borage at the bottom of the plot;
for the bubble of the acorn
exploding underground;
for the dewlaps on cattle
chewing cud in the fields beyond,
their calves impatient
at their udders;
for the kazoo of insects
busy at the nectaries
of cowslips & daffodils;
for the fresco of morning;
for the whole gamut & hex of spring;
for your mother
in her workshop,
unloading the kiln;
for the hubbub & jabber
of her radio;
for the hoop of love
that rolls on
with no beginning & no end;
for the unknowable nuances
of change;
for the nub of pleasures which elude me;
for the koan of 'Why?'
for the ingots of your eyes;
for the honey of your dribble;
for your *tabula rasa*;
for 'upsy-daisy'.

Grace Ingoldby

The Song of the Sparrow

'And one of the King's chief men presently said: Thus
seems it to me, thou King, the present life of man on
earth against that time which is unknown to us: it is as
if thou wert sitting at a feast with thy chief men and
thy thanes in the winter-time; the fire burns and the hall
is warmed and outside it rains and snows and storms.
Comes a sparrow and swiftly flies through the house; it
comes through one door and goes out another. Lo, in
the time in which he is within he is not touched by the
winter storm, but that time is the flash of an eye and
the least of times, and he soon passes from winter to
winter again. So is the life of man revealed for a brief
space, but what went before and what follows after we
know not.'

> – Coifi, chief of the pagan priests in council with
> King Edwin of Northumbria.

This is a cold night
A caught in the grasp night
Squeezed between tools invented for squeezing
Wishbone is walking
The cold's on his shoulder, the tongs of cold hold him
By the buttocks and hips
Bent to go forward, almost marching
Propelled along a gully path
To his right and his left the holly and scrub oaks
Deep layers of leaf mould indented as he is
Where the beeches have fallen
Trunks smooth like pewter
The cup on the table, the cup on the floor
Strokable skin yet asleep to sensation

Skin of the loved ones alseep in all innocence
Skin of the loved ones asleep by the fireside
Skin that was air to him, gone

This evening he's cut his own hair with the scissors
Walks further than usual, a mile on to Penquit
The night before Christmas and lights in the chapel
One or two gathered who turn at the sight of him
As if calamity had itself walked in
And he who's not spoken one month to another
Leans hard against a pillar by the door

The priest is a stranger, gorgeous by candlelight
A vision got up in amethyst and silver gilt
His chasuble worked in stem stitch and satin stitch
All sprigged with strawberries
He has embroidered entirely on his own
His voice – used to talking – coos Filius meus es tu,
          you are my son
Then something or other of Caesar Augustus a new
          dawn of glory
Eyes down Bone attempts to gather months to him
To peer into the year that has gone
And not for the life of him can he remember
The actions that brought him to this cold December
Flint above and flint below
For though he's recorded the cuckoo and corncrake
The swing of the seasons has not in any sense
          impinged
One end to the other, nothing and everything
And all encountered on his own
Why can't he recall the detail to feed him
The hands and the gestures, the eyes and the faces
Above all the postures, their own ways of standing
The actual matter of his dead?
Death wrapped about him and all he remembers
Is work on the river, the clutch of its dampness
The mist barely rising, the squelching his boot makes

The sole that needs stitching
More knots that take patience
Curving needle and waxed thread

'There were wolves,' says the priest, his voice
                languidly beautiful
Voice practised on the river where the bank sends out
                an echo
Voice that brings wolves, thin-flanked right into the
                chancel of the church
'Wolves set to their purpose
Outrageous in daylight, watchful on outcrops of rocks
Their silhouettes stood out against the winter sun
The sun on the old olive terraces, little more lovely
Than the delicate olive leaves
A lesson for us for they live a long time and yet they
                remain lovely.
He pauses, taking in the figure of Bone
Recoils just a little, the movement's invisible
This priest has no wish to cosy the peasantry
He won't tell of shepherds though they be a part of
                Christmas
He doesn't do shepherds and he doesn't do sheep
Uplift is what he does, exclusively, brilliantly
Kings and their retinue
A glitter for Christmas
A gloss to the century which – Bone has reminded
                him –
Is flint above and flint below, so –
'Down', says the priest his gaze fixed short of
                Wishbone
'Down the old olive terraces
Skirting the watching wolves who would strike if they
                wanted to
Could strike if they cared to do –
Kings came on
The kings and their retinue
Pages on foot, kings riding on horses

Their boots looked like liquid so lively and glinting
A sheen off their boots which glimmered in the winter
          sun
Their pages wore yellow, the colour of moonlight
Hunting dogs ran with them, white as the snow that
          they stepped through
Their collars bejewelled
Encrusted with preciousness – not something you say
          about sheep
And their masters were splendid
The pearls at their necks glowed like shells under
          water
Some black as the olives but more heavy and pendant
Suspended from scrolled golden chains
The pinks that they wore were so soft and translucent
You might say they'd been wafted towards the
          material
Not spun. Babies heel pink the colour of blushes
The time that they came was a time of abundance
Fish filled the rivers then
Fruit filled the trees
And the buildings they made reflected creation
Their palaces patterned on God's many roomed
          mansion
Mi casa su casas all fitted with fountains that plashed
          on tiled pavements
Refracting the sunshine in streaks.'

A clink at the altar of silver and pewter
The shrilling of a tiny sacring-bell
Smell of the candles not tallow but church kind
Flame that dips and flickers with a sudden rush of air
As, dressed in the costumes of asses and oxen
Seers out of Hoppels Tor
Announce themselves at the church door

'We will not be forgotten.'
Brays the ass to the oxen

'Though a mile is two in winter.' Lows the oxen to
        the ass
'We will make our presence felt.'
Says the ass to the oxen
'We are part of the picture.' Says the oxen to the ass
'You the colour of chestnut warmed beneath the
            waistcoat.'
'You a serious figure with the cross upon your back.'
'Your eyes are so wise.' Says the oxen to the ass
And the ox turns his ear which is seven times beautiful
Soft like the skin on Wishbone's soft belly
Alas

'I wish,' said the ass, 'that an angel might enter
The cabin that Wishbone has left.'
'Yes,' the oxen agrees, 'for an angel is sensitive'
The noise of his door-latch would harrow an angel.'
'Yes harrow him completely.' Says the ass.
'The door latch, the clack of it
'And the outhouse, so pitiful
The hatchet that hangs there—
'The hatchet he's considered.' Says the oxen to the ass
'It's the one cup on the table
It's what happened at his fireside
It's the slab of lonely knowledge that he bears
It's the turned out contents of his pockets
All placed so neatly on the table
Alas
His knife and some coin
And his sharpening stone—'
'For the hatchet!' says the oxen to the ass
'Cheese rind and heel of bread
His bed and the river running yellow
And his cold catkin view
I wish for an angel and I know that you do too.'

We were walking and talking in the wood –
Near to Wishbone –
We were walking where he walks

Beneath the lattice of the trees
'And I was weary.' Says the oxen to the ass
'You wandered off the path.'
'You showed me where it was easy for me to climb
      the bank.'
'We felt the leaf mould, smooth and soft beneath our
      feet.'
'And you rubbed your back against a holly tree.'
'And you got down on your haunches –
Seven times beautiful the brown of your haunches –
And we knelt together where the winds of October
Had uprooted an enormous tree
What did we see?

Tiny nativity
In the bowl where the roots had been
Minuscule baby
Bedded in moss
Triangular angels that fluttered quite close to the
      ground.'
'Your breath warmed the wind flower
That broke from its winter
Small white anemone bell
The milk of its colour
The blue veining visible
On the skin of the baby.'

They end with a flourish, a bow and a curtsy
'Time to go.' Says the oxen
'Story's told.' Replies the ass

Now the priest lifts his wafer to wake the believers
All elbows and overclothes, thighs like big gammons
And Wishbone is seized with a fresh sense of
            shipwreck – going down
A sense that he's sinking in the strong scent of candles
In the warmth that surrounds him

Out from the chapel
No taste for a blessing

Winter his master now
World as it ever was
Flint above and flint below

This man is walking
And out beyond Penquit
The stories slough off him
The colours congeal as the silence engulfs him
As the cold of the night starts slowly to impinge
And instinct is uppermost
Offering himself to it
Letting it grasp him
By the shoulders
By the buttocks
The hips
Kings to the margin
Miracles to the credulous
Back to the crosspost
Where the sky's much more open
And the stars come into view
Uncountable Pleiades
Sailing so far above
Cold that draws him by the hand
The country is freezing
In the way that the blood clots
A weave that spreads outwards
A bridge made of filaments
Strong enough for Bone to stand upon
Cold that presents him
As ice to the skater
A freedom of movement
A joy unexpected
Slab of knowledge made lovely
By the ice that preserves it
Cold that is burning to cleave to
Revealed in the flash of an eye.

Biographical Notes

Elspeth Barker's novel *O Caledonia* (Penguin) won the David Higham Prize and was shortlisted for the Whitbread First Novel award. Her second novel was published in 2000.

Carol Baxendale was born in Broughty Ferry in 1955. She studied fine art in Cheltenham, and printmaking at the Slade School of Art. She has taught printmaking, held exhibitions and, more recently, published stories in *Spiked, Birdsuit* and *Front to Back*. Now resident in the UK, she has also travelled and worked extensively in Norway.

Beverley Bie lives in Paris, where she teaches at the British School. Her poems have been published in *Ambit, London Magazine, Poetry Nottingham, Poetry Wales* and *Smiths Knoll*; a translation of Francis Ponge's 'Le parti pris des choses' has been published by Guernica Editions.

Ranjit Bolt is one of Britain's leading theatrical translators. He read Greats at Oxford, then worked in the City for eight years before giving up his job eleven years ago to concentrate on translation. Five of his translations have been produced by Sir Peter Hall, and three by the National Theatre. He has also worked with the RSC and there have been a number of productions of his work in North America. His first novel (in verse) was published by John Murray in 2001.

Alison Booth is an Australian, who moved from Sydney to England in 1979 to study at the London School of Economics. She is a professor of economics at the University of Essex. She started writing short stories recently, and this is her first published piece of fiction.

Andy Brown's three poetry collections are *From A Cliff* (Arc), *The Wanderer's Prayer* (Arc) and *West of Yesterday* (Stride). He edited two volumes of critical correspondences with poets and editors, *Binary Myths 1 and 2* (Stride) and is writing a novel. He is Centre Director for the Arvon Foundation in Devon.

Alan Brownjohn's *Collected Poems* appeared in 1988, and two further volumes of verse have appeared since, the most recent being *In the Cruel Arcade*. The novel from which this excerpt is taken will be his third, following *The Way You Tell Them* (1990), winner of the Authors' Club first novel prize, and *The Long Shadows* (1997).

John Burnside has published seven books of poetry, of which the most recent is *The Asylum Dance* (Jonathan Cape, 2000), as well as two novels and a recent book of short stories, *Burning Elvis* (Jonathan Cape, 2000). He has just finished work on a new novel, *The Locust Room*, due for publication in May 2001 (Jonathan Cape).

Kee Thuan Chye is a Malaysian playwright, actor and literary editor best known for his plays *1984 Here and Now*, a critique of political oppression and racial discrimination, and *We Could **** You, Mr Birch*, a satire on power and the clash of cultures. He has been a judge of the Commonwealth Writers' Prize.

Julia Darling is a playwright, and a writer of short and long fiction. Her short stories have appeared in many anthologies and she is currently compiling a second collection of stories, following her first collection, *Bloodlines*. Her first novel, *Crocodile Soup*, was published in 1998 by Transworld, and has subsequently been published in Canada and America and translated into Danish. She is working on her second novel, and a new play, and is currently resident at Newcastle University as a literary 'fellow' for the Royal Literary Fund. She lives in Newcastle.

Louis de Bernières was born in 1954. He is the author of *The War of Don Emmanuel's Nether Parts*, *Señor Vivo and the Coca Lord* (Commonwealth Writers' Prize, Eurasia Region, 1992), *The Troublesome Offspring of Cardinal Guzman* and *Captain*

Corelli's Mandolin (Commonwealth Writers' Prize, 1995). His play, *Sunday Morning at the Centre of the World*, was first broadcast on BBC Radio 4 in March 1999.

Patricia Debney received her MA in Creative Writing from the UEA in 1992, and lives and teaches in Kent. She has had stories and translations published, and wrote the libretto for a chamber opera, *The Juniper Tree*, performed at the Munich Biennale and the Almeida Theatre in London in 1997. *Losing You* is currently seeking a publisher.

Des Dillon. Writer of fiction, poet, dramatist and screenwriter. Born Coatbridge, 1960. Studied English at Strathclyde University. Taught English. Awarded SAC writer's bursary, 1996. Writer in residence Castlemilk, Glasgow, 1998–2000. Novels – *Me and Ma Gal, The Big Empty, Duck, Itchycooblue, Return of the Busby Babes, The Big Q*. Working on a screenplay for BBC Films based on *The Big Q*. Lives in Galloway.

Isobel Dixon was born in South Africa in 1969, and studied at Stellenbosch University and Edinburgh University. Her poetry has been widely published in South Africa, where she also won the Sanlam Literary Award 2000. In the UK her work has appeared in several journals and in *New Writing 8* (1999). She now works in London as a literary agent.

Helen Dunmore is a novelist, poet and short-story writer. She has published two collections of short stories: *Love of Fat Men* (Penguin, 1997) and *Ice-Cream* (Viking, 2000). Her latest novel is *With Your Crooked Heart* (Penguin, 1999). She won the inaugural Orange Prize for Fiction for her novel *A Spell of Winter*.

Geoff Dyer was born in Cheltenham in 1958 and educated at the local grammar school and Corpus Christi College, Oxford. He is the author of three novels, *The Colour of Memory, The Search* and *Paris Trance*; a critical study of John Berger, *Ways of Telling*; and three genre-defying titles, *But Beautiful, The Missing of the Somme* and *Out of Sheer Rage*. His most recent book is *Anglo-English Attitudes, Essays, Reviews and Misadventures*

1984–99, a collection of his freelance writing of the last fifteen years.

Ruth Fainlight's eleventh collection of poems, *Sugar-Paper Blue*, was published by Bloodaxe Books in 1997 and shortlisted for the Whitbread Prize that year. She has also published two collections of short stories, translations from Portuguese and Spanish, and written libretti for the Royal Opera House and Channel 4. In 1994 she received the Cholmondeley Award for Poetry.

Janice Galloway's work includes novels, *The Trick is to Keep Breathing, Foreign Parts*, short stories, *Blood, Where You Find It*, collaborative poetry texts (with visual artists) and music texts (mainly for Sally Beamish). Her literary prizes include the American Academy's E. M. Forster Award and the McVitie's and MIND/Allen Lane Awards. Her third novel is currently under completion.

Francis Gilbert was born in 1968. He grew up in Cambridge, London and Northumberland, and attended Sussex University and the University of East Anglia. He teaches part-time at a comprehensive and also writes on a freelance basis for the *New Statesman* and *The Times*. He lives in London with his wife, Erica Wagner, and their son Theodore.

Michael Hofmann was born in Freiburg in 1957, and lives in London. His poetry is published by Faber & Faber, who have just brought out *Behind the Lines*, a collection of his criticism. He has translated six books by Joseph Roth, as well as sundry other works by Brecht, Kafka, Koeppen, and his father, Gert Hofmann.

Andrea Holland was born in London, but studied in the USA, completing a Master's degree in Creative Writing at the University of Massachusetts. She taught in Virginia for several years but now resides in the UK, teaching and writing. She has poems in *The Rialto, Other Poetry, Ibid* and many US publications.

Grace Ingoldby has published five novels. The last, *Bring Out Your Dead*, was published by Peter Owen.

together for the first time all Merseyside-born Garrett's stories, reportage and critical essays from the 1930s.

Caitríona O'Reilly was born in Dublin in 1973 and educated at Trinity College Dublin, where she wrote a doctoral thesis on American poetry. She has published poetry and criticism in many journals, including *Thumbscrew Metre*, *Oxford Poetry*, the *Irish Times*, *PN Review* and *Verse*. She is also a member of the editorial board of *Metre* magazine. In 1999 she received a bursary in literature from the Arts Council of Ireland. Her first collection, *The Nowhere Birds*, will be published by Bloodaxe in 2001.

Andrew Pidoux was born in High Wycombe in 1974. He won an Eric Gregory Award in 1999. He is currently living in Tucson, Arizona, where he is a high school English teacher.

Tom Pow is author of four books of poems – *Rough Seas* (1987), *The Moth Trap* (1990), *Red Letter Day* (1996) and *Landscapes* (1999) – a travel book about Peru, *In The Palace of Serpents* (1992), two books for children, *Who is the World For?* and *Callum's Big Day* (both 2000) and three radio plays. He is lecturer in Creative and Cultural Studies at Glasgow University's Crichton Campus in Dumfries.

Deryn Rees-Jones' most recent collection of poems is *Signs Round A Dead Body* (Seren, 1998), a PBS Special Commendation. She is also the author of *Carol Ann Duffy* (1999) and co-editor of *Contemporary Women's Poetry: Reading, Writing, Practice* (Macmillan, 2000).

Peter Robinson is the author of four books of poetry, the most recent being *Lost and Found* (1997). Carcanet Press will publish his fifth *About Time Too* in March 2001. He has recently co-edited *The Thing About Roy Fisher: Critical Studies* (Liverpool University Press) and *News for the Ear: A Homage to Roy Fisher* (Stride Publications).

Stephen Romer was born in Hertfordshire in 1957. He has lived much of his adult life in France, first in Paris and now in Tours where he is Maître de Conférences at the University. He has published three collections of poetry with OUP, *Idols, Plato's*

Ladder and most recently *Tribute* (1998). He is currently preparing *A Choice of 20th Century French Poetry* for Faber.

Chris Rose went to visit Naples for three months, and has now been there for ten years.

Joseph Roth was born near Lvov in East Galicia (present-day Ukraine) in 1894, and died in Paris in 1939. He was one of the foremost journalists of his day, and the author of fifteen novels, all of them now translated into English. *The Wandering Jew*, a book-length essay on the Jews in Europe, was published earlier this year by Granta. 'The Leviathan' is included in *Strawberries: Collected Shorter Fiction*, forthcoming from the same publisher.

Lawrence Sail has published seven collections of poems, most recently *Building Into Air* (Bloodaxe, 1995) and *Out of Land: New & Selected Poems* (Bloodaxe, 1992): a new collection is forthcoming. He has edited several anthologies, including (with Kevin Crossley-Holland) *The New Exeter Book of Riddles* (Enitharmon, 1999). He is a Fellow of the Royal Society of Literature.

Eva Salzman was born in New York City. Publications include *Bargain with the Watchman* (OUP, 1997) and *The English Earthquake* (Bloodaxe, 1992). Currently Royal Literary Fund Fellow at Ruskin College, Oxford. Ongoing projects include a novel and two operas for the English National Opera Studio and Performing Arts Lab: *One Two*, with composer Gary Carpenter, showcased at the Royal Opera House Studio Theatre, and *Shawna and Ron's Half Moon*, performed by The Knack at Hoxton Hall, London.

William Scammell was born in Hampshire in 1939 but has lived and worked in Cumbria for many years. He has published nine books of poems, including *Bleeding Heart Yard* (1992) and *All Set To Fall Off the Edge of the World* (1998), and edited several others, including Ted Hughes's *Winter Pollen*. He has won awards from the Society of Authors, the Arts Council, Northern Arts, and won the National Poetry Competition in 1989. His *New & Selected Poems* is forthcoming, together with a book of critical prose. William Scammell sadly died in December 2000 while this book was going to press.

Peter Scupham was born in 1933. He taught, founded, with John Mole, the Mandeville Press and published his poetry with Oxford. His most recent collection, *Night Watch*, came out in 1999 with Anvil, and his *Collected Poems* will be published by Carcanet. He is a Fellow of the Royal Society of Literature.

Alan Sillitoe was born in 1928. He left school at fourteen and enlisted in 1946 into the RAFVR. At the end of 1949 he was invalided out of service. He began writing and lived for six years in France and Spain. His first stories were printed in the *Nottinghamshire Weekly Guardian*. In 1958, *Saturday Night and Sunday Morning* was published, and *The Loneliness of the Long-Distance Runner*, which won the Hawthornden Prize for Literature, came out in 1959. Both these books were made into films. Further works include *Key to the Door, The General, A Start in Life*, and *The Widower's Son*, as well as eight volumes of poetry. He has also written plays, essays and books for children. His recent novels include *The Broken Chariot* and *The German Numbers Woman*. His next novel, *Birthday*, which is the sequel to *Saturday Night and Sunday Morning* is to be published in April 2001.

Helen Simpson's first collection of short stories, *Four Bare Legs in a Bed* (Heinemann, 1990), won the *Sunday Times* Young Writer of the Year Award and a Somerset Maugham Award. Her suspense novella, *Flesh and Grass* (Pandora, 1990), appeared with Ruth Rendell's *The Strawberry Tree* under the general title of *Unguarded Hours*. She was chosen as one of Granta's Twenty Best of Young British Novelists in 1993. She has written a play, *Pinstripe*. *'Dear George' and other stories* was published in 1995 and her latest collection of short stories, *Hey Yeah Right Get a Life*, is published by Jonathan Cape in 2000.

Matt Simpson was born in Bootle and has lived most of his life in Liverpool. He is the author of three Bloodaxe collections: *Making Arrangements* (1982), *An Elegy for the Galosherman: New and Selected* (1990), and *Catching Up With History* (1995); his last book, *Cutting the Clouds Towards* (1995), was published by Liverpool University Press, who will also be bringing out his next collection *The Idea of Order at Hunts Cross* in 2001. He has published two collections for children: *The Pigs' Thermal Underwear* (Headland, 1992) and *Lost Property Box* (Macmillan, 1995 and 1998).

Atima Srivastava was born in Mumbai and lives in London. Her two novels are *Transmission* and *Looking for Maya*. She has been Writer in Residence at the University of Singapore and the University of Sofia (Bulgaria). She has won first prize in the Bridport Arts Short Story competition, Arts Council Awards for her second novel, and third novel in progress, and a Hawthornden Fellowship. Having worked in television for over thirteen years as a film editor, she is at present working on a libretto, and a play for the National Theatre.

Anne Stevenson, born in England of American parents, grew up in the United States and was educated at the University of Michigan where she studied music and wrote lyrics for dance drama and an opera. After bringing out two volumes of poetry in the States, she made her home in Britain where she published *Travelling Behind Glass* and an epistolary narrative, *Correspondences*, in 1974. Five further collections appeared before OUP published her *Collected Poems* in 1996 (Bloodaxe). In May 2000 Bloodaxe brought out her most recent collection, *Granny Scarecrow*. All Anne Stevenson's published poems are included in the full-text database of *Literature Online, Twentieth Century English Poetry*. Stevenson is also the author of *Bitter Fame, A Life of Sylvia Plath* (1989) and *Five Looks at Elizabeth Bishop* (1998). Her literary essays have been published by the University of Michigan Press. Married with three children and three grandchildren, she lives in Durham and in North Wales.

Anthony Thwaite was born in 1930. He has published fourteen books of poems, most recently *Selected Poems 1956–1996* (1997) and a limited edition of new poems, *A Different Country* (2000). Another recent publication is his edition of Philip Larkin's uncollected reviews and other miscellaneous writing, *Further Requirements.*

Barbara Trapido was born in Cape Town but came to England in 1963. She has written five novels including *Brother of the More Famous Jack* (which won a Whitbread Award in 1982), *Juggling* and, most recently, *The Travelling Hornplayer* (shortlisted for the 1998 Whitbread Novel Award). She lives in Oxford.

Erica Wagner was born in New York City and now lives in London with her husband, Francis Gilbert, and their son Theodore. She is the author of *Gravity*, a book of short stories (Granta, 1997) and *Ariel's Gift: Ted Hughes, Sylvia Plath and the Story of Birthday Letters* (Faber & Faber, 2000), and her work has been widely anthologized and broadcast on Radio 4. She is the Literary Editor of *The Times*.

Clare Wigfall was born in Greenwich during the summer of 1976. Her early childhood was spent in Berkeley, California, before returning, age eight, to London. At twenty-two, she moved to Prague, in the Czech Republic, and lives there now. Her first book will be published by Faber & Faber in August 2001.

Copyright information